Dr. Robert L. Mc Cornack

To A Damn Good

Instructor From

The Psych 710 Class,

Fall, 1955.

Advanced Statistical Methods in Biometric Research

WILEY PUBLICATIONS IN STATISTICS

Walter A. Shewhart, Editor

Mathematical Statistics

RAO—Advanced Statistical Methods in Biometric Research.

KEMPTHORNE—The Design and Analysis of Experiments.

DWYER—Linear Computations.

FISHER—Contributions to Mathematical Statistics.

WALD—Statistical Decision Functions.

FELLER—An Introduction to Probability Theory and Its Applications, Volume One.

WALD—Sequential Analysis.

HOEL—Introduction to Mathematical Statistics.

Applied Statistics

GOULDEN—Methods of Statistical Analysis (*in press*).

HALD—Statistical Theory with Engineering Applications.

HALD—Statistical Tables and Formulas.

YOUDEN — Statistical Methods for Chemists.

MUDGETT—Index Numbers.

TIPPETT—Technological Applications of Statistics.

DEMING—Some Theory of Sampling.

COCHRAN and COX—Experimental Designs.

RICE—Control Charts.

DODGE and ROMIG—Sampling Inspection Tables.

Related Books of Interest to Statisticians

HAUSER and LEONARD—Government Statistics for Business Use.

Advanced Statistical Methods in Biometric Research

C. RADHAKRISHNA RAO
Professor of Statistics
Indian Statistical Institute
Calcutta

New York • John Wiley & Sons, Inc.
London • Chapman & Hall, Limited

In memory of
my father
the late C. D. Naidu

The statistician is no longer an alchemist expected to produce gold from any worthless material offered him. He is more like a chemist capable of assaying exactly how much of value it contains, and capable also of extracting this amount, and no more. In these circumstances, it would be foolish to commend a statistician because his results are precise or to reprove because they are not. If he is competent in his craft, the value of the result follows solely from the value of the material given him. It contains so much information and no more. His job is only to produce what it contains.

R. A. FISHER

Preface

The ever-increasing need for more searching and finer analyses of statistical data in various domains of human activity has constantly been giving rise to new concepts and improved methods. The vast amount of research carried out during the past few decades in the field of theoretical and applied statistics has been responsible for the discarding or recasting of some of the older methods in statistics and for the creation of a wealth of new statistical tools for the research worker and the routine analyst. The popularity and range of application of any statistical method, however, has always remained in great measure dependent on the logical elucidation it received and the simplicity of procedure it was capable of, mainly because more often a method that is powerful is also complex in theory and procedure.

The object in writing this book is to present a number of statistical techniques, keeping in view the requirements of both the student who questions the basis of a particular method employed and the practical worker who seeks a recipe for the reduction of his data. I have therefore endeavored first to provide a theoretical groundwork for the different methods to satisfy the former and second to illustrate computational procedures by working out a number of problems in full to meet the demands of the latter.

Throughout this book, efforts have been made to integrate a large collection of computational schemes into consistent patterns. Thus the problems of regression and analysis of variance and covariance reduce to fitting of constants by the method of least squares and evaluation of the least sum of squares. The problems of multivariate analysis resolve themselves into an analysis of the dispersion matrix and reduction of determinants. The reduction of a matrix by the method of pivotal condensation emerges as the most useful technique which at the same time does not present any computational difficulty. The check column, properly carried, ensures numerical accuracy. The different computational schemes have been illustrated in detail with the help of original data. These data have also been reproduced, either in full or, in the case of extensive data, in the form of necessary statistics such as totals, sums of squares, products, etc., giving reference to the sources from which they are taken.

The material presented for illustrative purposes has been restricted mainly to anthropometric studies, but without prejudicing the statistical methods used in their applicability to problems in various other branches of knowledge such as general biology, psychology, economics, and other social sciences. The problem of neurotic groups considered in section 9d.1 provides an example from psychology. For the psychological findings appearing in that section I am indebted to Mr. Patrick Slater.

In the development of the text, the first chapter is devoted entirely to mathematical procedures in modern algebra. In the second chapter it is shown that most of the distribution problems connected with uni-variate and multivariate normal populations can be solved by a funda-mental theorem on least squares, whose proof needs only a knowledge of linear transformations.

The third chapter first deals with applications of the least square tech-nique in the estimation of parameters. It next traces as the starting point of exact sampling theory the fundamental discovery by W. S. Gosset, now known as "studentization," that the probability of the error in the observed average expressed as a multiple of the sample standard deviation admits a precise evaluation independently of the unknown standard deviation of the population. Then it proceeds with tests of linear hypotheses. The tests discussed in this chapter, exact for small samples, are due to R. A. Fisher, who, having developed the theory of these tests, also put forward the elegant computational scheme of the analysis of variance table.

The fourth chapter contains some observations on the general theories of estimation and certain applications of the method of maximum likelihood. The scoring system of R. A. Fisher discussed and elaborated in this chapter introduces great simplicity and mechanization in the use of the maximum likelihood principle, thus providing a complete answer to critics who hold that the method of maximum likelihood leads to intractable equations. Certain alternative methods of deriving asymp-totically best estimates advocated by some authors neither have gen-eral applicability nor would admit mechanized computation.

Problems of specification and associated tests of homogeneity form the subject matter of the fifth chapter. The choice of a mathematical model from which the observations could be deemed to have arisen is of fundamental importance because subsequent statistical computations have to be built on the framework of the chosen model. The choice is necessarily empirical, "but this empiricism could be cleared of its dangers if we can apply a rigorous and objective test of the adequacy with which the proposed population represents the whole of the available facts." Karl Pearson was the first to visualize this approach. The χ^2 goodness of fit introduced by him has been found extremely useful in many other directions too.

The next chapter gives tests of homogeneity of variances and co-variances, and these form the preliminary investigation in multivariate analysis which is detailed in the seventh chapter. The eighth and ninth chapters relate to the utilization of multiple measurements in problems of biological classification. Biologists are usually confronted with the problem of assigning an individual to one of several groups to which he might belong. An objective method which minimizes the errors of classification is provided in the eighth chapter, utilizing the modern theories of inference as developed by J. Neyman and A. Wald. Chapter 9 is devoted to a study of the interrelationships between a number of populations or groups of individuals. The methods of this chapter are based on the researches carried out in the Indian Statistical Institute under the inspiring guidance of P. C. Mahalanobis, who introduced the concept of group distance.

C. R. RAO

Calcutta, India
June 1952

Contents

CHAPTER 1· ALGEBRA OF VECTORS AND MATRICES

1a VECTOR SPACES 1

    1a.1 Vectors.   1a.2 Linear Independence and Orthogonality.   1a.3 Vector Spaces and the Sweep-Out Method.   1a.4 The Orthogonal Vector Space and the Deficiency Matrix.   1a.5 Linear Equations.

1b THEORY OF MATRICES AND DETERMINANTS 6

    1b.1 Matrices.   1b.2 Partitioned Matrices.   1b.3 Determinants.

1c QUADRATIC FORMS 18

    1c.1 Definitions.   1c.2 Linear Transformations.   1c.3 Classification of Quadratic Forms.   1c.4 The Latent Roots of a Matrix and the Characteristic Vectors.   1c.5 Pairs of Quadratic Forms.   1c.6 Reduction of an Asymmetric Matrix.

1d NUMERICAL APPENDIX 29

    1d.1 The Evaluation of Determinants, Reciprocals, and Solutions of Equations.

CHAPTER 2· THEORY OF DISTRIBUTIONS

2a SOME ANALYTICAL METHODS IN DISTRIBUTION PROBLEMS 32

    2a.1 Binomial Distribution.   2a.2 Multinomial Distribution.   2a.3 The Poisson Distribution.   2a.4 Normal Distribution.   2a.5 Gamma Distribution.   2a.6 Beta Distribution.   2a.7 Cauchy Distribution. 2a.8 Pearson's P_λ Distribution.   2a.9 Summary of Results.

2b DISTRIBUTIONS RELATING TO THE UNIVARIATE NORMAL DISTRIBUTION 46

    2b.1 Mean and Variance in Normal Samples.   2b.2 Student's Distribution.   2b.3 Fisher's z Distribution.   2b.4 Cochran's Theorem. 2b.5 Distribution of Non-Central χ^2.

2c MULTIVARIATE NORMAL POPULATIONS 51

    2c.1 The Multivariate Normal Distribution.   2c.2 The Distribution of a Set of Linear Functions of Normal Variates.   2c.3 The Distribution of Quadratic Forms.

2d LEAST SQUARES FUNDAMENTAL IN DISTRIBUTION THEORY 58

    2d.1 Two Theorems on Least Squares.   2d.2 Multivariate Distributions.

CHAPTER 3· THE THEORY OF LINEAR ESTIMATION
AND TESTS OF HYPOTHESES

3a LINEAR ESTIMATION 75

3a.1 Observational Equations. 3a.2 Best Unbiased Estimates. 3a.3 The Necessary and Sufficient Condition for the Existence of an Unbiased Estimate. 3a.4 Normal Equations. 3a.5 Linear Functions with Zero Expectations. 3a.6 Standard Errors of Estimates and Intrinsic Properties of Normal Equations. 3a.7 Principle of Substitution. 3a.8 Observational Equations with Linear Restrictions on Parameters. 3a.9 Observational Equations with Correlated Variables.

3b TESTS OF LINEAR HYPOTHESES 82

3b.1 Nature of Linear Hypotheses. 3b.2 Test for H_0. 3b.3 Test for H_0 when R_0 Is Not True.

3c THE COMBINATION OF WEIGHTED OBSERVATIONS 85

3c.1 Transformation to Unweighted Observations. 3c.2 An Example of Weighted Observations.

3d TESTS OF HYPOTHESES WITH A SINGLE DEGREE OF FREEDOM 87

3d.1 Student's t Test. 3d.2 Asymmetry of Right and Left Femora.

3e ANALYSIS OF VARIANCE 89

3e.1 One-Way Classification. 3e.2 Two-Way Classification with a Single Observation in a Cell. 3e.3 Two-Way Classification with Multiple but Equal Numbers in Cells. 3e.4 Two-Way Classification with Unequal Numbers in Cells.

3f THE THEORY OF STATISTICAL REGRESSION 102

3f.1 The Concept of Regression. 3f.2 Prediction of Cranial Capacity. 3f.3 Test for the Equality of Regression Equations. 3f.4 The Test for an Assigned Regression Function.

3g THE GENERAL PROBLEM OF LEAST SQUARES WITH TWO SETS OF PARAMETERS 118

3g.1 Concomitant Variables. 3g.2 Adjustment for Concomitant Variation. 3g.3 An Illustrative Example. 3g.4 A Problem of Inheritance in Man.

CHAPTER 4· THE GENERAL THEORY OF ESTIMATION
AND THE METHOD OF MAXIMUM LIKELIHOOD

4a BEST UNBIASED ESTIMATES 129

4a.1 Estimation by Minimizing the Variance. 4a.2 The Information Limit to Variance: A Single Parameter. 4a.3 Distributions Admitting Estimates with the Information Limit to Variance. 4a.4 Sufficient Statistics and Unbiased Estimates. 4a.5 Distributions Admitting Sufficient Statistics. 4a.6 An Optimum Property of Sufficient Statistics. 4a.7 More Stringent Inequalities for the Variance of an Estimate.

4a.8 The Case of Several Parameters.   4a.9   Properties of Distributions Admitting Sufficient Statistics: Several Parameters.

4b ESTIMATION BY THE METHOD OF MAXIMUM LIKELIHOOD 150
4b.1 The Principle of Maximum Likelihood.   4b.2 Consistency and Bias.   4b.3 The Concept of Efficiency.   4b.4 Some Optimum Properties of Maximum Likelihood Estimates.

4c SOME EXAMPLES OF MAXIMUM LIKELIHOOD ESTIMATES 161
4c.1 Improved Estimates of Means from Incomplete Data on Several Variables.   4c.2 The Method of Scoring for the Estimation of Parameters.   4c.3 Combination of Data.

APPENDIX: SOME LIMITING THEOREMS 172

CHAPTER 5· LARGE SAMPLE TESTS OF HYPOTHESES WITH APPLICATIONS TO PROBLEMS OF ESTIMATION

5a THE GENERAL THEORY OF TESTS IN LARGE SAMPLES 176
5a.1 The Nature of Statistical Hypotheses.   5a.2 The Problem of Distribution.

5b APPLICATIONS OF THE GENERAL THEORY 179
5b.1 The χ^2 Test of Departure from a Simple Hypothesis.   5b.2 The χ^2 Test of Goodness of Fit.   5b.3 Tests of Homogeneity of Parallel Samples.

5c CONTINGENCY TABLES 191
5c.1 The Probability of an Observed Configuration and Tests in Large Samples.   5c.2 Tests of Independence in a Contingency Table.   5c.3 Tests of Independence in Small Samples.

5d TESTS IN POISSON POPULATIONS 205

5e TRANSFORMATION OF STATISTICS 207
5e.1 A General Lemma.   5e.2 The Square Root Transformation of the Poisson Variate.   5e.3 The Sin^{-1} Transformation of the Binomial Proportion.   5e.4 Other Useful Transformations.

5f LARGE SAMPLE STANDARD ERRORS OF MOMENTS 215
5f.1 Variances and Covariances of Raw Moment Statistics.   5f.2 Large Sample Tests of Difference between Means and an Illustration of the P_λ Test.   5f.3 Tests of Normality.

CHAPTER 6· TESTS OF HOMOGENEITY OF VARIANCES AND CORRELATIONS

6a HOMOGENEITY OF VARIANCES 221
6a.1 Test for a Specified Variance.   6a.2 Test for a Specified Inequality of Two Estimated Variances.   6a.3 The Likelihood Criterion and Its

Use. 6a.4 Practical Applications. 6a.5 Problems Requiring an Exact Treatment.

6b HOMOGENEITY OF CORRELATIONS 230
6b.1 Exact Test for Zero Correlation. 6b.2 Fisher's Tanh^{-1} Transformation. 6b.3 Test for a Given ρ. 6b.4 Test for the Equality of Two Correlation Coefficients. 6b.5 Test for the Homogeneity of a Set of Correlation Coefficients. 6b.6 Correction for Bias in the Test for Homogeneity and the Best Estimate of ρ.

CHAPTER 7· TESTS OF SIGNIFICANCE IN MULTIVARIATE ANALYSIS

7a REVIEW OF WORK ON MULTIVARIATE ANALYSIS 236

7b TESTS WITH DISCRIMINANT FUNCTIONS 237
7b.1 Two Fundamental Distributions. 7b.2 Problems of a Single Sample. 7b.3 Mahalanobis' D^2 and Problems of Two Samples. 7b.4 Test for an Assigned Discriminant Function. 7b.5 Tests for Discriminant Function Coefficients. 7b.6 The Additional Information Supplied by Some Characters.

7c GENERALIZATION OF D^2 AND THE LARGE SAMPLE THEORY FOR SEVERAL GROUPS 257

7d TESTS WITH WILKS'S Λ CRITERION 258
7d.1 Analysis of Dispersion and the Theoretical Aspects of the Λ Criterion. 7d.2 The Distribution of Λ and Its Practical Use. 7d.3 Test of Differences in Mean Values for Several Populations. 7d.4 Internal Analysis of a Set of Variates. 7d.5 Barnard's Problem of Secular Variations in Skull Characters.

CHAPTER 8· STATISTICAL INFERENCE APPLIED TO CLASSIFICATORY PROBLEMS

8a TESTS OF NULL HYPOTHESES 273
8a.1 Problems in Biological Research. 8a.2 Null Hypotheses. 8a.3 Power Function of Neyman and Pearson. 8a.4 Locally Most Powerful Unbiased Tests. 8a.5 Test for a Finite Number of Alternatives. 8a.6 Tests When the Alternatives Are Continuous.

8b PROBLEMS OF DISCRIMINATION 286
8b.1 The General Problem. 8b.2 The Discriminant Function of R. A. Fisher. 8b.3 Some Difficulties in the Use of the Best Discriminating Solution. 8b.4 Uncertainty of the A Priori Information That One of the Alternatives Is Correct. 8b.5 The Doubtful Region. 8b.6 Resolution of a Mixed Series into Two Gaussian Components. 8b.7 Sexing of Osteometric Material. 8b.8 The Problem of Three and More Groups. 8b.9 Application to Multivariate Normal Populations. 8b.10 Allocation of a Number of Individuals to Two or More Groups.

8c Discriminant Function for Selecting Genetically Desirable Types 329
8c.1 Prediction Formula for the Genotypic Value.   8c.2 The Genetic
Advance.

8d Problems of Optimum Selection 336
8d.1 A Single Predictor for Dichotomy.   8d.2 The Problem of Differential Predictors.

Appendix A 339
A1 A Lemma of Neyman and Pearson.   A2 A Generalization of the
Neyman-Pearson Lemma.   A3 A Slight Variation of Lemma A1.
A4 A Lemma on Power Functions.   A5 Two Lemmas Useful in
Classificatory Problems.

Appendix B 345
B1 On a Transformation Useful in Multivariate Computations.   B2
An Alternative Computational Scheme.

CHAPTER 9· THE CONCEPT OF DISTANCE AND THE
PROBLEM OF GROUP CONSTELLATIONS

9a Distance between Two Populations 351
9a.1 The Need for a Distance Function.   9a.2 Mathematical Concepts (Discriminatory Topology).   9a.3 Mahalanobis' Generalized
Distance.   9a.4 Karl Pearson's Coefficient of Racial Likeness.

9b An Illustrative Example 357
9b.1 Calculation of D^2.   9b.2 The Determination of Group Constellations.

9c The Use of Canonical Variates in Deriving Group Constellations 364
9c.1 Graphical Methods of Representing the Groups.   9c.2 The
Problem of Maximal Average D^2.   9c.3 An Illustrative Example.

9d A Test for Reduction in the Number of Dimensions 370
9d.1 The Analysis of Neurotic Cases.

APPENDIX: Miscellaneous Problems 379

INDEX 383

CHAPTER 1

Algebra of Vectors and Matrices

1a Vector Spaces

1a.1 Vectors

A set of ordered elements $(x_1, \cdots, x_n)$ is called a vector which may be simply denoted by $\mathbf{x}$. The elements may be n observations obtained in the order $x_1, x_2, \cdots, x_n$ from a population, in which case $\mathbf{x}$ is called the vector of observations.

Suppose that these observations are standardized by multiplying each of them by a constant c, otherwise known as a scalar. The resulting vector is $(cx_1, \cdots, cx_n)$ which may be represented by $c\mathbf{x}$. This is the rule for multiplying a vector $\mathbf{x}$ by a scalar c.

The weighted sum of observations with the vector $\mathbf{w}$ of weights $(w_1, \cdots, w_n)$ is

$$w_1 x_1 + \cdots + w_n x_n$$

This may be represented by $\mathbf{w} \cdot \mathbf{x}$, denoting the product of two vectors $\mathbf{w}$ and $\mathbf{x}$. The simple average of the observations is the result of multiplying the observation vector $\mathbf{x}$ by the weight vector $(1/n, \cdots, 1/n)$. The sum of squares of observations is the result of multiplying $\mathbf{x}$ by itself, i.e., $\mathbf{x} \cdot \mathbf{x} = \mathbf{x}^2 = x_1^2 + \cdots + x_n^2$.

If $\mathbf{x} = (x_1, \cdots, x_p)$ is the vector of p measurements on an individual and $\mathbf{y} = (y_1, \cdots, y_p)$ on another, then the sum of the measurements is the vector $(x_1 + y_1, \cdots, x_p + y_p)$ which may be represented by $\mathbf{x} + \mathbf{y}$. From the definitions given above we find the vector of average measurements

$$\frac{1}{2}(\mathbf{x} + \mathbf{y}) = \left(\frac{x_1 + y_1}{2}, \cdots, \frac{x_p + y_p}{2} \right)$$

In general,

$$a\mathbf{x} + b\mathbf{y} + c\mathbf{z} = (ax_1 + by_1 + cz_1, \cdots, ax_p + by_p + cz_p)$$

where a, b, c are scalars and $\mathbf{x}$, $\mathbf{y}$, $\mathbf{z}$ are vectors. The vector $\mathbf{0} = (0, \cdots, 0)$ is called the null vector. It is easy to verify that any vector

1

added to the null one remains unchanged and any vector multiplied by the null vector reduces to zero.

1a.2   Linear Independence and Orthogonality

A set of vectors $(\mathbf{x}, \mathbf{y}, \cdots)$ are said to be independent if none of them can be expressed as a linear combination of the rest. For instance, the vectors $(1, 0, 1, -1, 2)$, $(3, 2, -1, 1, 2)$, and $(9, 4, 1, -1, 10)$ are not independent since the last vector is the sum of 3 times the first and 2 times the second. Two non-null vectors are said to be orthogonal if their product is zero. A set of orthogonal vectors with real elements are necessarily independent. If not, then

$$\mathbf{x} = a\mathbf{y} + b\mathbf{z} + \cdots$$

Multiplying by $\mathbf{x}$

$$\mathbf{x} \cdot \mathbf{x} = a\mathbf{x} \cdot \mathbf{y} + b\mathbf{x} \cdot \mathbf{z} + \cdots = 0$$

$$\mathbf{x} \cdot \mathbf{x} = x_1^2 + x_2^2 + \cdots = 0$$

which means that $x_1 = x_2 = \cdots = 0$ or $\mathbf{x}$ is a null vector.

1a.3   Vector Spaces and the Sweep-Out Method

The totality of vectors obtained by linear combinations of a set of vectors is called a vector space. Such a totality can be generated by a set of independent vectors called a basis of the vector space. If the number of vectors in a basis is m, then the vector space is said to be of rank or dimensions m. In practical problems it is sometimes necessary to obtain the rank of a vector space formed by the vectors

$$
\begin{array}{cccc}
a_{11} & a_{12} & \cdots & a_{1n} \\
a_{21} & a_{22} & \cdots & a_{2n} \\
\cdot & \cdot & \cdots & \cdot \\
a_{r1} & a_{r2} & \cdots & a_{rn}
\end{array}
$$

The arrangement of the elements a_{ij} in rows and columns as above is known as a matrix. A convenient way of finding the rank is by a method known as "sweep out," consisting in the following operations:

(i) Any vector having a non-zero value for the first element is taken, and all its elements are divided by the first so that the resulting vector is of the form

$$(1, \quad c_2, \quad \cdots, \quad c_n)$$

If the elements of the first column are all zero, then it is omitted to start with.

(ii) From every other vector is subtracted a vector obtained by multiplying $(1, c_2, \cdots, c_n)$ by the first element of the former vector so that the resulting vectors, except the one chosen in (i), have zero as their first element. The first column is said to be swept out by the vector called the pivotal row chosen above.

(iii) Omission of the pivotal row and the first column results in a reduced matrix on which operations (i) and (ii) are repeated until a single non-zero row or all null rows are left over. A single non-zero row left over may be regarded as the last pivotal row, in which case the rank of the matrix or of the vector space is equal to the number of pivotal rows. An example is given below with four rows.

Column No.					
Row No.	(1)	(2)	(3)	(4)	
(1)	0	1	2	3	
(2)	2	−1	5	4	
(3)	4	0	6	1	
(4)	0	−2	4	7	
					Operations on rows
(5)	1	−0.5	2.5	2	$(2) \div 2$ 1st pivotal row
(6)		1	2	3	$(1) - (5) \times 0$
(7)		2	−4	− 7	$(3) - (5) \times 4$
(8)		−2	4	7	$(4) - (5) \times 0$
(9)		1	2	3	$(6) \div 1$ 2nd pivotal row
(10)			−8	−13	$(7) - (9) \times 2$
(11)			8	13	$(8) - (9) \times -2$
(12)			1	$1\frac{3}{8}$	$(10) \div -8$ 3rd pivotal row
(13)				0	$(11) - (12) \times 8$

The rank of the vector space is, therefore, 3, the independent vectors being the pivotal rows

$$\begin{array}{cccc} 1 & -0.5 & 2.5 & 2 \\ 0 & 1 & 2 & 3 \\ 0 & 0 & 1 & 1\frac{3}{8} \end{array}$$

1a.4   The Orthogonal Vector Space and the Deficiency Matrix

The set of vectors orthogonal to all the vectors in a matrix generates an orthogonal vector space since any linear combination in it satisfies the orthogonality condition. The basis of the orthogonal vector space can be found in a simple way by an extension of the sweep-out process described above. Consider the basis of the vector space in the above example and sweep out the third and second columns using the third and second rows, yielding

$$1 \quad 0 \quad 0 \quad -{}^{35}\!\!/_{16}$$

$$0 \quad 1 \quad 0 \quad -\,{}^{1}\!\!/_{4}$$

$$0 \quad 0 \quad 1 \quad \quad {}^{13}\!\!/_{8}$$

which forms another basis for the same vector space. In general, the sweep-out method gives a reduced matrix (after a suitable rearrangement of columns if necessary to bring the unit elements to the diagonal) of the form

$$S: \quad \begin{matrix} 1 & 0 & \cdots & 0 & b_{11} & \cdots & b_{1k} \\ 0 & 1 & \cdots & 0 & b_{21} & \cdots & b_{2k} \\ \cdot & \cdot & \cdots & \cdot & \cdot & \cdots & \cdot \\ 0 & 0 & \cdots & 1 & b_{r1} & \cdots & b_{rk} \end{matrix}$$

All these vectors are independent. Consider the set of independent vectors

$$D: \quad \begin{matrix} b_{11} & b_{21} & \cdots & b_{r1} & -1 & 0 & \cdots & 0 \\ b_{12} & b_{22} & \cdots & b_{r2} & 0 & -1 & \cdots & 0 \\ \cdot & \cdot & \cdots & \cdot & \cdot & \cdot & \cdots & \cdot \\ b_{1k} & b_{2k} & \cdots & b_{rk} & 0 & 0 & \cdots & -1 \end{matrix}$$

which is obtained by a rearrangement of the elements in S. The vectors in D are mutually orthogonal to those in S. Since $(r + k)$ is the total number of independent vectors possible, D contains all vectors orthogonal to S and for this reason is termed the deficiency matrix. In the above example, the deficiency matrix consists of the single row

$$D: \quad -\tfrac{35}{16} \quad -\tfrac{1}{4} \quad \tfrac{13}{8} \quad -1$$

Example 1. In a matrix the number of independent row vectors is equal to the number of independent column vectors.

Example 2. If each vector consists of n elements, then there cannot be more than n independent vectors in a set.

Example 3. Any vector of n elements can be expressed as a linear combination of any given set of vectors with rank n.

Example 4. The rank of the matrix

$$
\begin{array}{cccc}
1 - \dfrac{1}{n} & -\dfrac{1}{n} & \cdots & -\dfrac{1}{n} \\[2mm]
-\dfrac{1}{n} & 1 - \dfrac{1}{n} & \cdots & -\dfrac{1}{n} \\[2mm]
\cdot & \cdot & \cdots & \cdot \\[2mm]
-\dfrac{1}{n} & -\dfrac{1}{n} & \cdots & 1 - \dfrac{1}{n}
\end{array}
$$

containing n rows and n columns, is $(n - 1)$.

1a.5 Linear Equations

The m equations in n unknowns $x_1, \cdots, x_n$

$$a_{11}x_1 + \cdots + a_{1n}x_n = 0$$
$$\cdot \quad \cdots \quad \cdot$$
$$a_{m1}x_1 + \cdots + a_{mn}x_n = 0$$

are called homogeneous linear equations. Since any solution considered as a vector is orthogonal to every vector of the matrix

$$
M: \qquad
\begin{array}{ccc}
a_{11} & \cdots & a_{1n} \\
\cdot & \cdots & \cdot \\
a_{m1} & \cdots & a_{mn}
\end{array}
$$

the totality of the solution vectors forms a space orthogonal to M. The basis of this orthogonal space is the deficiency matrix D to be determined as in the previous section. If the rank of M is r, then the solution space has a basis consisting of $(n - r)$ independent vectors.

Replacing the zeros in the above equations by $b_1, \cdots, b_m$, we obtain a set of non-homogeneous equations which can be regarded as homogeneous in $(n + 1)$ unknowns.

$$a_{11}x_1 + \cdots + a_{1n}x_n - b_1 x_{n+1} = 0$$
$$\cdot \quad \cdots \quad \cdot \quad \cdot \quad \cdot$$
$$a_{m1}x_1 + \cdots + a_{mn}x_n - b_m x_{n+1} = 0$$

Only those solutions for which $x_{n+1} \neq 0$ will yield solutions to the non-homogeneous equations. If $\mathbf{c} = (c_1, \cdots, c_m)$ is any vector orthogonal to column vectors in M, then, multiplying the above equations by

$c_1, \cdots, c_m$ and adding, we obtain

$$x_{n+1}(b_1 c_1 + \cdots + b_m c_m) = 0$$

If $\Sigma b_i c_i \neq 0$ for at least one $\mathbf{c}$, then $x_{n+1} = 0$. On the other hand, if $(b_1, \cdots, b_m)$ is dependent on the column vectors in M, then $\Sigma b_i c_i = 0$ for all $\mathbf{c}$ orthogonal to M, in which case the number of independent column vectors in N, obtained by adding the column vector with elements $b_1, b_2, \cdots, b_m$ to M, remains the same as before. This means that the homogeneous equations in $(n + 1)$ unknowns have $(n + 1 - r)$ independent solutions. Of these, $(n - r)$ independent solutions are the vectors in D, the deficiency matrix of M, with zeros added to form the $(n + 1)$th elements. The one more independent solution must necessarily have a non-zero value of x_{n+1}, for otherwise it leads to a contradiction. Hence the necessary and sufficient condition for the non-homogeneous equations to have a solution is that $(b_1, \cdots, b_m)$ is dependent on the column vectors or that the ranks of N and M are equal.

Example 1. Find the value of δ for which the equations in three unknowns

$$2x_1 - x_2 + 5x_3 = 4$$

$$4x_1 + 6x_3 = 1$$

$$-2x_2 + 4x_3 = 7 + \delta$$

admit a solution.

1b   Theory of Matrices and Determinants

1b.1   Matrices

A matrix is, in general, an arrangement of pq elements in p rows and q columns. If A and B are two matrices of the form (p, q)

$$A = \begin{pmatrix} a_{11} & \cdots & a_{1q} \\ \cdot & \cdots & \cdot \\ a_{p1} & \cdots & a_{pq} \end{pmatrix} \quad \text{and} \quad B = \begin{pmatrix} b_{11} & \cdots & b_{1q} \\ \cdot & \cdots & \cdot \\ b_{p1} & \cdots & b_{pq} \end{pmatrix}$$

then matrix addition is defined by

$$A + B = \begin{pmatrix} a_{11} + b_{11} & \cdots & a_{1q} + b_{1q} \\ \cdot & \cdots & \cdot \\ a_{p1} + b_{p1} & \cdots & a_{pq} + b_{pq} \end{pmatrix}$$

When there is no ambiguity about the number of rows and columns, it may be convenient to denote the matrices A and B by (a_{ij}) and (b_{ij}), in which case $A + B = (a_{ij} + b_{ij})$. This process is known as matrix addition. Just as in the case of vectors, a matrix can be multiplied by a scalar c, the law of multiplication being

$$cA = \begin{pmatrix} ca_{11} & \cdots & ca_{1q} \\ \cdot & \cdots & \cdot \\ ca_{p1} & \cdots & ca_{pq} \end{pmatrix} = (ca_{ij})$$

Consider two matrices A and B such that the number of columns in the first is equal to the number of rows in the second. For instance,

$$A = \begin{pmatrix} a_{11} & a_{12} \\ a_{21} & a_{22} \end{pmatrix} \quad \text{and} \quad B = \begin{pmatrix} b_{11} & b_{12} & b_{13} \\ b_{21} & b_{22} & b_{23} \end{pmatrix}$$

are two such matrices. The product AB of A and B is defined to be a matrix whose (i, j)th element is the product of the ith row vector of A and the jth column vector of B.

$$AB = \begin{pmatrix} a_{11}b_{11} + a_{12}b_{21} & a_{11}b_{12} + a_{12}b_{22} & a_{11}b_{13} + a_{12}b_{23} \\ a_{21}b_{11} + a_{22}b_{21} & a_{21}b_{12} + a_{22}b_{22} & a_{21}b_{13} + a_{22}b_{23} \end{pmatrix}$$

In general, two matrices A and B can be multiplied in the above manner only when the number of rows in A is equal to the number of columns in B. The resulting matrix has the same number of rows as in A and the same number of columns as in B.

The product AB is not, in general, equal to the product BA. When the product AB is considered, A is said to be post-multiplied by B or B pre-multiplied by A.

The product law is associative so that the product of three matrices A, B, C can be done in any of the following ways:

$$ABC = A(BC) = (AB)C$$

For multiplication to be compatible the matrices A, B, C should be of the form (p, q), (q, r), (r, s), in which case the triple product is of the form (p, s). Observe the rule:

$$(p, q)(q, r)(r, s) = (p, s)$$

The matrix A' obtained by interchanging the rows and columns of A is called the transpose of A. From the definition it follows that

$$(AB)' = B'A' \qquad (ABC)' = C'B'A' \qquad \text{etc.}$$

If **x** is a row vector, then **x**′ will be a column vector, in which case the vector multiplication **x**·**y** of two vectors **x** and **y** can also be written **xy**′. Both representations will be used throughout.

A matrix that contains all zero elements is called a null matrix. It is easy to verify that the addition of a null matrix leaves any matrix unaltered whereas multiplication by a null matrix reduces any other matrix to a null matrix.

A matrix with equal number of rows and columns having unity for all its diagonal elements and zero elsewhere is called a unit matrix represented by I. It is easy to verify that

$$AI = A \qquad \text{and} \qquad IA = A$$

provided that multiplication is permissible. The distributive law holds for matrix multiplication.

$$A(B + C) = AB + AC$$

$$(A + B)(C + D) = AC + AD + BC + BD$$

A matrix of the form (n, n) is said to be a square matrix. A square matrix is said to be symmetric if the elements in the ith row, jth column and the jth row, ith column are equal.

The rank of a matrix, as defined in 1a.3, is the number of independent rows it contains. This is also equal to the number of independent columns (example 1, 1a.4). The method of sweep out discussed in 1a.3 is very convenient for determining the rank of a matrix. The following examples concerning the rank of a matrix will be useful.

Example 1. If A is a square symmetric matrix of the form (n, n), such that

$$A(I - A) = 0$$

where I is the unit matrix, then rank A + rank $(I - A) = n$.

The condition $A(I - A) = 0$ implies that vectors in A, being orthogonal to the vectors in $(I - A)$, are independent of the vectors in $(I - A)$. If r and s are the numbers of independent vectors or the ranks of A and $(I - A)$, then the number of independent vectors in A and $(I - A)$ put together is $(r + s)$. If every row in $(I - A)$ is replaced by the sum of the corresponding rows in $(I - A)$ and A, then n rows of the form

$$
\begin{matrix}
1 & 0 & \cdots & 0 \\
0 & 1 & \cdots & 0 \\
\cdot & \cdot & \cdots & \cdot \\
0 & 0 & \cdots & 1
\end{matrix}
$$

are obtained. These being independent, it follows that the number of independent vectors in A and $(I - A)$ is not less than n. Since there are only n elements in a vector, this is the maximum possible number of independent vectors. Hence $(r + s) = n$.

Example 2. The rank of the product AB is not greater than the rank of A or the rank of B.

The product AB can be obtained from B by suitable linear combinations of rows. This process does not increase the number of independent rows in B. Therefore rank $AB \not> $ rank B. Also $(AB)' = B'A'$, so that the above argument leads to the result rank $(AB)' \not> $ rank A', which means that rank $AB \not> $ rank A.

Example 3. Let $\alpha_1, \cdots, \alpha_r$ be a set of r vectors generating a vector space. If $\beta_1, \cdots, \beta_s$ are s independent vectors, then the maximum number of independent vectors belonging to the β space and lying entirely in the α space is equal to t, where $(s - t)$ is the rank of the matrix $(\delta_i \cdot \beta_j)$, $(i = 1, \cdots, j = 1, \cdots, s)$, and $\delta_1, \delta_2 \cdots$ are the independent vectors generating the vector space orthogonal to the α space. In other words, there are t independent linear functions of β which can be expressed as linear functions of α only.

Consider any linear function

$$\gamma = l_1 \beta_1 + \cdots + l_s \beta_s$$

and express the condition that it is orthogonal to $\delta_1, \delta_2, \cdots$.

$$l_1 \delta_i \cdot \beta_1 + \cdots + l_s \delta_i \cdot \beta_s = 0 \qquad i = 1, 2, \cdots$$

The number of independent solutions is evidently s minus the rank of $(\delta_i \cdot \beta_j)$. Each solution supplies a linear combination of β lying in the α space. If $\gamma_1, \cdots, \gamma_t$ are these vectors, then there are $(s - t)$ more vectors belonging to the β space, $\gamma_{t+1}, \cdots, \gamma_s$ such that no linear combination of $\gamma_{t+1}, \cdots, \gamma_s$ belongs to the α space, for otherwise a contradiction is obtained.

Example 4. If the row vectors of a square matrix are all mutually orthogonal and the square of each row vector is unity, so are its column vectors.

1b.2 Partitioned Matrices

Sometimes it is convenient to represent a matrix obtained by the juxtaposition of two or more matrices in a partitioned form. Thus a partitioned matrix A is represented by

$$A = \left(\begin{array}{c|c} P & Q \\ \hline R & S \end{array} \right)$$

where the rows in P equal in number those in Q, the columns in P equal those in R, and so on. By definition,

$$A' = \left(\begin{array}{c|c} P' & R' \\ \hline Q' & S' \end{array} \right)$$

If

$$B = \left(\begin{array}{c|c} E & F \\ \hline G & H \end{array} \right)$$

then

$$AB = \left(\begin{array}{c|c} P & Q \\ \hline R & S \end{array} \right)\left(\begin{array}{c|c} E & F \\ \hline G & H \end{array} \right) = \left(\begin{array}{c|c} PE + QG & PF + QH \\ \hline RE + SG & RF + SH \end{array} \right)$$

provided that the products PE, etc., are permissible.

1b.3　Determinants

A determinant is a real valued function of the elements of a square matrix. If $x_1, x_2, \cdots, x_p$ denote the row vectors, then the function may be represented by $D(x_1, \cdots, x_p)$. We shall choose the function to satisfy the following conditions:

(a) $D(x_1, \cdots, cx_m, \cdots, x_p) = cD(x_1, \cdots, x_m, \cdots, x_p)$, where c is a scalar.

(b) $D(x_1, \cdots, x_m + x_k, \cdots, x_p) = D(x_1, \cdots, x_m, \cdots, x_p)$, for $m \neq k$.

(c) $D(e_1, \cdots, e_p) = 1$, where $e_1, \cdots, e_p$ constitute the vectors of a unit matrix and are called elementary vectors.

Let D exist when the following properties hold:

(1) If $x_i = 0$, then $x_i = 0x_i$; hence, by (a), $D = 0$, putting $c = 0$.

(2) $D(x_1, \cdots, x_m + cx_k, \cdots, x_p) = D(x_1, \cdots, x_m, \cdots, x_p)$.

This is true when $c = 0$. If c is not zero, then

$$D(x_1, \cdots, x_m + cx_k, \cdots, x_p)$$

$$= -\frac{1}{c} D(x_1, \cdots, x_m + cx_k, \cdots, -cx_k, \cdots, x_p) \qquad \text{by (a)}$$

$$= -\frac{1}{c} D(x_1, \cdots, x_m, \cdots, -cx_k, \cdots, x_p) \qquad \text{by (b)}$$

$$= D(x_1, \cdots, x_p) \qquad \text{by (a)}$$

(3) From (2) it follows that, if the rows are dependent, then $D = 0$. As a particular case, if two rows are identical the determinant vanishes.

(4) If two rows are interchanged, then D changes sign.

$$D = D(\mathbf{x}_1, \cdots, \mathbf{x}_m + \mathbf{x}_k, \cdots, \mathbf{x}_k, \cdots, \mathbf{x}_p)$$

$$= D(\mathbf{x}_1, \cdots, \mathbf{x}_m + \mathbf{x}_k, \cdots, \mathbf{x}_k - \mathbf{x}_m - \mathbf{x}_k, \cdots, \mathbf{x}_p)$$

$$= D(\mathbf{x}_1, \cdots, \mathbf{x}_m + \mathbf{x}_k, \cdots, -\mathbf{x}_m, \cdots, \mathbf{x}_p)$$

$$= D(\mathbf{x}_1, \cdots, \mathbf{x}_k, \cdots, -\mathbf{x}_m, \cdots, \mathbf{x}_p)$$

$$= -D(\mathbf{x}_1, \cdots, \mathbf{x}_k, \cdots, \mathbf{x}_m, \cdots, \mathbf{x}_p)$$

In general, an even permutation of rows does not alter the determinant whereas an odd permutation changes sign.

(5)

$$D(\mathbf{x}_1, \cdots, \mathbf{x}_m + \mathbf{y}, \cdots, \mathbf{x}_p)$$
$$= D(\mathbf{x}_1, \cdots, \mathbf{x}_m, \cdots, \mathbf{x}_p) + D(\mathbf{x}_1, \cdots, \mathbf{y}, \cdots, \mathbf{x}_p)$$

If $\mathbf{x}_m$ depends on the rest of $\mathbf{x}$, the result is established by subtracting a suitable linear combination of other vectors from the mth vector in each of the above determinants. If the other vectors are themselves dependent, then each term above is zero. The only alternative is that all $\mathbf{x}$ are independent, in which case $\mathbf{y}$ is necessarily a linear function of $\mathbf{x}$ (because there cannot be more than p independent vectors).

$$\mathbf{y} = \Sigma c_i \mathbf{x}_i$$

$$D(\mathbf{x}_1, \cdots, \mathbf{x}_m + \Sigma c_i \mathbf{x}_i, \cdots, \mathbf{x}_p) = (1 + c_m) D(\mathbf{x}_1, \cdots, \mathbf{x}_m, \cdots, \mathbf{x}_p)$$

$$= D(\mathbf{x}_1, \cdots, \mathbf{x}_m, \cdots, \mathbf{x}_p) + D(\mathbf{x}_1, \cdots, c_m \mathbf{x}_m, \cdots, \mathbf{x}_p)$$

$$= D(\mathbf{x}_1, \cdots, \mathbf{x}_m, \cdots, \mathbf{x}_p) + D(\mathbf{x}_1, \cdots, \Sigma c_i \mathbf{x}_i, \cdots, \mathbf{x}_p)$$

(6) $D(\mathbf{x}_1 + \mathbf{y}_1, \cdots, \mathbf{x}_p + \mathbf{y}_p) = \Sigma D(\mathbf{z}_1, \cdots, \mathbf{z}_p)$, where $\mathbf{z}_i$ can be $\mathbf{x}_i$ or $\mathbf{y}_i$ and the summation is over 2^p possible sets, $\mathbf{z}_1, \cdots, \mathbf{z}_p$. This follows by repeated application of (5).

(7) Any vector $\mathbf{x}_m = a_{m1}\mathbf{e}_1 + a_{m2}\mathbf{e}_2 + \cdots + a_{mp}\mathbf{e}_p$, where $\mathbf{e}_1, \cdots, \mathbf{e}_p$ are elementary vectors. Therefore

$$D(\mathbf{x}_1, \cdots, \mathbf{x}_m, \cdots, \mathbf{x}_p) = D(\Sigma a_{1i}\mathbf{e}_i, \mathbf{x}_2, \cdots, \mathbf{x}_p)$$

$$= \Sigma a_{1i} D(\mathbf{e}_i, \mathbf{x}_2, \cdots, \mathbf{x}_p)$$

$$= \Sigma a_{1i} a_{2j} D(\mathbf{e}_i, \mathbf{e}_j, \cdots, \mathbf{x}_p)$$

$$= \Sigma a_{1i} a_{2j} \cdots a_{pk} D(\mathbf{e}_i, \mathbf{e}_j, \cdots, \mathbf{e}_k)$$

In the final summation,

$$D(\mathbf{e}_i, \mathbf{e}_j, \cdots, \mathbf{e}_k) = 0 \qquad \text{whenever two suffixes are equal}$$

$$= +1 \qquad \text{when } i, j, \cdots \text{ is an even permutation of}$$
$$1, 2, \cdots, p$$

$$= -1 \qquad \text{when } i, j, \cdots \text{ is an odd permutation}$$

Hence

$$D = \Sigma \pm a_{1i}a_{2j} \cdots a_{pk}$$

The function so derived satisfies the conditions (a), (b), and (c) given above and is called the value of the determinant of the square matrix (a_{ij}) and is also denoted by $|\, a_{ij}\,|$ or simply $|\, A\,|$.

(8)

$$D = \Sigma a_{mi}D(\mathbf{x}_1, \cdots, \mathbf{e}_i, \cdots, \mathbf{x}_p)$$

$$= \Sigma a_{mi}A_{mi}$$

where A_{mi} is the determinant obtained by replacing the mth vector by $\mathbf{e}_i$ and is called the *cofactor* of a_{mi}. The minor of a_{mi} is defined as the determinant obtained by omitting the mth row and ith column. The cofactor is obtained from the minor by the relation

$$A_{mi} = (-1)^{i+m} \times \text{the minor of } a_{mi}$$

(9) It is easy to verify that

$$\sum_i a_{mi}A_{si} = 0 \qquad \text{if} \qquad m \neq s$$

because this is the value of a determinant with the mth and sth rows identical.

From the definition it follows that, when the rank of the matrix A of the type (n, n) is less than n, then $|\, A\,| = 0$. To prove the converse, it is necessary to recall the sweep-out method described in 1a.3. When a column is swept out the only operation that changes the value of the determinant is the division by a non-zero element, also called the pivotal element, to obtain the pivotal row. The pivotal row may be moved to the first position if necessary by an interchange of rows in which case the determinant changes sign. Expanding by the first column, it is seen the determinant of this altered matrix is same as the determinant of the reduced matrix of one order less obtained by the omission of the pivotal row and the swept-out column. This means that $|\, A\,|$ is, apart from a sign, equal to the determinant of the reduced matrix at any stage multiplied by the product of the pivotal elements used up to that stage. If the rank of A is less than n, a zero row will be encountered at some stage leading to a null value of the reduced matrix. If A has full rank, then the sweep-out process can be carried out to the last row giving a non-zero value to $| A |$. Hence,

(i) If $| A | = 0$, the rank of A must be less than n.

(ii) If $| A | \neq 0$, the rank of A is n, or in other words the rows and columns of A are all independent.

Example 1. If $| A |$, the determinant of A, is not zero, in which case A is called a non-singular matrix, then there exists a matrix represented by A^{-1} such that

$$AA^{-1} = A^{-1}A = I$$

Defining the matrix

$$A^{-1} = (a^{ij})$$

where $a^{ij} = A_{ji}/| A |$, A_{ji} being the cofactor of a_{ji}, it is easy to verify that the above result is true. The matrix A^{-1} is called the reciprocal of A and is defined only when $| A | \neq 0$.

Example 2. If X is an unknown matrix involved in the equation $XA = Y$, then $X = YA^{-1}$, provided that A^{-1} exists.

Example 3. If B is a matrix of the form (m, n) and A of the form (n, n) with rank n, then

$$\text{Rank } B = \text{Rank } BA$$

Let s be the rank of B and r that of BA. Since B is the product of BA and A^{-1}, s is not greater than r. This in conjunction with the earlier result (example 2, 1b.1) yields $s = r$.

Example 4. If the rank of a matrix A is r, then all subdeterminants of the order $(r + 1)$ or greater vanish. This is true because there are not more than r independent rows or columns. Conversely, if all determinants of the order $(r + 1)$ or greater vanish and at least one determinant of the order r does not vanish, then the rank of A is r.

Example 5. The rank of a matrix A is unaltered by pre- or post-multiplication by an elementary matrix $E_{rs}(\lambda)$ where $E_{rs}(\lambda)$ is defined by (e_{ij}).

$$e_{ii} = 1 \quad \text{for all } i$$

$$e_{ij} = \lambda \quad \text{for } i = r \text{ and } j = s$$

$$e_{ij} = 0 \quad \text{for other values of } i \text{ and } j$$

The proposition is true because $| E_{rs}(\lambda) | \neq 0$. Pre-multiplication by $E_{rs}(\lambda)$ means replacing the rth row of A by its rth row $+ \lambda$ times the sth row. Post-multiplication means replacing the sth column of A by the sth column $+ \lambda$ times the rth column.

Example 6. If A is a square symmetric matrix, then there exists a non-singular matrix B such that the matrix BAB' is in the diagonal form.

If there is a non-zero diagonal element in A, then it may be used as a pivot and the row and column in which it occurs can be swept out, leaving a reduced matrix. This method consists in only row and column additions or, in other words, pre- and post-multiplications by elementary matrices. Since the matrix is symmetrical, the symmetrical elements in a row and column can be swept out by pre- and post-multiplying by elementary matrices which are only transposes. Thus, sweeping out a row and column is equivalent to pre- and post-multiplying by products of elementary matrices which are transposes. The reduced matrix is also symmetrical. The above process can be carried on whenever a non-zero diagonal element can be found. If a non-zero diagonal element cannot be found, then, by the addition of a row and the corresponding column a non-zero element can be brought to the diagonal position and the above process continued. This is also a symmetrical operation by the use of elementary matrices, so that it follows that the matrix A can be reduced to the diagonal form by pre- and post-multiplying by B and B' where B is a product of elementary matrices.

It can be easily seen that any non-symmetrical square matrix A can be reduced to the diagonal form by pre- and post-multiplications by matrices which need not be transposes.

Example 7. If the product AB of two square matrices is zero, then either $A = 0$, or $B = 0$, or both A and B are singular matrices.

Example 8. If A and B are square matrices of order n and ranks r and s, then

$$\text{Rank } AB \geq r + s - n$$

From example 6 there exist two non-singular matrices C and D such that

$$CAD = \begin{pmatrix} I & 0 \\ \hline 0 & 0 \end{pmatrix}$$

where I is the unit matrix (r, r).

$$\text{Rank of } AB = \text{Rank of } CAB \quad \text{since } C \text{ is non-singular}$$

$$= \text{Rank of } CADD^{-1}B$$

$$= \text{Rank of } \begin{pmatrix} I & 0 \\ \hline 0 & 0 \end{pmatrix} B_1$$

where $B_1 = D^{-1}B$ and hence has rank s. The last product is a matrix obtained by choosing the first r rows of B_1 and the rest consisting of zero rows. Therefore the rank of AB is equal to the rank of the first r rows of B_1. If this is equal to t, then the number of dependent rows is $(r - t)$. By considering all rows of B, we get $(n - s)$ dependent rows which must not be less than the dependent vectors in a subset. Hence

$$r - t \leq n - s$$

or

$$t \geq r + s - n$$

Example 9. $\left| AB \right| = \left| A \right| \left| B \right|$ where A and B are two square matrices.

There exist matrices E and F which are products of elementary matrices such that

$$EAF = D$$

where D is diagonal with elements $d_1, \cdots, d_p$ so that $\left| A \right| = d_1 \cdots d_p$.

$$AB = AFF^{-1}B$$

$$\left| AB \right| = \left| EAFF^{-1}B \right|$$

Since the determinant is not altered on multiplication by elementary matrices,

$$\left| AB \right| = \left| DF^{-1}B \right|$$

$$= d_1 d_2 \cdots d_p \left| F^{-1}B \right| = d_1 \cdots d_p \left| B \right| = \left| A \right| \left| B \right|$$

Example 10. If A is a matrix of the type (m, n), then

$$\left| AA' \right| \geq 0 \qquad \text{if } m \leq n$$

$$= 0 \qquad \text{if } m > n$$

If $m \leq n$, there exists * a matrix B of the type $(n - m, n)$ containing row vectors which are orthogonal to those in A (i.e., $AB' = 0$) and satisfying the condition $BB' = I$. Consider the product

$$\binom{B}{A} (B' \; A') = \left(\frac{BB' \; | \; BA'}{AB' \; | \; AA'} \right) = \left(\frac{I \; | \; 0}{0 \; | \; AA'} \right)$$

Taking determinants,

$$\left| \frac{B}{A} \right|^2 = \left| AA' \right| \geq 0$$

* Consider the equations $xA' = 0$. This has at least $(n - m)$ independent solution vectors which may be replaced by an equivalent set of standardized orthogonal vectors. These vectors form the matrix B.

If $m > n$, then

$$(A \mid 0) \left(\frac{A'}{0} \right) = AA' + 0 = AA'$$

where 0 stands for a null matrix. Taking determinants,

$$\mid AA' \mid = \mid A \mid 0 \mid^2 = 0$$

Example 11. If A is a matrix of the type (m, n), $m \leq n$, then:
(i) $\mid AA' \mid$ = the sum of squares of all possible m columned determinants in A.
(ii) Rank of AA' = Rank of A.
Let $A = (a_{ij})$, in which case

$$AA' = (\Sigma a_{ir} a_{jr})$$

$$\mid AA' \mid = \Sigma \begin{vmatrix} a_{1r}a_{1r} & a_{2s}a_{1s} & \cdots & a_{mt}a_{1t} \\ \cdot & \cdot & \cdots & \cdot \\ a_{1r}a_{mr} & a_{2s}a_{ms} & \cdots & a_{mt}a_{mt} \end{vmatrix}$$

summed over all n^m sets of $(r, s, \cdots, t)$; $(r, s, \cdots, t = 1, 2, \cdots, n)$. In this summation it is easy to see that the determinants in which any two of the symbols $(r, s, \cdots, t)$ are equal vanish so that the summation is over sets in which $r \neq s \cdots \neq t$. Corresponding to any set $(r, s, \cdots, t)$ there are m^m permutations, the determinants arising out of which can be grouped into a single determinant. Thus

$$\mid AA' \mid = \Sigma \begin{vmatrix} a_{1r}a_{1r} + \cdots + a_{1t}a_{1t} & \cdots & a_{1r}a_{mr} + \cdots + a_{1t}a_{mt} \\ \cdot & \cdots & \cdot \\ a_{mr}a_{1r} + \cdots + a_{mt}a_{1t} & \cdots & a_{mr}a_{mr} + \cdots + a_{mt}a_{mt} \end{vmatrix}$$

summed over the ^nc_m combinations $(r, s, \cdots, t)$ from 1 to n,

$$= \Sigma \begin{vmatrix} a_{1r} & a_{1s} & \cdots & a_{1t} \\ a_{2r} & a_{2s} & \cdots & a_{2t} \\ \cdot & \cdot & \cdots & \cdot \\ a_{mr} & a_{ms} & \cdots & a_{mt} \end{vmatrix}^2$$

which proves result (i).

To prove (ii), let the rank of A be r so that there are r independent vectors which may be marked. In the product AA', the marked rows and the corresponding columns in A' give rise to a determinant of order r which, by the above proposition, is equal to the sum of squares of all possible r columned determinants chosen out of the r marked rows.

Since the r rows in A are independent, there is at least one determinant containing r independent columns in it, so that the rth-order determinant obtained from the marked rows and columns in A and A' is not zero. Therefore, the rank of $AA' \not< r$. But the rank of the product AA' cannot exceed the rank of A, which is r. Therefore, the rank of AA' = the rank of A.

Example 12. Defining for any $x_1, \cdots, x_n$

$$S_j = (x_1 - \bar{x})^j + (x_2 - \bar{x})^j + \cdots + (x_n - \bar{x})^j = d_1^{\ j} + d_2^{\ j} + \cdots + d_n^{\ j}$$

$$\bar{x} = \frac{x_1 + x_2 + \cdots + x_n}{n}$$

$$d_i = (x_i - \bar{x}) \qquad i = 1, 2, \cdots, n$$

show that the determinant

$$\begin{vmatrix} S_0 & S_1 & \cdots & S_i \\ S_1 & S_2 & \cdots & S_{i+1} \\ \cdot & \cdot & \cdots & \cdot \\ S_i & S_{i+1} & \cdots & S_{i+i} \end{vmatrix}$$

is not less than zero for all i.

This follows from the fact that the above determinant is $\left| AA' \right| \geq 0$ (example 10 above), where

$$A = \begin{vmatrix} 1 & 1 & \cdots & 1 \\ d_1 & d_2 & \cdots & d_n \\ \cdot & \cdot & \cdots & \cdot \\ d_1^{\ i} & d_2^{\ i} & \cdots & d_n^{\ i} \end{vmatrix}$$

This proves the consistency relations to be satisfied by the moments calculated from any sample of observations.

Example 13. The jth moment of a number of variables is defined by $\mu_j = S_j/n$, where S_j is as in example 12. Two constants β_1 and β_2 defined by K. Pearson are

$$\beta_1 = \frac{\mu_3^{\ 2}}{\mu_2^{\ 3}} \qquad \beta_2 = \frac{\mu_4}{\mu_2^{\ 2}}$$

To show that $\beta_2 \geq 1 + \beta_1$, consider the determinant of example 12 for $i = 2$.

$$\begin{vmatrix} n & 0 & n\mu_2 \\ 0 & n\mu_2 & n\mu_3 \\ n\mu_2 & n\mu_3 & n\mu_4 \end{vmatrix} \geq 0$$

Expanding,
$$n^3(\mu_2\mu_4 - \mu_3{}^2 - \mu_2{}^3) \geq 0$$
Hence the result.

1c Quadratic Forms

1c.1 Definitions

The general quadratic form in n variables $x_1, \cdots, x_n$ is

$$a_{11}x_1{}^2 + a_{12}x_1x_2 + \cdots + a_{1n}x_1x_n$$

$$+ a_{21}x_2x_1 + a_{22}x_2{}^2 + \cdots + a_{2n}x_2x_n$$

$$\cdots \qquad \cdots \qquad \cdots \qquad \cdots$$

$$+ a_{n1}x_nx_1 + a_{n2}x_nx_2 + \cdots + a_{nn}x_n{}^2$$

where $a_{ij} = a_{ji}$. Adopting the matrix notation, the above quadratic form can be written

$$\mathbf{x}A\mathbf{x}'$$

where $\mathbf{x}$ is the vector $(x_1, \cdots, x_n)$ and A is the symmetric matrix (a_{ij}). The matrix A is called the matrix of the quadratic form $\mathbf{x}A\mathbf{x}'$, and $|A|$, its discriminant.

The *rank of the quadratic* form $\mathbf{x}A\mathbf{x}'$ is the same as the rank of the matrix A.

1c.2 Linear Transformations

Let the variables in $\mathbf{x}$ be transformed to those in $\mathbf{y} = (y_1, \cdots, y_n)$ by means of the transformation

$$\mathbf{x} = \mathbf{y}C$$

(i) Under this transformation the quadratic form $\mathbf{x}A\mathbf{x}'$ changes to $\mathbf{y}CAC'\mathbf{y}'$ so that the matrix of the new form is CAC'. The discriminant of the transformed quadratic form is $|C|^2|A|$.

(ii) It has been shown in example 6 of 1b.3 that there exists a matrix B, $|B| \neq 0$, such that the matrix BAB' is in the diagonal form. If this matrix B is chosen as the matrix of transformation from $\mathbf{x}$ to $\mathbf{y}$, then the quadratic form can be reduced to the form $c_1y_1{}^2 + \cdots + c_ry_r{}^2$ containing the square terms only. The value of $|B| = 1$ since B is a product of elementary matrices which have a unit determinant.

By making a further transformation $\sqrt{|c_i|}\, y_i = z_i$ the quadratic form becomes $\pm z_1{}^2 \pm z_2{}^2 \pm \cdots \pm z_r{}^2$.

(iii) If the rank of the matrix A is r, then the reduced quadratic form contains only r square terms. This follows, for the ranks of A and BAB', where $|B| \neq 0$ (example 3, 1b.3), are the same.

(iv) A linear transformation $\mathbf{x} = \mathbf{y}C$ is said to be orthogonal if $CC' = I$. The transformation is non-singular since $|\,C\,|^2 = 1$. The quadratic form $x_1^2 + \cdots + x_n^2 = \mathbf{x}I\mathbf{x}'$ changes over to

$$\mathbf{y}CIC'\mathbf{y}' = \mathbf{y}CC'\mathbf{y}' = \mathbf{y}I\mathbf{y}' = y_1^2 + y_2^2 + \cdots + y_n^2$$

This is referred to as the invariance property of the distance function under an orthogonal transformation. Also let $\mathbf{x}_1$ and $\mathbf{x}_2$ be two vectors transforming to $\mathbf{y}_1$ and $\mathbf{y}_2$. Then

$$\mathbf{x}_1\mathbf{x}_2' = \mathbf{y}_1CC'\mathbf{y}_2' = \mathbf{y}_1\mathbf{y}_2'$$

so that the angles are also invariant. Also, if $\mathbf{x}$ transforms to $\mathbf{y}$ and $\mathbf{a}$ to $\mathbf{b}$, then

$$(\mathbf{x} - \mathbf{a})^2 = (\mathbf{y} - \mathbf{b})^2$$

and

$$(\mathbf{x}_1 - \mathbf{a}_1)(\mathbf{x}_2 - \mathbf{a}_2)' = (\mathbf{y}_1 - \mathbf{b}_1)(\mathbf{y}_2 - \mathbf{b}_2)'$$

1c.3 Classification of Quadratic Forms

The real quadratic form $\mathbf{x}A\mathbf{x}'$ is said to be definite if it is positive (or negative) for every set of real values $x_1, \cdots, x_n$ other than the set $x_1 = \cdots = x_n = 0$. A quadratic form which is never negative but which assumes zero value for some non-null values of $x_1, x_2, \cdots, x_n$ is called semi-positive definite. Similarly, semi-negative forms can be defined.

(i) The definiteness of a quadratic form is invariant under non-singular transformations.

Since the transformation $\mathbf{x} = \mathbf{y}B$ is non-singular, there exists the inverse transformation $\mathbf{y} = \mathbf{x}B^{-1}$, which establishes a one-to-one correspondence. If the quadratic form is positive (or negative) for a given vector $\mathbf{x}$, then the transformed form is positive (or negative) for the corresponding $\mathbf{y}$, and vice versa. Also $\mathbf{y} = (0, \cdots, 0)$ when and only when $\mathbf{x} = (0, \cdots, 0)$.

(ii) Every real positive definite quadratic form can be transformed by a real transformation matrix of unit modulus to the form

$$c_{11}y_1^2 + \cdots + c_{nn}y_n^2$$

where each $c_{ii} > 0$.

It is shown in (ii) of 1c.2 that every quadratic form can be reduced to a form consisting of the square terms only. No coefficient is negative, for otherwise it implies that the quadratic form is negative for some values of $\mathbf{y} \neq \mathbf{0}$ and hence of $\mathbf{x}$. Also, no coefficient can be zero, for, if $c_{ii} = 0$, then the quadratic form vanishes for $y_i \neq 0$ and others equal to zero, which is contrary to the assumption of the definiteness of the quadratic form.

(iii) The necessary and sufficient condition that a real quadratic form $\mathbf{x}A\mathbf{x}'$ is positive definite is that

$$a_{11} > 0, \quad \begin{vmatrix} a_{11} & a_{12} \\ a_{21} & a_{22} \end{vmatrix} > 0, \quad \cdots \quad \begin{vmatrix} a_{11} & \cdots & a_{1i} \\ \cdot & \cdots & \cdot \\ a_{i1} & \cdots & a_{ii} \end{vmatrix} > 0, \quad \cdots$$

Let the positive definite quadratic form under the transformation $\mathbf{x} = \mathbf{y}B$ be reduced to $c_1 y_1^2 + \cdots + c_n y_n^2$, where $c_1, \cdots, c_n$ are positive. In such a case

$$BAB' = \begin{bmatrix} c_1 & 0 & \cdots & 0 \\ 0 & c_2 & \cdots & 0 \\ \cdot & \cdot & \cdots & \cdot \\ 0 & 0 & \cdots & c_n \end{bmatrix}$$

$$|B|^2|A| = c_1 c_2 \cdots c_n > 0$$

Therefore $|A| > 0$. Consider the set of values of $x_1, \cdots, x_n$ in which $x_n = 0$. Then, from the above argument, it can be shown that

$$\begin{vmatrix} a_{11} & \cdots & a_{1(n-1)} \\ \cdot & \cdots & \cdot \\ a_{(n-1)1} & \cdots & a_{(n-1)(n-1)} \end{vmatrix} > 0$$

and so on, which establishes the necessity of the condition. To prove sufficiency, let

$$\Delta_i = \begin{vmatrix} a_{11} & \cdots & a_{1i} \\ \cdot & \cdots & \cdot \\ a_{i1} & \cdots & a_{ii} \end{vmatrix}$$

Since $a_{11} > 0$, the first column and row in A can be swept out. The resulting matrix is

$$\begin{bmatrix} a_{11} & 0 & \cdots & 0 \\ 0 & b_{22} & \cdots & b_{2n} \\ \cdot & \cdot & \cdots & \cdot \\ 0 & b_{n2} & \cdots & b_{nn} \end{bmatrix}$$

where $a_{11}b_{22} = \Delta_2$, for the value of any subdeterminant including the first row and column is unaltered. Also $\Delta_2 > 0$. Hence it follows that $b_{22} = \Delta_2/a_{11} > 0$. With b_{22} as a pivot the second row and column can be swept out. The resulting matrix is

$$\begin{bmatrix} a_{11} & 0 & 0 & \cdots & 0 \\ 0 & b_{22} & 0 & \cdots & 0 \\ 0 & 0 & c_{33} & \cdots & c_{3n} \\ \cdot & \cdot & \cdot & \cdots & \cdot \\ 0 & 0 & c_{n3} & \cdots & c_{nn} \end{bmatrix}$$

where $a_{11}b_{22}c_{33} = \Delta_3$. Therefore $c_{33} = \Delta_3/\Delta_2 > 0$, and so on. Finally the matrix A can be reduced to the diagonal form

$$
\begin{bmatrix}
\Delta_1 & 0 & \cdots & 0 \\
0 & \Delta_2/\Delta_1 & \cdots & 0 \\
0 & 0 & \cdots & 0 \\
\cdot & \cdot & \cdots & \cdot \\
0 & 0 & \cdots & \Delta_n/\Delta_{n-1}
\end{bmatrix}
$$

where each diagonal element is positive. This shows that the quadratic form $\mathbf{x}A\mathbf{x}'$ can be transformed to the positive definite form

$$
\Delta_1 y_1{}^2 + \frac{\Delta_2}{\Delta_1} y_2{}^2 + \cdots + \frac{\Delta_n}{\Delta_{n-1}} y_n{}^2
$$

which establishes the sufficiency of the condition. It should be noted that sweeping out is equivalent to pre- and post-multiplication by a product of elementary matrices which are transposes. This product of the elementary matrices provides the transformation matrix.

(iv) The necessary and sufficient condition that a real quadratic form $\mathbf{x}A\mathbf{x}'$ is negative definite is that

$$
\Delta_1 < 0, \quad \Delta_2 > 0, \quad \Delta_3 < 0, \quad \cdots
$$

This is true, since $-\mathbf{x}A\mathbf{x}'$ is positive definite.

1c.4   The Latent Roots of a Matrix and the Characteristic Vectors

Let $\mathbf{x}A\mathbf{x}'$ be a quadratic form in n variables. Let us find a vector $\mathbf{x}$ which maximizes $\mathbf{x}A\mathbf{x}'$ subject to the condition $\mathbf{x}\mathbf{x}' = 1$. This is obtained by differentiating *

$$
\mathbf{x}A\mathbf{x}' - \lambda(\mathbf{x}\mathbf{x}' - 1)
$$

* The following rules of differentiation with respect to vectors (i.e., simultaneously with respect to all the variables) will be useful.

Since $\mathbf{x}\mathbf{x}' = x_1{}^2 + x_2{}^2 + \cdots + x_n{}^2$,

$$
\left(\frac{\partial}{\partial x_1}, \frac{\partial}{\partial x_2}, \cdots, \frac{\partial}{\partial x_n} \right) (x_1{}^2 + \cdots + x_n{}^2) = 2(x_1, \cdots, x_n)
$$

Therefore

$$
\frac{\partial}{\partial \mathbf{x}} \mathbf{x}\mathbf{x}' = 2\mathbf{x}
$$

Similarly

$$
\frac{\partial}{\partial \mathbf{x}} \mathbf{x}A\mathbf{x}' = 2\mathbf{x}A
$$

where λ is a Lagrangian multiplier. The equations are

$$xA - \lambda xI = 0$$

$$xx' = 1$$

In order that a non-null x may exist, λ must be chosen to satisfy the determinantal equation

$$|A - \lambda I| = 0$$

This is called the *characteristic equation* of the matrix A. Any value of λ which satisfies this equation is called a *latent root*, and the x corresponding to a given λ is called a *characteristic vector*.

(i) The degree of the characteristic equation for roots other than $\lambda = 0$ is equal to the rank of A.

This can be verified by expanding the determinantal equation. The coefficients of λ^{n-r-1}, $\cdots$, λ, λ^0, being the sums of determinants containing more than r columns and rows, will be zero if the rank of A is r.

(ii) If A is real, all the roots are real.

Let $x + iy$ be the characteristic vector corresponding to a complex root λ. Then

$$(x + iy)A - \lambda(x + iy) = 0$$

Multiplying by $(x - iy)$

$$\lambda(x^2 + y^2) = (x + iy)A(x - iy)'$$

$$= xAx' + yAy' + i(yAx' - xAy')$$

$$= xAx' + yAy'$$

Hence λ is real.

(iii) The value of the quadratic form for a given characteristic vector x is equal to the value of the latent root λ associated with it. Since

$$xA - \lambda xI = 0$$

Then

$$xAx' = \lambda xx' = \lambda$$

The maximum and minimum values of xAx' subject to the condition $xx' = 1$ are then the largest and the least latent roots.

(iv) If the quadratic form is positive definite, then all the latent roots are positive. This is true, since the latent roots are the values of the quadratic form for some values of the variables.

(v) The characteristic vectors corresponding to two different latent roots are orthogonal.

Let λ_1, λ_2 be two roots and $\mathbf{x}$, $\mathbf{y}$ the corresponding vectors. Then

$$\mathbf{x}A - \lambda_1\mathbf{x} = 0$$

$$\mathbf{y}A - \lambda_2\mathbf{y} = 0$$

Multiplying the first by $\mathbf{y}'$, the second by $\mathbf{x}'$, and subtracting,

$$(\lambda_1 - \lambda_2)\mathbf{xy}' = \mathbf{x}A\mathbf{y}' - \mathbf{y}A\mathbf{x}' = 0$$

From this it follows that $\mathbf{xy}' = 0$, since $\lambda_1 \neq \lambda_2$.

(vi) There exists an orthogonal transformation which transforms a quadratic form $\mathbf{x}A\mathbf{x}'$ into $\mathbf{y}\Lambda_n\mathbf{y}'$, where Λ_n is a diagonal matrix containing all the latent roots of A.

Assume that X_i is a matrix of the form (i, n), the rows of which are the characteristic vectors corresponding to the latent roots λ_1, $\cdots$, λ_i, *not all of which need be different.* Also, let the rows of X_i be orthogonal. We will show that under these conditions there exists a vector $\mathbf{x}$ which is orthogonal to the rows in X_i and is a characteristic vector corresponding to the latent root λ_{i+1}.

Since the row vectors are orthogonal and normalized

$$X_iX_i' = I$$

Since the jth vector satisfies the relation

$$\mathbf{x}_jA - \lambda_j\mathbf{x}_j = 0$$

it follows that

$$X_iA - \Lambda_iX_i = 0$$

where Λ_i is a diagonal matrix containing λ_1, $\cdots$, λ_i in the diagonal.

Let us find a vector $\mathbf{x}$, $(\mathbf{xx}' = 1)$, orthogonal to the rows in X_i (i.e., $X_i\mathbf{x}' = 0$) and which maximizes $\mathbf{x}A\mathbf{x}'$. Introducing the vector $\mathbf{\mu} = (\mu_1, \cdots, \mu_i)$ of Lagrangian multipliers, the quantity to be differentiated is

$$\mathbf{x}A\mathbf{x}' - 2\mathbf{\mu}X_i\mathbf{x}' - \lambda\mathbf{xx}'$$

Differentiating, we obtain

$$2\mathbf{x}A - 2\mathbf{\mu}X_i - 2\lambda\mathbf{x}I = 0 \tag{1c.4.1}$$

Eliminating $\mathbf{x}$ and $\mathbf{\mu}$, the equation giving λ is

$$\begin{vmatrix} \underset{(n,\,n)}{A - \lambda I} & \underset{(n,\,i)}{X_i'} \\ \underset{(i,\,n)}{X_i} & \underset{(i,\,i)}{0} \end{vmatrix} = 0 \tag{1c.4.2}$$

Pre-multiplying this by

$$\left| \begin{array}{c|c} \underset{(n,\,n)}{I} & \underset{(n,\,i)}{0} \\ \hline \underset{(i,\,n)}{X_i} & \underset{(i,\,i)}{\lambda I - \Lambda_i} \end{array} \right| = (\lambda - \lambda_1) \cdots (\lambda - \lambda_i),$$

we get

$$\left| \begin{array}{c|c} A - \lambda I & X_i' \\ \hline 0 & I \end{array} \right| = \left| A - \lambda I \right| = 0$$

Equation (1c.4.2) can be written

$$\frac{\left| A - \lambda I \right|}{(\lambda - \lambda_1) \cdots (\lambda - \lambda_i)} = 0$$

Hence all λ satisfying (1c.4.2) are the latent roots of $\left| A - \lambda I \right| = 0$ other than those already considered. Let us consider the latent root λ_{i+1} and solve for $\mathbf{x}$ and μ from the set of equations (1c.4.1). Representing the solution for $\mathbf{x}$ by $\mathbf{x}_{i+1}$, we have

$$\mathbf{x}_{i+1}A - \mu X_i - \lambda \mathbf{x}_{i+1} = 0$$

$$X_i \mathbf{x}'_{i+1} = 0$$

Or, multiplying by X_i',

$$\mathbf{x}_{i+1}A X_i' - \mu X_i X_i' - \lambda \mathbf{x}_{i+1} X_i' = 0$$

i.e.,

$$\mathbf{x}_{i+1} X_i' \Lambda_i - \mu I - \lambda \mathbf{x}_{i+1} X_i' = 0$$

i.e.,

$$0\Lambda_i - \mu I - 0 = 0$$

Therefore

$$\mu = 0$$

which shows that $\mathbf{x}_{i+1}$ satisfies the equations

$$\mathbf{x}_{i+1}(A - \lambda_{i+1}I) = 0$$

$$X_i \mathbf{x}'_{i+1} = 0$$

Therefore $\mathbf{x}_{i+1}$ is a characteristic vector corresponding to λ_{i+1} and is orthogonal to X_i.

Starting from the first characteristic vector, all the n can be constructed so that there exists an orthogonal transformation X_n such that

$$X_n A = \Lambda_n X_n$$

and hence

$$X_n A X_n' = \Lambda_n$$

Corollary. If λ_i is a root of multiplicity r, then there are r and only r orthogonal vectors satisfying the equation

$$\mathbf{x}(A - \lambda_i I) = 0$$

so that the rank of $A - \lambda_i I$ is $(n - r)$.

Corresponding to a latent root λ_i of multiplicity r_i there are, by the above result, r_i orthogonal characteristic vectors. Since $(r_1 + r_2 + \cdots)$ $= n$ and there can be only n orthogonal vectors, it follows that there are only r_i characteristic vectors correspnding to λ_i. Hence the rank of $(A - \lambda_i I)$ is $(n - r)$.

To obtain the characteristic vectors corresponding to the root λ_i of multiplicity r_i, the best method is to find the space orthogonal to $(A - \lambda_i I)$ and choose any set of orthogonal vectors in this space.

1c.5 Pairs of Quadratic Forms

Let A and B be two symmetric matrices and $\mathbf{x}$ a vector such that

$$\mathbf{x}(A - \lambda B) = 0$$

where λ satisfies the determinantal equation $\left| A - \lambda B \right| = 0$. If $\left| B \right| \neq 0$, then B^{-1} exists, in which case $\mathbf{x}$ satisfies the equation

$$\mathbf{x}(AB^{-1} - \lambda I) = 0 \tag{1c.5.1}$$

and λ is the latent root of the matrix AB^{-1}. The determination of the vectors satisfying (1c.5.1) thus reduces to the case considered in the previous section.

(i) If λ_1 and λ_2 are two different roots, then

$$\mathbf{x}_1 AB^{-1} - \lambda_1 \mathbf{x}_1 = 0$$

or

$$\mathbf{x}_1 A - \lambda_1 \mathbf{x}_1 B = 0$$

$$\mathbf{x}_2 A - \lambda_2 \mathbf{x}_2 B = 0$$

Multiplying the first equation by $\mathbf{x}_2'$ and the second by $\mathbf{x}_1'$ and subtracting,

$$(\lambda_1 - \lambda_2)\mathbf{x}_1 B \mathbf{x}_2' = 0 \quad \text{or} \quad \mathbf{x}_1 B \mathbf{x}_2' = 0$$

(ii) If λ is a root of multiplicity r, then the rank of $(AB^{-1} - \lambda I)$ can be shown to be $(n - r)$ as in the previous section. The number of independent vectors satisfying the equation $\mathbf{x}(AB^{-1} - \lambda I) = 0$ is r. The vectors in this set may be chosen such that any two vectors $\mathbf{x}$ and $\mathbf{y}$ satisfy the relation $\mathbf{x} B \mathbf{y}' = 0$. Thus, corresponding to the n latent roots we obtain n vectors which may be represented by a matrix X_n

satisfying the condition that

$$X_n B X_n' = C \qquad \text{a diagonal matrix}$$

Let the leading diagonal of C contain the elements $c_1, \cdots, c_n$.

(iii) If Λ_n denotes the diagonal matrix containing $\lambda_1, \cdots, \lambda_n$ in the diagonal, then

$$X_n A B^{-1} - \Lambda_n X_n = 0$$

or

$$X_n A - \Lambda_n X_n B = 0$$

Multiplying by X_n'

$$X_n A X_n' = \Lambda_n X_n B X_n' = \Lambda_n C$$

This shows that the transformation $\mathbf{x} = \mathbf{y} X_n$ transforms the quadratic forms $\mathbf{x} A \mathbf{x}'$ and $\mathbf{x} B \mathbf{x}'$ into

$$c_1 \lambda_1 y_1{}^2 + \cdots + c_n \lambda_n y_n{}^2$$

and

$$c_1 y_1{}^2 + \cdots + c_n y_n{}^2$$

(iv) If B is positive definite, then the transformation $\sqrt{c_i} y_i = Y_i$ carries the above quadratic forms to

$$\lambda_1 Y_1{}^2 + \cdots + \lambda_n Y_n{}^2$$

and

$$Y_1{}^2 + \cdots + Y_n{}^2$$

(v) If the quadratic form $\mathbf{x} A \mathbf{x}'$ is never negative, then no λ is negative.

Example 1. If A and B are symmetric matrices such that B is positive definite and $(A - B)$ is positive or semi-positive definite, then $|A| \geq |B|$.

Consider the equation

$$|A - B - \lambda B| = 0$$

where no root is negative since $(A - B)$ is positive or semi-positive definite and B is positive definite. Since

$$|A - B(1 + \lambda)| = 0$$

it follows that $|A|/|B| = (1 + \lambda_1) \cdots (1 + \lambda_n)$, where $\lambda_1, \lambda_2, \cdots, \lambda_n$ are the roots. None of the factors in the product $(1 + \lambda_1) \cdots (1 + \lambda_n)$ is less than one so that

$$\frac{|A|}{|B|} \geq 1$$

which proves the result. This result also shows that the matrix A is also positive definite.

Example 2. The rank of the quadratic form $\Sigma(x_i - \bar{x})^2$, where $\bar{x}$ is the average of $x_1, x_2, \cdots, x_n$, is $(n - 1)$. (Use example 4, 1a.4.)

Example 3. Consider the matrix (x_{ij}) of measurements, $i = 1, 2, \cdots, p; j = 1, 2, \cdots, n$. If

$$\sum_{j=1}^{n} x_{ij} = n\bar{x}_i$$

$$S_{tu} = \Sigma(x_{tj} - \bar{x}_t)(x_{uj} - \bar{x}_u)$$

then the matrix (S_{tu}), $(t, u = 1, 2, \cdots, p)$, is

(i) positive definite or semi-definite if $n \geq p$;

(ii) positive semi-definite if $n < p$; and

(iii) positive definite if the rank of $(x_{ij} - \bar{x}_i)$ is equal to p and semi-definite if it is less than p.

(Use examples 10 and 11, 1b.3.)

Example 4. The solution of

$$\left| d_i d_j - \lambda a_{ij} \right| = 0$$

is

$$\lambda = \Sigma\Sigma a^{ij} d_i d_j = \mathbf{d} A^{-1} \mathbf{d}'$$

where $A = (a_{ij})$ and $\mathbf{d} = (d_1, \cdots, d_p)$.

Example 5. If A and C are two matrices such that with respect to a symmetric definite matrix Λ

$$A\Lambda C' = 0$$

then the rows in A are independent of the rows in C.

If any vector $\mathbf{x}$ in A is dependent on the vectors in C, then $\mathbf{x}\Lambda\mathbf{x}' = 0$, which is impossible since Λ is a definite matrix.

Example 6. Consider the quadratic form in $y_1, \cdots, y_t$

$$\sum_{i=1}^{n} (y_1 + d_i y_2 + d_i^2 y_3 + \cdots + d_i^t y_t)^2$$

where $d_1, \cdots, d_n$ are as defined in example 12 of 1b.3, and deduce the result about the moments. When the variable x is continuous, the summation is replaced by integration. We thus deduce the consistency relations to be satisfied by the moments of any distribution.

1c.6 Reduction of an Asymmetric Matrix

In population studies it is often necessary to determine the powers of an asymmetric matrix called the generation matrix. If A represents the generation matrix of the type (k, k) and $\mathbf{f}_0$, $\mathbf{f}_n$ represent the initial and the nth generation frequencies in some well-defined classes, then

$$\mathbf{f}_n = \mathbf{f}_0 A^n$$

The calculations can be simplified by the following steps. Let $\lambda_1, \cdots,$ λ_p be the distinct roots of the determinantal equation

$$\left| A' - \lambda I \right| = 0$$

with the multiplicity of the root λ_i being equal to m_i, $\Sigma m_i = k$. Let it be possible to find m_i independent solutions $\mathbf{x}_{i1}, \cdots, \mathbf{x}_{im_i}$ of the equation

$$\mathbf{x}_i(A' - \lambda_i I) = 0 \qquad (1\text{c}.6.1)$$

If P stands for the matrix containing the vectors $\mathbf{x}_{ij}$, then

$$PA' = \Lambda P$$

where Λ is the matrix containing the latent roots allowing repetitions and arranged in the same order as the corresponding vectors. If $\mathbf{x}_1$, $\cdots$, $\mathbf{x}_p$ are any characteristic vectors corresponding to the distinct roots $\lambda_1, \cdots, \lambda_p$, then they are all independent. If there were a relation

$$\rho_1 \mathbf{x}_1 + \cdots + \rho_p \mathbf{x}_p = 0 \qquad (1\text{c}.6.2)$$

where the terms with zero coefficients are omitted, then from the relations $\mathbf{x}_i A' = \lambda_i \mathbf{x}_i$ it follows that

$$\lambda_1 \rho_1 \mathbf{x}_1 + \cdots + \lambda_p \rho_p \mathbf{x}_p = 0 \qquad (1\text{c}.6.3)$$

Using (1c.6.3), one variable in (1c.6.2) is eliminated and a new relation obtained. This gives rise to a relation similar to (1c.6.3). After repeated eliminations the relation (1c.6.2) reduces to an absurd result that one of the vectors is zero. Therefore no such relation as (1c.6.2) is true. From this it follows that P is a non-singular matrix in which case

$$A = (P^{-1}\Lambda P)' = Q^{-1}\Lambda Q$$

where $P' = Q^{-1}$. Hence

$$A^2 = Q^{-1}\Lambda Q Q^{-1}\Lambda Q = Q^{-1}\Lambda^2 Q$$

and generally

$$A^n = Q^{-1}\Lambda^n Q$$

so that an easy rule is provided once the P matrix is evaluated. Such a simple representation breaks down when it is not possible to find m_i independent solutions of (1c.6.1) where λ_i is a root of multiplicity m_i.

It is seen that the linear functions of frequencies $\mathbf{x}_{ij}\mathbf{f}'$ transform in a simple way from generation to generation. In fact

$$\mathbf{x}_{ij}\mathbf{f}_n' = \lambda_i^n \mathbf{x}_{ij}\mathbf{f}_0' \qquad (1c.6.4)$$

so that, knowing the initial values of these linear functions, the vector $\mathbf{f}_n$ can be solved from the equations (1c.6.4).

1d   Numerical Appendix

1d.1   The Evaluation of Determinants, Reciprocals, and Solutions of Equations

The theoretical expression for the value of the determinant given in 1b.3 is not convenient for practical computations. The method of pivotal condensation will be useful in (i) determining the value of a determinant, (ii) solving linear equations, and (iii) obtaining the reciprocal of a matrix. These three techniques are simultaneously illustrated in the example below. Only the relevant computations need be retained in any problem. In this illustration a non-symmetrical matrix is chosen. In most of the statistical computations symmetric matrices are met with. This results in a certain amount of reduction in computations, and the layout of a simplified procedure in such cases is discussed in the text.

References

LEVI, F. W. (1942). Algebra, Calcutta University.
TURNBULL, H. W., and A. C. AITKEN (1932). An introduction to the theory of canonical matrices. Blackie, London.

Notes on the Computations in Table 1d.1α

(i) Row 10 is obtained from row 01 by reducing the first element to unity. This is called a pivotal row and the first element, 0.1228 underlined in the table, is the first pivotal element. By multiplying row 10 by 0.1281 and subtracting from row 02, row 11 is obtained in which the first element is zero. Similarly, by eliminating the first element in rows 03 and 04, rows 12 and 13 are obtained. Starting with the reduced matrix in rows 11, 12, and 13, the whole operation is repeated.

(ii) Rows 10, 20, 30, and 40 are pivotal rows, and the product of the four elements

$$0.12280 \times 0.18719 \times 0.21601 \times 0.37510 = 0.0018625$$

is the value of the determinant of the matrix of equations. If only the value of the determinant is needed, the calculations beyond column 4 should be omitted.

(iii) Calculations up to column 5 give the solutions of non-homogeneous equations, and columns 6, 7, 8, and 9 are intended for the solutions of non-homogeneous equations whose right-hand elements are columns of a unit matrix. The four sets of solutions will form the elements of the reciprocal matrix.

(iv) The pivotal row 40 gives the solutions for x_4, and, by substituting this value of x_4 in row 30, row 30' giving the solutions for x_3 is obtained. By substituting the values of x_3 and x_4 in row 20, row 20' is obtained, and so on. Thus the last four rows in the *reverse order* (in columns 6, 7, 8, and 9) give the reciprocal matrix.

(v) To start, the matrix has only four significant figures. But it is better to keep more places (usually one more) in subsequent calculations to keep a check on the rounding-off errors.

(vi) A sum check provided in the last column ensures accuracy of all the calculations. To start, the sum of the elements in each of the initial rows (here four) is written in the last column. For subsequent operations this is treated as an extra column. Any derived row has the property that the last element is the sum of the other elements. This may be checked whenever a new row is obtained, either by reducing the first coefficient to unity or by sweeping out a first column.

TABLE 1d.1α. Computations for the Evaluation of a Determinant, Reciprocal Matrix, etc.

Row No.	Matrix of Linear Equations				Right-Hand Elements	Unit Matrix for the Reciprocal				Sum Check
0	1	2	3	4	5	6	7	8	9	10
01	0.1228	-0.0508	0.1434	0.2016	0.8430	1	·	·	·	2.2600
02	0.1281	0.1342	0.0196	0.4703	0.6713	·	1	·	·	2.4235
03	0.0434	0.2172	0.1034	0.1056	1.3412	·	·	1	·	2.8108
04	0.2023	0.1523	0.2045	0.8562	0.8235	·	·	·	1	3.2388
10	1	-0.41368	1.16775	1.64169	6.86482	8.14332	·	·	·	18.40391
11		0.18719	-0.12999	0.26000	- 0.20808	- 1.04316	1	·	·	0.06596
12		0.23515	0.05272	0.03436	1.04327	- 0.35342	·	1	·	2.01207
13		0.23599	-0.03173	0.52409	0.56525	- 1.64739	·	·	1	- 0.48431
20		1	-0.69443	1.38896	- 1.11160	- 5.57273	5.34217	·	·	0.35237
21			0.21601	-0.29225	1.30466	0.95701	- 1.25621	1	·	1.92921
22			0.13215	0.19631	- 0.30292	- 0.33228	- 1.26070	·	1	- 0.56746
30			1	-1.35295	6.03981	4.43040	- 5.81552	4.62941	·	8.93111
31				0.37510	- 1.10108	- 0.91776	- 0.49218	- 0.61178	1	- 1.74771
40				1	- 2.93543	- 2.44671	- 1.31213	- 1.63098	2.66595	- 4.65932
30'			1		2.06832	1.12012	7.59077	2.42278	3.60690	2.62728
20'		1			4.40190	- 1.39650	1.89341	3.94782	-1.19816	8.64844
10'	1				11.08958	10.27434	11.80150	1.48150	-9.08428	26.56275

CHAPTER 2

Theory of Distributions

2a Some Analytical Methods in Distribution Problems

2a.1 Binomial Distribution

Binomial distribution is the simplest problem in the theory of distribution. The observations consist of n independent stochastic variables, each of which can assume two values, 1 and 0, with probabilities p and q, $(p + q = 1)$. If we attach the value 1 to success and 0 to failure in a trial, then the sum of observations in n independent trials gives the total number of successes. What is the probability distribution of the number of successes in n trials?

If we denote by r the number of successes, then

$$r = x_1 + x_2 + \cdots + x_n$$

where $x_i = 1$ for success and 0 for failure. Since the events are independent, the probability for any series of x with r, 1 and $(n - r)$, 0 is $p^r q^{n-r}$. To obtain the probability of r successes we have to sum up the probabilities corresponding to all possible series of x containing 1, r times and 0, $(n - r)$ times. This number is $\binom{n}{r}$, the number of combinations of r out of n things. Since each such series has the probability $p^r q^{n-r}$, the total probability of r is $\binom{n}{r} p^r q^{n-r}$. This is the rth term in the binomial expansion $(p + q)^n$.

If n_1 trials give r_1 successes and an independent set of n_2 trials gives r_2 successes, the probability of success being the same for both sets, the probability of $r = (r_1 + r_2)$ should be the same as that of r successes in $n = (n_1 + n_2)$ trials. This can be formally derived in the following manner. The probability of r_1 and r_2 is

$$P(r_1, r_2) = \binom{n_1}{r_1} p^{r_1} q^{n-r_1} \binom{n_2}{r_2} p^{r_2} q^{n-r_2}$$

$$= \binom{n_1}{r_1} \binom{n_2}{r_2} p^{r_1+r_2} q^{n_1+n_2-r_1-r_2}$$

32

Therefore

$$P(r = r_1 + r_2) = \sum_{r=r_1+r_2} P(r_1, r_2)$$

$$= p^r q^{n-r} \sum_{r=r_1+r_2} \binom{n_1}{r_1}\binom{n_2}{r_2}$$

$$= p^r q^{n-r} \binom{n}{r}$$

Thus the sum of two binomial variates is also a binomial variate.

Corresponding to a probability distribution there is a distribution function which gives the probability of a variate's assuming a value less than or equal to an assigned value. If $P(x)$ denotes the probability distribution, the corresponding distribution function will be denoted by $F(x)$.

In the binomial case

$$F(r) = \sum_{s=0}^{r} P(s)$$

$$= \Sigma \binom{n}{s} p^s q^{n-s}$$

$$= \Sigma \frac{n!}{r!(n-r-1)!} q^{n-s} \frac{r!}{s!(r-s)!} p^s \frac{(n-r-1)!(r-s)!}{(n-s)!}$$

$$= \frac{n!}{r!(n-r-1)!} q^{n-r} \Sigma \int_0^1 \binom{r}{s} p^s q^{r-s} t^{r-s} (1-t)^{n-r-1} \, dt$$

$$= \frac{n!}{r!(n-r-1)!} q^{n-r} \int_0^1 (1-t)^{n-r-1} (p+qt)^r \, dt$$

Putting $t = 1 - x/q$, the above expression becomes

$$\frac{n!}{r!(n-r-1)!} \int_0^q x^{n-r-1} (1-x)^r \, dx$$

This is an incomplete beta function which is extensively tabulated in *Tables of Incomplete Beta Function* (edited by K. Pearson). If r is small, then each term in the above summation can be separately calculated and added to obtain $F(r)$.

Example 1. For a binomial distribution $(p + q)^n$,

$$E\left(\frac{r}{n}\right) = p \qquad V\left(\frac{r}{n}\right) = \frac{pq}{n} \qquad \mathrm{cov}\left(\frac{r}{n}, \frac{n-r}{n}\right) = -\frac{pq}{n}$$

where E stands for expectation, V for variance, and cov for covariance.

Example 2. If μ_t is the tth corrected moment of the observed number of successes, then

$$\mu_{t+2} = pq \left\{ \frac{d}{dp} \mu_{t+1} + n(t+1)\mu_t \right\} \qquad \text{(Romanovsky, 1925)}$$

Hence

$$\beta_1 = \frac{\mu_3^2}{\mu_2^3} = \frac{(q-p)^2}{npq}$$

$$\beta_2 = \frac{\mu_4}{\mu_2^2} = 3 + \frac{1 - 6pq}{npq}$$

2a.2 Multinomial Distribution

If there are k mutually exclusive events with probabilities $\pi_1, \pi_2, \cdots, \pi_k$, $(\Sigma \pi_i = 1)$, then the probability of occurrence of n_1 events of the first kind, n_2 of the second, $\cdots$, etc., in a total of n independent trials is

$$P(n_1, n_2, \cdots, n_k) = \frac{n!}{n_1! \cdots n_k!} \pi_1^{n_1} \cdots \pi_k^{n_k}$$

The product $\pi_1^{n_1} \cdots \pi_k^{n_k}$ refers to the probability of events occurring in some order; $n!/n_1! \cdots n_k!$ represents the number of arrangements of n_1 things of one kind, n_2 of another kind, and so on. Therefore the total probability of the desired number of events of the various kinds is the product of these two expressions, the argument being similar to that used for the binomial. The above probability is a term of the multinomial expansion.

$$(\pi_1 + \pi_2 + \cdots + \pi_k)^n$$

Since

$$\Sigma \frac{n!}{n_1! \cdots n_k!} \pi_1^{n_1} \cdots \pi_k^{n_k} = (\pi_1 + \cdots + \pi_k)^n$$

$$\pi_i \frac{\partial}{\partial \pi_i} \Sigma \frac{n!}{n_1! \cdots n_k!} \pi_1^{n_1} \cdots \pi_k^{n_k} = \Sigma n_i P(n_1, \cdots, n_k)$$

$$= \pi_i \frac{\partial}{\partial \pi_i} (\pi_1 + \cdots + \pi_k)^n$$

$$= n\pi_i (\pi_1 + \cdots + \pi_k)^{n-1}$$

$$\pi_j \frac{\partial}{\partial \pi_j} \Sigma n_i P(n_1, \cdots, n_k) = \Sigma n_i n_j P(n_1, \cdots, n_k)$$

$$= \pi_j \frac{\partial}{\partial \pi_j} n\pi_i (\pi_1 + \cdots + \pi_k)^{n-1}$$

$$= n(n-1)\pi_i \pi_j (\pi_1 + \cdots + \pi_k)^{n-2}$$

Similarly

$$\pi_i \frac{\partial}{\partial \pi_i} \Sigma n_i P(n_1, \cdots, n_k) = \Sigma n_i^2 P(n_1, \cdots, n_k)$$

$$= n\pi_i(\pi_1 + \cdots + \pi_k)^{n-1}$$

$$+ n(n-1)\pi_i^2(\pi_1 + \cdots + \pi_k)^{n-2}$$

These results give

$$E(n_i) = n\pi_i$$

$$E(n_i n_j) = n(n-1)\pi_i \pi_j$$

$$E(n_i^2) = n\pi_i + n(n-1)\pi_i^2$$

Therefore

$$V(n_i) = E(n_i^2) - [E(n_i)]^2 = n\pi_i(1 - \pi_i)$$

$$\text{cov } (n_i, n_j) = E(n_i n_j) - E(n_i)E(n_j) = -n\pi_i \pi_j$$

which are similar to the results obtained for the binomial. From these results the variances and covariances of linear functions of frequencies in k classes can be obtained in a simple way.

$$V(l_1 n_1 + \cdots + l_k n_k) = \Sigma l_i^2 V(n_i) + 2\Sigma\Sigma l_i l_j \text{ cov } (n_i, n_j)$$

$$= \Sigma l_i^2 n\pi_i(1 - \pi_i) + 2\Sigma\Sigma l_i l_j(-n\pi_i \pi_j)$$

$$= n\{\Sigma l_i^2 \pi_i - (\Sigma l_i \pi_i)^2\}$$

Similarly

$$\text{cov } \{(l_1 n_1 + \cdots + l_k n_k), (m_1 n_1 + \cdots + m_k n_k)\}$$

$$= n\{\Sigma l_i m_i \pi_i - (\Sigma l_i \pi_i)(\Sigma m_i \pi_i)\}$$

Higher moments of the multinomial can be derived by extending the differentiation processes, but they are not of much use in practice.

2a.3 The Poisson Distribution

This is a discrete distribution where the stochastic variable assumes values $0, 1, 2, \cdots$, with the probability for r equal to

$$e^{-\mu} \frac{(\mu)^r}{r!}$$

where μ is a parameter. Since,

$$e^{\mu} = \sum_{0}^{\infty} \frac{\mu^r}{r!}$$

$$\Sigma r \frac{\mu^r}{r!} = \mu \frac{d}{d\mu} e^{\mu} = \mu e^{\mu}$$

$$\Sigma r^2 \frac{\mu^r}{r!} = \mu \frac{d}{d\mu}(\mu e^{\mu}) = \mu^2 e^{\mu} + \mu e^{\mu}$$

These give

$$E(r) = \mu \qquad V(r) = \mu$$

so that the mean and variance of this distribution are equal. The higher moments can be derived from the relation

$$\mu_{t+1} = t\mu\mu_{t-1} + \mu \frac{d\mu_t}{d\mu}$$

obtained in a manner similar to the corresponding relation in the binomial distribution. This gives

$$\mu_3 = \mu \qquad \mu_4 = \mu + 3\mu^2 \qquad \text{etc.}$$

Hence

$$\beta_1 = \frac{1}{\mu} \qquad \beta_2 = 3 + \frac{1}{\mu}$$

If $r_1, r_2, \cdots, r_k$ are independent variates from the same Poisson distribution,

$$P(r_1, r_2, \cdots, r_k) = e^{-k\mu} \frac{(\mu)^{r_1+r_2+\cdots+r_k}}{r_1!r_2! \cdots r_k!}$$

$$P(r = r_1 + r_2 + \cdots + r_k) = e^{-k\mu}(\mu)^r \Sigma \frac{1}{r_1!r_2! \cdots r_k!}$$

$$= e^{-k\mu}\mu^r \frac{k^r}{r!} = e^{-k\mu} \frac{(k\mu)^r}{r!}$$

which shows that the sum of k Poisson variates, each with parameter μ, is itself a Poisson variate with the parameter $k\mu$.

The conditional distribution

$$P(r_1, r_2, \cdots, r_k, \mid r) = \frac{P(r_1, r_2, \cdots, r_k)}{P(r)}$$

$$= \frac{r!}{r_1! \cdots r_k!} \left(\frac{1}{k}\right)^{r_1} \cdots \left(\frac{1}{k}\right)^{r_k}$$

is a multinomial with index r and probability in each class equal to $1/k$. If $r_1, \cdots, r_k$ are Poisson variates with parameters $\mu_1, \cdots, \mu_k$, then

$$P(r_1, \cdots, r_k) = e^{-(\mu_1 + \cdots + \mu_k)} \frac{\mu_1^{r_1}}{r_1!} \cdots \frac{\mu_k^{r_k}}{r_k!}$$

$$P(r = r_1 + \cdots + r_k) = e^{-\mu} \Sigma \frac{\mu_1^{r_1}}{r_1!} \cdots \frac{\mu_k^{r_k}}{r_k!}$$

$$= e^{-\mu} \frac{\mu^r}{r!}$$

where $\mu = \mu_1 + \cdots + \mu_k$, which shows that the sum of k independent Poisson variates is in general a Poisson variate. This is true in the case of a binomial variate only when the binomial proportions are the same. The conditional distribution

$$P(r_1, \cdots, r_k \mid r) = \frac{P(r_1, \cdots, r_k)}{P(r)}$$

$$= \frac{r!}{r_1! \cdots r_k!} \left(\frac{\mu_1}{\mu}\right)^{r_1} \cdots \left(\frac{\mu_k}{r_k}\right)^{r_k}$$

is multinomial with probabilities $\mu_1/\mu, \cdots, \mu_k/\mu$ in the k classes.

In general, any multinomial distribution

$$\frac{n!}{n_1! \cdots n_k!} \pi_1^{n_1} \cdots \pi_k^{n_k}$$

can be written as the ratio of

$$P(n_1, \cdots, n_k) = e^{-n\pi_1} \frac{(n\pi_1)^{n_1}}{n_1!} \cdots e^{-n\pi_k} \frac{(n\pi_k)^{n_k}}{n_k!}$$

to

$$P(n = n_1 + \cdots + n_k) = e^{-n} \frac{n^n}{n!}$$

which is the relative probability of k Poisson variates with parameters $\mu_i = n\pi_i$, $(i = 1, 2, \cdots k)$, subject to the condition that the sum of the variables is equal to n.

The distribution function for the Poisson distribution is obtained below.

$$F(r) = e^{-\mu}\left(1 + \frac{\mu}{1!} + \cdots + \frac{\mu^r}{r!}\right)$$

$$= \sum_s \frac{e^{-\mu}\mu^s}{s!(r-s)!} \int_0^\infty e^{-x}x^{r-s}\,dx$$

$$= \frac{e^{-\mu}}{r!} \int_0^\infty e^{-x}(\mu + x)^r\,dx$$

$$= \frac{1}{r!} \int_\mu^\infty e^{-y}y^r\,dy$$

which is the incomplete gamma integral, tables for which have been edited by K. Pearson.

The Poisson probability can be deduced from the binomial when n, the number of trials, is large and p is small. For instance, the probability for no success is

$$P(0) = q^n = (1-p)^n = \left(1 - \frac{np}{n}\right)^n \sim e^{-np} = e^{-\mu}$$

$$\frac{P(r+1)}{P(r)} = \frac{\binom{n}{r+1}p^{r+1}q^{n-r-1}}{\binom{n}{r}p^r q^{n-r}}$$

$$= \frac{n-r}{r+1}\frac{p}{q} \sim \frac{\mu}{r+1}$$

where $\mu = np$. The successive terms of the binomial then tend to

$$e^{-\mu},\ e^{-\mu}\frac{\mu}{1!},\ e^{-\mu}\frac{\mu^2}{2!},\ \cdots$$

yielding the Poisson series. Thus, when the probability is small and the number of trials is indefinitely large, the Poisson distribution may be used.

2a.4 Normal Distribution

This is a continuous distribution with the probability differential of the stochastic variable x equal to

$$N(\mu, \sigma)\,dx = \frac{1}{\sigma\sqrt{2\pi}}e^{-(x-\mu)^2/2\sigma^2}\,dx$$

The rth moment of this distribution is

$$\frac{1}{\sigma\sqrt{2\pi}} \int_{-\infty}^{+\infty} (x - \mu)^r e^{-(x-\mu)^2/2\sigma^2} \, dx$$

$$= \frac{1}{\sigma\sqrt{2\pi}} \int_{-\infty}^{+\infty} y^r e^{-y^2/2\sigma^2} \, dy \qquad \text{putting } y = x - \mu$$

$$= 0 \qquad \text{if } r \text{ is odd}$$

$$= \frac{1}{\sigma\sqrt{2\pi}} \int_{0}^{\infty} z^{(r-1)/2} e^{-z/2\sigma^2} \, dz \qquad \text{putting } z = y^2 \text{ if } r \text{ is even}$$

$$= \frac{(2\sigma^2)^{(r+1)/2}}{\sigma\sqrt{2\pi}} \Gamma\left(\frac{r+1}{2}\right) = \sigma^r (r - 1)(r - 3) \cdots \quad (1)$$

$$= \frac{\sigma^r (r - 1)!}{\left(\dfrac{r - 2}{2}\right)! \, 2^{(r-2)/2}}$$

whence we have the following results:

$$\mu_2 = \sigma^2 \qquad \mu_3 = 0 \qquad \mu_4 = 3\sigma^4$$

$$\beta_1 = 0 \qquad \beta_2 = 3$$

If x and y are two independent normal variates with mean values m_1 and m_2 and standard deviations σ_1 and σ_2, then their joint distribution is

$$\text{const. } e^{-\frac{1}{2}Q(x,y)} \, dx \, dy$$

where

$$Q(x, y) = \frac{(x - m_1)^2}{\sigma_1^2} + \frac{(y - m_2)^2}{\sigma_2^2}$$

$$= \frac{[(x - m_1) + (y - m_2)]^2}{\sigma_1^2 + \sigma_2^2} + \frac{[(x - m_1) - \lambda(y - m_2)]^2}{\sigma_1^2 + \lambda^2\sigma_2^2}$$

where $\sigma_1^2 = \lambda\sigma_2^2$. Make the transformation

$$u = x + y \qquad v = x - \lambda y$$

so that the joint distribution of u and v becomes

$$\text{const. } e^{-\frac{1}{2}Q(u,v)} \, du \, dv$$

where

$$Q(u, v) = \frac{(u - m_1 - m_2)^2}{\sigma_1^2 + \sigma_2^2} + \frac{(v - m_1 + \lambda m_2)^2}{\sigma_1^2 + \lambda^2\sigma_2^2}$$

The distributions of u and v are independent as their joint distribution turns out to be a product of two functions. The distribution of u is

$$\text{const. } e^{-\frac{1}{2}(u-m_1-m_2)^2/(\sigma_1^2+\sigma_2^2)}\, du$$

which shows that $u = (x + y)$, the sum of two normal variates, is itself a normal variate with mean equal to the sum of the means and variance equal to the sum of the variances. In general, the sum of k normal variates is distributed as a normal variate with mean equal to the sum of the individual means and variance equal to the sum of the individual variances.

Example 1. If x is $N(\mu, \sigma)$, what is the distribution of x^2?

The distribution of x is

$$\frac{1}{\sigma\sqrt{2\pi}}\, e^{-(x-\mu)^2/2\sigma^2}\, dx$$

Let $y = x^2$ so that $dy = 2x\, dx$. The range of y is from 0 to ∞, and that of x is from $-\infty$ to ∞. Corresponding to a given y there are two values of x ($\pm x$). The probability density at $+x$ transforms to

$$\frac{1}{\sigma\sqrt{2\pi}}\, e^{-(y-2\sqrt{y}\mu+\mu^2)/2\sigma^2}\, \frac{dy}{2\sqrt{y}}$$

and that at $-x$ to

$$\frac{1}{\sigma\sqrt{2\pi}}\, e^{-(y+2\sqrt{y}\mu+\mu^2)/2\sigma^2}\, \frac{dy}{2\sqrt{y}}$$

so that the total probability differential of y is the sum of the above two expressions, i.e.,

$$\frac{1}{\sigma\sqrt{2\pi}}\, e^{-(y/2\sigma^2)-(\mu^2/2\sigma^2)}\, \frac{(e^{\sqrt{y}\mu/\sigma^2}+e^{-\sqrt{y}\mu/\sigma^2})}{2\sqrt{y}}dy$$

$$= \frac{1}{\sigma\sqrt{2\pi}}\, e^{-(y+\mu^2)/2\sigma^2}\, \frac{\cosh \sqrt{y}\mu/\sigma^2}{\sqrt{y}}\, dy$$

If $\mu = 0$, the distribution of y is

$$\frac{1}{\sigma\sqrt{2\pi}}\, e^{-y/2\sigma^2}y^{-\frac{1}{2}}\, dy$$

which is $G(1/2\sigma^2, \frac{1}{2})$ defined in 2a.5.

2a.5 Gamma Distribution

The gamma distribution is defined by

$$G(\alpha, p)\, dx = \frac{\alpha^p}{\Gamma(p)}\, e^{-\alpha x}x^{p-1}\, dx$$

where the range of x is $(0, \infty)$, $\alpha > 0$, and $p \geq 1$. The rth raw moment of this distribution is

$$\int_0^\infty \frac{\alpha^p}{\Gamma(p)} e^{-\alpha x} x^{p+r-1} \, dx = \frac{\Gamma(p+r)}{\Gamma(p)} \frac{1}{\alpha^r}$$

so that

$$E(x) = \frac{p}{\alpha} \qquad V(x) = \frac{p}{\alpha^2}$$

If $\alpha = 1$, the mean and the variance of the gamma variate are equal, as in the case of a Poisson variate.

Let x and y be two independent gamma variates with parameters (α, p) and (α, q); then their joint distribution is

$$\text{const. } e^{-\alpha(x+y)} x^{p-1} y^{q-1} \, dx \, dy$$

Put $x = r \cos^2 \theta$ and $y = r \sin^2 \theta$, so that $dx \, dy = 2r \cos \theta \sin \theta \, dr \, d\theta$. The distribution of r and θ is

$$\text{const. } e^{-\alpha r} r^{p+q-1} (\cos \theta)^{2p-1} (\sin \theta)^{2q-1} \, dr \, d\theta$$

and that of r alone is $ce^{-\alpha r} r^{p+q-1} \, dr$, which is again a gamma variate with parameters $(\alpha, p+q)$. In general the sum of k gamma variates with parameters (α, p_1), (α, p_2), $\cdots$, (α, p_k) is distributed as a gamma variate with parameters $(\alpha, p_1 + p_2 + \cdots + p_k)$. The distribution of $z = x/(x+y)$ is that of $\cos^2 \theta$, i.e.,

$$\frac{1}{\beta(p, q)} z^{p-1} (1 - z)^{q-1} \, dz \qquad \beta(p, q) = \frac{\Gamma(p) \Gamma(q)}{\Gamma(p+q)}$$

which is $B(p, q)$ defined in 2a.6. A special case of the gamma distribution is the χ^2 distribution,

$$\chi^2(k) = \text{const. } e^{-x^2/2} (\chi^2)^{(k-2)/2} \, d\chi^2 = G\left(\frac{1}{2}, \frac{k}{2}\right)$$

which is specified by one parameter k known as the degrees of freedom of χ^2.

2a.6 Beta Distribution

A stochastic variable in the range $(0, 1)$ having the probability distribution

$$B(a, b) \, dx = \frac{1}{\beta(a, b)} x^{a-1} (1 - x)^{b-1} \, dx$$

is said to follow the beta distribution with parameters a and b. The rth moment about the origin is

$$\frac{1}{\beta(a, b)} \int x^{r+a-1}(1 - x)^{b-1} \, dx = \frac{\beta(a + r, b)}{\beta(a, b)}$$

The mean and variance of x are

$$\frac{a}{a + b} \quad \text{and} \quad \frac{ab}{(a + b)^2(a + b + 1)}$$

If x and y are two independent beta variates with parameters (a, b) and (c, d), then their joint distribution is

$$\text{const.} \ x^{a-1}(1 - x)^{b-1}y^{c-1}(1 - y)^{d-1} \, dx \, dy$$

Put $u = x$ and $z = xy$, so that $\partial(x, y)/\partial(u, z) = 1/u$. The joint distribution of u and z is

$$\text{const.} \ u^{a-c-d}(1 - u)^{b-1}z^{c-1}(u - z)^{d-1} \, du \, dz$$

$$= \text{const.} \ (1 - u)^{b-1}z^{c-1}(u - z)^{d-1} \, du \, dz \quad \text{if } a = c + d$$

Integrating over u, the distribution of z is obtained as

$$\frac{1}{\beta(c, b + d)} z^{c-1}(1 - z)^{b+d-1} \, dz$$

This shows that the product of two beta variables, with parameters (a, b) and (c, d) such that $a = (c + d)$, is distributed as a beta variable with parameters $(c, b + d)$. In general, the product of beta variables, with parameters $(a_1, b_1), (a_2, b_2) \cdots (a_k, b_k)$ such that $a_i = (a_{i+1} + b_{i+1})$, is distributed as a beta variable with parameters $(a_k, b_1 + \cdots + b_k)$.

2a.7 Cauchy Distribution

The Cauchy distribution is defined by

$$\frac{1}{\pi} \frac{dx}{1 + (x - \mu)^2}$$

where x ranges from $-\infty$ to ∞. This is a symmetrical distribution with the modal value at $x = \mu$.

$$E(x) = \frac{1}{\pi} \int_{-\infty}^{+\infty} \frac{x \, dx}{1 + (x - \mu)^2}$$

This integral does not exist but has the principal value μ since

$$\lim_{l \to \infty} \frac{1}{\pi} \int_{-l}^{+l} \frac{x \, dx}{1 + (x - \mu)^2} \quad \text{exists}$$

The second moment

$$E(x^2) = \frac{1}{\pi} \int_{-\infty}^{+\infty} \frac{x^2 \, dx}{1 + (x - \mu)^2} = \infty$$

so that the Cauchy variable has infinite variance. This is an example of a continuous distribution for which the mean and variance do not exist.

Consider two independent Cauchy variates x and y with parameters μ_1 and μ_2. Their joint distribution is

$$\frac{1}{\pi^2} \frac{dx}{1 + (x - \mu_1)^2} \frac{dy}{1 + (y - \mu_2)^2}$$

Putting $u = x - \mu_1$ and $v = y - \mu_2$, we find the distribution of $(u + v)/2$ and hence derive that of $(x + y)/2$ by the substitution $u + v = (x + y - \mu_1 - \mu_2)$. Transforming from u, v to u, z connected by the relations $u = u$ and $u + v = 2z$, the joint distribution of u and z is given by

$$\text{const.} \frac{du \, dz}{\{1 + u^2\}\{1 + (2z - u)^2\}}$$

$$\frac{1}{\{1 + u^2\}\{1 + (2z - u)^2\}} = \frac{1}{4z^2(4 + 4z^2)}$$
$$\left\{ \frac{4zu}{1 + u^2} + \frac{4z^2}{1 + u^2} + \frac{8z^2 - 4zu}{1 + (2z - u)^2} + \frac{4z^2}{1 + (2z - u)^2} \right\}$$

Integrating term by term with respect to u from $-\infty$ to ∞, we obtain

$$\text{const.} \frac{dz}{(4z^2 + 4)4z^2} \left[2z \log (1 + u^2) - 2z \log \{1 + (2z - u)^2\} \right.$$
$$\left. + 4z^2 \tan^{-1} u + 4z^2 \tan^{-1} (u - 2z) \right]_{-\infty}^{+\infty} = \text{const.} \frac{dz}{1 + z^2}$$

The distribution of $z = (x + y)/2$ obtained by changing z to $z - (\mu_1 + \mu_2)/2$ in the above expression is

$$\frac{1}{\pi} \frac{dz}{1 + \left(z - \dfrac{\mu_1 + \mu_2}{2}\right)^2}$$

which shows that the mean of two Cauchy variables with parameters μ_1 and μ_2 is distributed as a Cauchy variable with the parameter equal to the mean of the two parameters. In general, the average of k Cauchy variables with parameters $\mu_1, \cdots, \mu_k$ is distributed as a Cauchy variable with the parameter $(\mu_1 + \cdots + \mu_k)/k$. If all μ are the same, we obtain the interesting result that the distributions of a single observation and that of the mean of any number of observations are the same.

2a.8 Pearson's P_λ Distribution

If a stochastic variable x has the probability density $f(x)$, then the variable

$$\int_{-\infty}^{x} f(x)\, dx$$

which represents the probability of an observation's being less than or equal to x, has probability density unity. Since

$$dy = \frac{d}{dx} \int_{-\infty}^{x} f(x)\, dx = f(x)\, dx$$

$f(x)\, dx$ transforms to dy with the range of y equal to $(0, 1)$.

Let $z = -2 \log_e y$, in which case $dz = -(2/y)\, dy$. Since the probability density of y is dy, that of z is

$$\frac{y}{2}\, dz = \frac{1}{2}\, e^{-z/2}\, dz$$

which is $G(\frac{1}{2}, 1)$.

If $y_1, y_2, \cdots, y_k$ are k probabilities derived from k independent observations $x_1, \cdots, x_k$ from k distributions, all of which may be different from one another, then their joint distribution is

$$dy_1 \cdots dy_k$$

If $z_i = -2 \log_e y_i$, then z_i is $G(\frac{1}{2}, 1)$ for all i. If P_λ is defined by $z_1 + \cdots + z_k$, then P_λ, being the sum of k gamma variates with parameters $(\frac{1}{2}, 1)$, is distributed as $G(\frac{1}{2}, k)$ or $\chi^2(2k)$. This distribution is useful in combining several independent tests.

2a.9 Summary of Results

Some of the important results of this section have been brought together for later use.

(i) If $n_1, \cdots, n_k$, $(\Sigma n_i = n)$, are the frequencies in k mutually exclusive classes with probabilities $\pi_1, \cdots, \pi_k$, then, as shown in 2a.2,

$$E(n_i) = n\pi_i$$

$$V(l_1 n_1 + \cdots + l_k n_k) = n\{\Sigma l_i^2 \pi_i - (\Sigma l_i \pi_i)^2\}$$

$$\text{cov}\,\{(l_1 n_1 + \cdots + l_k n_k),\, (m_1 n_1 + \cdots + m_k n_k)\}$$

$$= n\{\Sigma l_i m_i \pi_i - (\Sigma l_i \pi_i)(\Sigma m_i \pi_i)\}$$

$$(2a.9.1)$$

(ii) Defining as in 2a.4,

$$N(\mu, \sigma, x) \, dx = \frac{1}{\sigma\sqrt{2\pi}} e^{-(x-\mu)^2/2\sigma^2} \, dx$$

$$\int_{\bar{x}} N(\mu_1, \sigma_1, x_1) \cdots N(\mu_n, \sigma_n, x_n) \, dx_1 \cdots dx_n = N(\mu, \sigma, \bar{x}) \, d\bar{x} \qquad (2a.9.2)$$

where $\mu = (\mu_1 + \cdots + \mu_n)/n$, $\sigma^2 = (\sigma_1^2 + \cdots + \sigma_n^2)/n^2$. The symbol $\int_{\bar{x}}$ is used to indicate that the integration is over constant values of $\bar{x}$. The distribution of $y = x^2$, where x is $N(\mu, \sigma)$, is

$$\frac{1}{\sigma\sqrt{2\pi}} e^{-\mu^2/2\sigma^2} e^{-y/2\sigma^2} \frac{\cosh\left(\sqrt{y}\mu/\sigma^2\right)}{\sqrt{y}} \, dy$$

$$= \frac{1}{\sigma\sqrt{2\pi}} e^{-\mu^2/2\sigma^2} e^{-y/2\sigma^2} y^{-\frac{1}{2}} \left\{ 1 + \frac{1}{2!}\left(\frac{\mu}{\sigma^2}\right)^2 y + \frac{1}{4!}\left(\frac{\mu}{\sigma^2}\right)^4 y^2 + \cdots \right\} \, dy$$

$$= e^{-\mu^2/2\sigma^2} \Sigma \left(\frac{\mu^2}{2\sigma^2}\right)^r \frac{1}{r!} G\left(\frac{1}{2\sigma^2}, r + \frac{1}{2}, y\right) dy \qquad (2a.9.3)$$

(iii) Defining

$$G(\alpha, p, x) \, dx = \frac{\alpha^p}{\Gamma(p)} e^{-\alpha x} x^{p-1} \, dx$$

the results obtained in 2a.5 are

$$\int_{X=x_1+\cdots+x_n} G(\alpha, p_1, x_1) G(\alpha, p_2, x_2) \cdots dx_1 \, dx_2 \cdots dx_n$$
$$= G(\alpha, p_1 + \cdots + p_n, X) \, dX \qquad (2a.9.4)$$

Also

$$\int_{z=x/(x+y)} G(\alpha, p, x) G(\alpha, q, y) \, dx \, dy = B(p, q, z) \, dz \qquad (2a.9.5)$$

and

$$\int_{f=x/y} G(\alpha, p, x) G(\alpha, q, y) \, dx \, dy = \frac{\Gamma(p+q)}{\Gamma(p)\Gamma(q)} \frac{f^{p-1} \, df}{(1+f)^{p+q}} \qquad (2a.9.6)$$

(iv) Defining as in 2a.6,

$$B(a, b, x) \, dx = \frac{\Gamma(a+b)}{\Gamma(a)\Gamma(b)} x^{a-1}(1-x)^{b-1} \, dx$$

$$\int_{z=xy} B(a, b, x) B(c, d, y) \, dx \, dy = B(c, b+d, z) \, dz \qquad (2a.9.7)$$

if $a = c + d$.

$$\int_{z=x_1 \cdots x_n} B(a_1, b_1, x_1) B(a_2, b_2, x_2) \cdots dx_1 \cdots dx_n$$

$$= B(a_n, b_1 + \cdots + b_n, z) \, dz \quad (2a.9.8)$$

provided that $a_1 = a_2 + b_2$, $a_2 = a_3 + b_3$, $\cdots$.

2b Distributions Relating to the Univariate Normal Distribution

2b.1 Mean and Variance in Normal Samples

Let $x_1, \cdots, x_n$ be n independent observations from a normal population $N(\mu, \sigma)$. The probability density is

$$\text{const. } e^{-\phi/2\sigma^2}$$

where

$$\phi = \Sigma(x_i - \mu)^2 = n(\bar{x} - \mu)^2 + S^2$$

$$\bar{x} = \frac{(x_1 + \cdots + x_n)}{n}$$

$$S^2 = \Sigma(x_i - \bar{x})^2$$

Consider an orthogonal transformation from x to z:

$$z_1 = \frac{(x_1 + \cdots + x_n)}{\sqrt{n}} = \sqrt{n}\bar{x}$$

$$z_i = a_{i1}x_1 + \cdots + a_{in}x_n \qquad i = 2, \cdots, n$$

Since the vectors of z_1 and z_i, $(i \neq 1)$, are orthogonal, $\sum_j a_{ij} = 0$, for $i = 2, \cdots, n$. Under this transformation

$$x_1, \cdots, x_n \sim z_1, \cdots, z_n$$

$$\mu, \cdots, \mu \sim \sqrt{n}\mu, 0, \cdots, 0$$

and, as shown in (iv) of 1c.2 (invariance of distance),

$$\Sigma(x_i - \mu)^2 = (z_1 - \sqrt{n}\mu)^2 + z_2^2 + \cdots + z_n^2$$

$$= n(\bar{x} - \mu)^2 + S^2$$

Therefore $S^2 = z_2^2 + \cdots + z_n^2$. The distribution of $z_1 \cdots z_n$ is

$$\text{const. } e^{-\{(z_1 - \sqrt{n}\mu)^2 + z_2^2 + \cdots + z_n^2\}/2\sigma^2} \, dz_1 \cdots dz_n$$

which shows that the distributions of z_1 and $z_2, \cdots, z_n$ are independent and hence those of $\bar{x} = z_1/\sqrt{n}$ and $S^2 = z_2^2 + \cdots + z_n^2$. The distribution of $\bar{x}$ is

$$\text{const. } e^{-n(\bar{x}-\mu)^2/2\sigma^2}\, d\bar{x} \qquad \text{const. } = \sqrt{\frac{n}{2\pi}}\frac{1}{\sigma}$$

Since z_i^2 is $G(1/2\sigma^2,\ \tfrac{1}{2})$ for $i \geq 2$, it follows from (2a.9.3) and (2a.9.4) that $z_2^2 + \cdots + z_n^2 = S^2$ is distributed as $G(1/2\sigma^2,\ (n-1)/2)$, i.e.,

$$\text{const. } e^{-S^2/2\sigma^2}(S^2)^{(n-3)/2}\, dS^2 \qquad \text{const. } = \frac{1}{(2\sigma^2)^{(n-1)/2}\Gamma\left(\dfrac{n-1}{2}\right)}$$

or that of $\chi^2 = S^2/\sigma^2$ is $\chi^2(n-1)$.

2b.2 Student's Distribution

The joint distribution of $\sqrt{n}(\bar{x} - \mu)$ and S^2 is

$$N(0,\ \sigma^2)\, d\sqrt{n}(\bar{x}-\mu)\ G\left(\frac{1}{2\sigma^2},\frac{n-1}{2}\right) dS^2$$

Student's t statistic is

$$t = \frac{\sqrt{n}(\bar{x}-\mu)}{s}$$

where $s^2 = S^2/(n-1)$ or, squaring and rearranging,

$$\frac{t^2}{n-1} = \frac{n(\bar{x}-\mu)^2}{S^2} = f$$

$n(\bar{x}-\mu)^2$ is distributed as $G(1/2\sigma^2,\ \tfrac{1}{2})$, so, from (2a.9.6), the distribution of f is

$$\frac{\Gamma\left(\dfrac{n}{2}\right)}{\Gamma\left(\dfrac{1}{2}\right)\Gamma\left(\dfrac{n-1}{2}\right)}\frac{f^{-1/2}}{(1+f)^{n/2}}\, df$$

and hence that of t, which is symmetrically distributed, is

$$\frac{\Gamma\left(\dfrac{n}{2}\right)}{\sqrt{n-1}\,\Gamma\left(\dfrac{1}{2}\right)\Gamma\left(\dfrac{n-1}{2}\right)}\frac{dt}{\left(1+\dfrac{t^2}{n-1}\right)^{n/2}} \qquad (2b.2.1)$$

This is called Student's t distribution based on $(n - 1)$ degrees of freedom. When $n = 2$, this reduces to Cauchy distribution.

Non-Null t^2 Distribution. To find the distribution of $t^2 = n\bar{x}^2/s^2$ when $\mu \neq 0$, we note that the joint density of S^2 and $y = n\bar{x}^2$ is (see 2a.9.3)

$$e^{-n\mu^2/2\sigma^2} G\left(\frac{1}{2\sigma^2}, \frac{n-1}{2}, S^2\right) \Sigma \left(\frac{n\mu^2}{2\sigma^2}\right)^r \frac{1}{r!} G\left(\frac{1}{2\sigma^2}, r + \frac{1}{2}, y\right) \quad (2b.2.2)$$

Making use of (2a.9.6) for each term of the infinite series we find the distribution of $f = y/S^2$ to be

$$e^{-n\mu^2/2\sigma^2} \Sigma \frac{1}{r!} \left(\frac{n\mu^2}{2\sigma^2}\right)^r \frac{\Gamma\left(\frac{n}{2} + r\right)}{\Gamma\left(r + \frac{1}{2}\right) \Gamma\left(\frac{n-1}{2}\right)} \frac{f^{r-\frac{1}{2}}}{(1 + f)^{(n/2)+r}} df$$

$$= \frac{\Gamma\left(\frac{n}{2}\right)}{\Gamma\left(\frac{n-1}{2}\right) \Gamma\left(\frac{1}{2}\right)} e^{-n\mu^2/2\sigma^2} \frac{f^{-\frac{1}{2}}}{(1 + f)^{n/2}} {}_1F_1\left(\frac{n}{2}, \frac{1}{2}, \frac{f}{1+f} \frac{n\mu^2}{2\sigma^2}\right) df$$

$$(2b.2.3)$$

where ${}_1F_1$ is the hypergeometric function defined above. The distribution of $t^2 = (n - 1)f$ can be obtained from this. Sometimes it is useful to use the distribution of $R = S^2/(y + S^2)$ which can be obtained by applying (2a.9.5) to each term in (2b.2.2).

$$e^{-n\mu^2/2\sigma^2} \Sigma \frac{1}{r!} \left(\frac{n\mu^2}{2\sigma^2}\right)^r B\left(\frac{n-1}{2}, r + \frac{1}{2}\right) dR \quad (2b.2.4)$$

2b.3   Fisher's z Distribution

If s_1^2 and s_2^2 are two independent estimates of variance based on n_1 and n_2 degrees of freedom, then $S_1^2 = n_1 s_1^2$ and $S_2^2 = n_2 s_2^2$ have the joint distribution

$$G\left(\frac{1}{2\sigma^2}, \frac{n_1}{2}, S_1^2\right) G\left(\frac{1}{2\sigma^2}, \frac{n_2}{2}, S_2^2\right) dS_1^2 \, dS_2^2$$

so that their ratio $f = S_1^2/S_2^2$ has the distribution

$$\frac{\Gamma\left(\frac{n_1 + n_2}{2}\right)}{\Gamma\left(\frac{n_1}{2}\right) \Gamma\left(\frac{n_2}{2}\right)} \frac{f^{(n_1/2)-1}}{(1 + f)^{(n_1+n_2)/2}} df$$

The distribution of $F = s_1^2/s_2^2 = n_2 f/n_1$ is

$$\left(\frac{n_1}{n_2}\right)^{n_1/2} \frac{\Gamma\left(\dfrac{n_1 + n_2}{2}\right)}{\Gamma\left(\dfrac{n_1}{2}\right)\Gamma\left(\dfrac{n_2}{2}\right)\left(1 + \dfrac{n_1}{n_2}F\right)^{(n_1+n_2)/2}} F^{(n_1/2)-1}\, dF$$

This is called the variance ratio distribution. Fisher defines

$$z = \frac{1}{2}\log_e \frac{s_1^2}{s_2^2} = \frac{1}{2}\log_e F$$

so that the z distribution is

$$\left(\frac{n_1}{n_2}\right)^{n_1/2} \frac{\Gamma\left(\dfrac{n_1 + n_2}{2}\right)}{\Gamma\left(\dfrac{n_1}{2}\right)\Gamma\left(\dfrac{n_2}{2}\right)\left(1 + \dfrac{n_1}{n_2}e^{2z}\right)^{(n_1+n_2)/2}} e^{n_1 z}\, 2\, dz$$

In practice it is convenient to use the F distribution instead of z.

2b.4 Cochran's Theorem

Let $x_1, \cdots, x_n$ be n normal variates with zero mean and unit variance. If $x_1^2 + \cdots + x_n^2 = q_1 + \cdots + q_k$, where q_i is a quadratic form of rank n_i, then the necessary and sufficient condition that $q_1, q_2, \cdots$ are independently distributed as χ^2 with $n_1, n_2, \cdots$ degrees of freedom is that $n = \Sigma n_i$.

Since q_i is a quadratic form of rank n_i, it can be expressed as (see ii in 1c.2)

$$\pm l_{i1}^2 \pm l_{i2}^2 \pm \cdots \pm l_{in_i}^2 \qquad (2b.4.1)$$

where l_{ij} is a linear function of $x_1, \cdots, x_n$. Also by hypothesis

$$\Sigma x_i^2 = \Sigma q_i = \sum_{i=1}^{k} \sum_{j=1}^{n_i} \pm l_{ij}^2$$

If $n = \Sigma n_i$, then there are n linear functions l_{ij}, which supply a transformation from x to l, viz.,

$$\mathbf{l} = \mathbf{x}A$$

with A as the matrix of transformation. If Δ denotes a diagonal matrix with ± 1 in the diagonal then

$$\mathbf{x}\mathbf{x}' = \Sigma\Sigma \pm l_{ij}^2 = \mathbf{l}\Delta\mathbf{l}' = \mathbf{x}A\Delta A'\mathbf{x}' = \mathbf{x}\mathbf{x}'$$

or

$$A\Delta A' = I \qquad |A|\,|\Delta|\,|A'| = 1$$

Since $|\Delta| \neq 0$, $|A| \neq 0$. This shows that the transformation is non-singular, in which case the positive definite form $\mathbf{xx}'$ remains positive even after transformation. Therefore the coefficients in (2b.4.1) should all be $+1$. The joint distribution of l is derived from that of x

$$\text{const. } e^{-\frac{1}{2}(x_1^2 + \cdots + x_n^2)}\, dx_1 \cdots dx_n \sim \text{const. } e^{-\frac{1}{2}\Sigma\Sigma l_{ij}^2}\, \Pi\, dl_{ij},$$

which shows that l_{ij} are independently distributed and so are q_1, q_2, $\cdots$, q_k, each of which depends on exclusive subsets of l_{ij}. Since q_i is the sum of squares of n_i independent normal variates $l_{i1}, \cdots, l_{in_i}$, it is distributed as χ^2 with n_i degrees of freedom. This establishes the sufficiency of the condition.

If q_i is distributed as χ^2 with n_i degrees of freedom, then Σq_i, being the sum of k independent χ^2, is also a χ^2 with Σn_i degrees of freedom. But $\Sigma q_i = \Sigma x_i^2$, being the sum of squares of n variates $N(0, 1)$, is a χ^2 with n degrees of freedom. Therefore $n = \Sigma n_i$.

2b.5 Distribution of Non-Central χ^2

Consider k independent normal variates $x_1, \cdots, x_k$ with means ν_1, $\nu_2, \cdots, \nu_k$ and standard deviations $\sigma_1, \sigma_2, \cdots \sigma_k$. The distribution of $(x_1/\sigma_1)^2 + (x_2/\sigma_2)^2 + \cdots$ is χ^2 with k degrees of freedom only when $\nu_1 = \cdots = \nu_k = 0$. To find the general distribution make the following transformations.

$$y_i = \frac{x_i}{\sigma_i} \qquad i = 1, 2, \cdots k$$

$$\mathbf{z} = \mathbf{y}A$$

where A is an orthogonal transformation such that the first transformed variable is

$$\frac{\left(\dfrac{\nu_1}{\sigma_1} y_1 + \cdots + \dfrac{\nu_k}{\sigma_k} y_k\right)}{\nu} \qquad \nu^2 = \Sigma\left(\frac{\nu_i^2}{\sigma_i^2}\right)$$

Then $E(z_1) = \nu$, $E(z_2) = \cdots = E(z_k) = 0$, and $z_1, \cdots, z_k$ are distributed as independent normal variates with unit variances.

Now

$$\chi^2 = \Sigma\left(\frac{x_i}{\sigma_i}\right)^2 = \Sigma y_i^2 = \Sigma z_i^2 = \chi_1^2 + \chi_2^2$$

where $\chi_1{}^2 = z_1{}^2$, and $\chi_2{}^2 = z_2{}^2 + \cdots + z_k{}^2$. The joint distribution of z_1 and $\chi_2{}^2$ is simply

$$\text{const. } e^{-\frac{1}{2}[(z_1-\nu)^2+\chi_2{}^2]}\chi_2{}^{k-2} \, dz_1 \, d\chi_2$$

The distribution of $\chi_2{}^2$ and $z_1{}^2$ is

$$e^{-\nu^2/2} G\left(\frac{1}{2}, \frac{k-1}{2}\right) d\chi_2{}^2 \, \Sigma \left(\frac{\nu^2}{2}\right)^r \frac{1}{r!} G\left(\frac{1}{2}, r + \frac{1}{2}\right) dz_1{}^2$$

Hence, by using (2a.9.4), each term of the above series can be reduced, yielding the distribution of $\chi^2 = z_1{}^2 + \chi_2{}^2$,

$$e^{-\nu^2/2} \Sigma \left(\frac{\nu^2}{2}\right)^r \frac{1}{r!} G\left(\frac{1}{2}, \frac{k}{2} + r\right) d\chi^2$$

2c Multivariate Normal Populations

2c.1 The Multivariate Normal Distribution

(i) A set of p variates $\mathbf{x} = (x_1, \cdots, x_p)$ is said to follow the p-variate normal distribution if the joint probability distribution of the variables is

$$C e^{-\frac{1}{2}(\mathbf{x}-\mathbf{\mu})\Lambda(\mathbf{x}-\mathbf{\mu})'} \, d\mathbf{x}$$

and, when $\mathbf{x}$ is measured from the origin $\mathbf{\mu} = (\mu_1, \cdots, \mu_p)$, the distribution reduces to

$$C e^{-\frac{1}{2}\mathbf{x}\Lambda\mathbf{x}'} \, d\mathbf{x}$$

where C is a constant and the quadratic form $\mathbf{x}\Lambda\mathbf{x}'$ is positive definite. The constant is determined from the relation

$$C \int e^{-\frac{1}{2}\mathbf{x}\Lambda\mathbf{x}'} \, d\mathbf{x} = 1$$

Since $\mathbf{x}\Lambda\mathbf{x}'$ is positive definite, there exists a non-singular transformation $\mathbf{x} = \mathbf{y}B$ such that

$$\mathbf{x}\Lambda\mathbf{x}' = \mathbf{y}B\Lambda B'\mathbf{y}' = \mathbf{y}\mathbf{y}'$$

$$\therefore \ B\Lambda B' = I \quad \text{or} \quad |B| = |\Lambda|^{-\frac{1}{2}}$$

The Jacobian of the transformation is

$$\frac{\partial(x_1, \cdots, x_p)}{\partial(y_1, \cdots, y_p)} = |B| = |\Lambda|^{-\frac{1}{2}}$$

The above integral transforms to

$$\frac{C}{|\Lambda|^{\frac{1}{2}}} \int e^{-\frac{1}{2}(y_1^2 + \cdots + y_p^2)} \, dy_1 \cdots dy_p$$

$$= \frac{C}{|\Lambda|^{\frac{1}{2}}} \int e^{-\frac{1}{2}y_1^2} \, dy_1 \int e^{-\frac{1}{2}y_2^2} \, dy_2 \cdots$$

$$= \frac{C}{|\Lambda|^{\frac{1}{2}}} (\sqrt{2\pi})^p = 1$$

$$C = \frac{|\Lambda|^{\frac{1}{2}}}{(2\pi)^{p/2}}$$

(ii) Since

$$\int x_i C e^{-\frac{1}{2}\mathbf{x}\Lambda\mathbf{x}'} \, d\mathbf{x} = 0$$

being an odd function of x_i and an even function of the rest, it follows that μ_i is the mean value of the original variable x_i. If $E(x_i x_j)$ is the covariance between the ith and jth variables, the expected values of the elements of the matrix $\mathbf{x}'\mathbf{x}$ will be the elements of variance covariance or the dispersion matrix to be represented by R.

$$R = C \int \mathbf{x}'\mathbf{x} e^{-\frac{1}{2}\mathbf{x}\Lambda\mathbf{x}'} \, d\mathbf{x}$$

If $\mathbf{x} = \mathbf{y}B$ such that $B\Lambda B' = I$, the above integral becomes

$$C|B| \int B'\mathbf{y}'\mathbf{y}B e^{-\frac{1}{2}\mathbf{y}\mathbf{y}'} \, d\mathbf{y} = \frac{1}{(2\pi)^{p/2}} \int B'\mathbf{y}'\mathbf{y}B e^{-\frac{1}{2}\mathbf{y}\mathbf{y}'} \, d\mathbf{y}$$

$$= B' \left\{ \frac{1}{(2\pi)^{p/2}} \int \mathbf{y}'\mathbf{y} e^{-\frac{1}{2}\mathbf{y}\mathbf{y}'} \, d\mathbf{y} \right\} B$$

$$= B'\{I\}B = B'B$$

Since $B\Lambda B' = I$, $\Lambda = B^{-1}B'^{-1} = (B'B)^{-1}$ or $B'B = \Lambda^{-1}$. This shows that the dispersion matrix of the variables is the reciprocal of the matrix of the quadratic form in the exponential. Alternatively, given the dispersion matrix R the probability density can be written as

$$\frac{1}{|R|^{\frac{1}{2}}(2\pi)^{p/2}} e^{-\frac{1}{2}\mathbf{x}R^{-1}\mathbf{x}'}$$

The above proof is due to Nair (1949).

2c.2 The Distribution of a Set of Linear Functions of Normal Variates

Starting from the joint distribution

$$Ce^{-\frac{1}{2}\mathbf{x}\Lambda\mathbf{x}'}\,d\mathbf{x}$$

it is required to find the distribution of $\mathbf{u} = (u_1, \cdots, u_k)$, $(k \leq p)$, defined by

$$\mathbf{u} = \mathbf{x}B$$

where B is a matrix (p, k) of rank k. Make the transformation

$$\mathbf{u} = \mathbf{x}B \qquad \mathbf{v} = \mathbf{x}A$$

where $\mathbf{v} = (v_1, \cdots, v_{p-k})$ and A is a matrix $(p, p - k)$ of rank $(p - k)$ and is such that $A'\Lambda^{-1}B = 0$. The total transformation may be represented by $(\mathbf{u} \mid \mathbf{v}) = \mathbf{x}(B \mid A)$. Now the rank of

$$\begin{pmatrix} B' \\ \cdots \\ A' \end{pmatrix} \Lambda^{-1}(B \mid A) = \left(\begin{array}{c|c} B'\Lambda^{-1}B & 0 \\ \hline 0 & A'\Lambda^{-1}A \end{array} \right)$$

is p, the same as that of $(B \mid A)$. This means that the rank of $B'\Lambda^{-1}B$ is k and that $A'\Lambda^{-1}A$ is $(p - k)$ in which case $(B'\Lambda^{-1}B)^{-1}$ and $(A'\Lambda^{-1}A)^{-1}$ exist. Let the quadratic form $\mathbf{x}\Lambda\mathbf{x}'$ change over to

$$\mathbf{u}D_1\mathbf{u}' + \mathbf{u}D_2\mathbf{v}' + \mathbf{v}D_3\mathbf{v}'$$

Substituting $\mathbf{u} = \mathbf{x}B$ and $\mathbf{v} = \mathbf{x}A$, we obtain

$$BD_1B' + BD_2A' + AD_3A' = \Lambda$$

Pre- and post-multiplying by $B'\Lambda^{-1}$ and $\Lambda^{-1}B$,

$$B'\Lambda^{-1}BD_1B'\Lambda^{-1}B = B'\Lambda^{-1}B$$

or

$$D_1 = (B'\Lambda^{-1}B)^{-1}$$

Similarly,

$$D_3 = (A'\Lambda^{-1}A)^{-1}$$

Pre- and post-multiplying by $B'\Lambda^{-1}$ and $\Lambda^{-1}A$, we find

$$B'\Lambda^{-1}BD_2A'\Lambda^{-1}A = 0$$

or

$$D_2 = 0$$

The joint distribution of $\mathbf{u}$ and $\mathbf{v}$ is

$$\text{const. } e^{-\frac{1}{2}(\mathbf{u}D_1\mathbf{u}' + \mathbf{v}D_3\mathbf{v}')}\,d\mathbf{u}\,d\mathbf{v}$$

Integrating out for $\mathbf{v}$, the distribution for $\mathbf{u}$ is

$$\text{const. } e^{-\frac{1}{2}\mathbf{u}(B'\Lambda^{-1}B)^{-1}\mathbf{u}'} \, d\mathbf{u}$$

which shows that a set of linear functions of normal variates follows a multivariate normal distribution. The dispersion matrix of $\mathbf{u} = \mathbf{x}B$ is

$$\{(B'\Lambda^{-1}B)^{-1}\}^{-1} = B'\Lambda^{-1}B$$

which can be obtained directly without finding the distribution of $\mathbf{u}$.

In particular, if $x_1, \cdots, x_p$ follow a p-variate normal distribution, the subset $x_1, \cdots, x_k$ follow a k-variate normal distribution. It is also of interest to determine the conditional distribution of $x_{k+1}, \cdots, x_p$, given $x_1, x_2, \cdots, x_k$. Consider the partitioned vector

$$(\mathbf{x}_1 \mid \mathbf{x}_2) = (x_1, \cdots, x_k \mid x_{k+1}, \cdots, x_p)$$

with its dispersion matrix

$$E\begin{pmatrix} \mathbf{x}_1' \\ \hline \mathbf{x}_2' \end{pmatrix} (\mathbf{x}_1 \mid \mathbf{x}_2) = \left(\begin{array}{c|c} A & B \\ \hline B' & C \end{array} \right)$$

Consider the linear functions

$$\mathbf{x}_2 - \mathbf{x}_1 T$$

where the matrix T is chosen such that

$$E[\mathbf{x}_1'(\mathbf{x}_2 - \mathbf{x}_1 T)] = 0$$

i.e.,

$$B - AT = 0 \qquad \text{or} \qquad T = A^{-1}B$$

$$E(\mathbf{x}_2 - \mathbf{x}_1 T)'(\mathbf{x}_2 - \mathbf{x}_1 T) = E(\mathbf{x}_2'\mathbf{x}_2) + T'E(\mathbf{x}_1'\mathbf{x}_1)T - 2E(\mathbf{x}_2'\mathbf{x}_1)T$$

$$= C + B'A^{-1}AA^{-1}B - 2B'A^{-1}B$$

$$= C - B'A^{-1}B = D \qquad \text{say}$$

The joint distribution of $\mathbf{x}_1$ and $\mathbf{y}_2 = (\mathbf{x}_2 - \mathbf{x}_1 T)$ is

$$\text{const. } e^{-\frac{1}{2}\mathbf{x}_1 A^{-1}\mathbf{x}_1' - \frac{1}{2}\mathbf{y}_2 D^{-1}\mathbf{y}_2'} \, d\mathbf{x}_1 \, d\mathbf{y}_2$$

and that of $\mathbf{x}_1$ and $\mathbf{x}_2$ is

$$\text{const. } e^{-\frac{1}{2}\mathbf{x}_1 A^{-1}\mathbf{x}_1' - \frac{1}{2}(\mathbf{x}_2 - \mathbf{x}_1 T)D^{-1}(\mathbf{x}_2 - \mathbf{x}_1 T)'} \, d\mathbf{x}_1 \, d\mathbf{x}_2$$

which shows that the distribution of $\mathbf{x}_2$, given $\mathbf{x}_1$, is the second part of the above expression. The matrices T and D are already determined in terms of known quantities.

2c.3 The Distribution of Quadratic Forms

(i) Given the joint distribution

$$Ce^{-\frac{1}{2}\mathbf{x}\Lambda\mathbf{x}'}\,d\mathbf{x}$$

to find the distribution of the quadratic form $\mathbf{x}\Lambda\mathbf{x}'$ make the transformation $\mathbf{y} = \mathbf{x}B$ such that

$$\mathbf{x}\Lambda\mathbf{x}' = \mathbf{y}\mathbf{y}'$$

in which case the joint distribution of y is

$$\text{const. } e^{-\frac{1}{2}(y_1{}^2 + \cdots + y_p{}^2)}\,dy_1, \cdots, dy_p$$

The distribution of $x\Lambda x' = \Sigma y_i{}^2$, being the sum of squares of p variates $N(0, 1)$, is distributed as χ^2 with p degrees of freedom.

(ii) Suppose that the x_i are subject to k restrictions specified by $\mathbf{x}B = 0$, where B is a matrix (p, k). As in 2c.2 the transformation

$$\mathbf{u} = \mathbf{x}B \qquad \mathbf{v} = \mathbf{x}A$$

such that $A'\Lambda^{-1}B = 0$ gives

$$\mathbf{x}\Lambda\mathbf{x}' = \mathbf{u}(B'\Lambda^{-1}B)^{-1}\mathbf{u}' + \mathbf{v}(A'\Lambda^{-1}A)^{-1}\mathbf{v}'$$

The value of the quadratic form $\mathbf{x}\Lambda\mathbf{x}'$ subject to the restriction $\mathbf{u} = \mathbf{x}B = 0$ is $\mathbf{v}(A'\Lambda^{-1}A)^{-1}\mathbf{v}'$. The distribution $\mathbf{v}$ for any $\mathbf{u}$ is independent of $\mathbf{u}$ and is given by

$$\text{const. } e^{-\frac{1}{2}\mathbf{v}D_3\mathbf{v}'}\,d\mathbf{v} \qquad D_3 = (A'\Lambda^{-1}A)^{-1}$$

By the result proved in (i), $\mathbf{v}D_3\mathbf{v}'$ is distributed as χ^2 with $(p - k)$ degrees of freedom. So the quadratic form $\mathbf{x}\Lambda\mathbf{x}'$ subject to the condition $\mathbf{x}B = 0$ is distributed as χ^2 with $(p - k)$ degrees of freedom.

(iii) If $\mathbf{x}\Lambda\mathbf{x}' = q_1 + \cdots + q_k$ where q_i is a quadratic form of rank p_i, then the necessary and sufficient condition that q are independently distributed as χ^2 is that $p = \Sigma p_i$. This is essentially Cochran's theorem with a general positive definite quadratic form $\mathbf{x}\Lambda\mathbf{x}'$ instead of $\mathbf{x}\mathbf{x}'$. The proof remains the same.

(iv) The necessary and sufficient condition that a quadratic form $\mathbf{x}D\mathbf{x}'$ of rank k is distributed as χ^2 when $\mathbf{x}$ follows the law, const. $\exp -\frac{1}{2}(\mathbf{x}\Lambda\mathbf{x}')\,d\mathbf{x}$, is that the quadratic form $\mathbf{x}(\Lambda - D)\mathbf{x}'$ is of rank $(p - k)$. The sufficiency condition follows from result (iii), since $\mathbf{x}\Lambda\mathbf{x}' = \mathbf{x}D\mathbf{x}' + \mathbf{x}(\Lambda - D)\mathbf{x}'$. To prove the necessity we observe that there exists a transformation $\mathbf{y} = \mathbf{x}B$ which transforms (see 1c.5).

$$\mathbf{x}\Lambda\mathbf{x}' \rightarrow y_1{}^2 + \cdots + y_p{}^2$$

$$\mathbf{x}D\mathbf{x}' \rightarrow \lambda_1 y_1{}^2 + \cdots + \lambda_k y_k{}^2$$

The quadratic form $\mathbf{x}D\mathbf{x}'$ is thus a linear compound of the squares of independent normal variates $N(0, 1)$. It may be verified that its distribution is χ^2 when and only when each λ is equal to unity. Otherwise the distribution is different from χ^2. Take, for instance, $\lambda_1 y_1^2 + \lambda_2 y_2^2$. If this is distributed as χ^2 with 2 degrees of freedom, then

$$E(\lambda_1 y_1^2 + \lambda_2 y_2^2) = \lambda_1 + \lambda_2 = 2$$

$$V(\lambda_1 y_1^2 + \lambda_2 y_2^2) = 3(\lambda_1 + \lambda_2)^2 - 4\lambda_1\lambda_2$$

$$= 3 \times 4 - 4\lambda_1\lambda_2 = 8$$

$$\lambda_1\lambda_2 = 1$$

which means $\lambda_1 = \lambda_2 = 1$. Similarly, it may be shown by considering k moments that $\lambda_1, \cdots, \lambda_k$ are the roots of an equation $(\lambda - 1)^k = 0$. Therefore $\mathbf{x}D\mathbf{x}'$ transforms to $y_1^2 + \cdots + y_k^2$, in which case $\mathbf{x}(\Lambda - D)\mathbf{x}'$ transforms to $y^2_{k+1} + \cdots + y_p^2$ or the rank of $\mathbf{x}(\Lambda - D)\mathbf{x}'$ is $(p - k)$.

(v) Let $\mathbf{x}D_1\mathbf{x}'$ and $\mathbf{x}D_2\mathbf{x}'$ be two quadratic forms distributed as χ^2 with k_1 and k_2 degrees of freedom. The necessary and sufficient condition that they are independently distributed is $D_1\Lambda^{-1}D_2 = 0$.

In (iv) it is seen that the transformation $\mathbf{y} = \mathbf{x}B$ transforms

$$\mathbf{x}D\mathbf{x}' \rightarrow y_1^2 + \cdots + y_k^2$$

$$\mathbf{x}(\Lambda - D)\mathbf{x}' \rightarrow y^2_{k+1} + \cdots + y_p^2$$

If $\mathbf{z}_1 = (y_1, \cdots, y_k)$ and $\mathbf{z}_2 = (y_{k+1}, \cdots, y_p)$, then

$$(\mathbf{z}_1 \mid \mathbf{z}_2) = \mathbf{x}(B_1 \mid B_2) = \mathbf{x}B$$

$$\mathbf{x}D\mathbf{x}' = \mathbf{z}_1\mathbf{z}_1' = \mathbf{x}B_1'B_1\mathbf{x}' \quad \text{or} \quad D = B_1'B_1$$

$$\mathbf{x}(\Lambda - D)\mathbf{x}' = \mathbf{z}_2\mathbf{z}_2' = \mathbf{x}B_2'B_2\mathbf{x}' \quad \text{or} \quad \Lambda - D = B_2'B_2$$

Since $\mathbf{z}_1$ and $\mathbf{z}_2$ are independently distributed,

$$B_1\Lambda^{-1}B_2' = 0$$

which gives

$$B_1'B_1\Lambda^{-1}B_2'B_2 = 0 \quad \text{or} \quad D\Lambda^{-1}(\Lambda - D) = 0$$

$$D = D\Lambda^{-1}D$$

This is another form of the necessary and sufficient * condition for $\mathbf{x}D\mathbf{x}'$ to be distributed as χ^2.

* It is not difficult to prove sufficiency because $D = D\Lambda^{-1}D$ means that $D\Lambda^{-1}(\Lambda - D) = 0$. From example 5 in 1c.5 it follows that D and $(\Lambda - D)$ have independent row vectors. The rank of the vectors in D and $(\Lambda - D)$ put together is obviously p. Therefore rank D + rank $(\Lambda - D) = p$. Then (iii) holds good.

Since xD_1x' is a χ^2, $D_1 = D_1\Lambda^{-1}D_1$. For the same reason $D_2\Lambda^{-1}D_2$ $= D_2$. If $D_1\Lambda^{-1}D_2 = 0$, then rank D_1 + rank D_2 + rank $(\Lambda - D_1 - D_2) = p$. This shows, by (iii), that xD_1x' and xD_2x' are independently distributed. On the other hand, if xD_1x' and xD_2x' are independently distributed, then $x(\Lambda - D_1 - D_2)x'$ is also an independent χ^2. Hence there exists a transformation which transforms the quadratic forms xD_1x', xD_2x', $x(\Lambda - D_1 - D_2)x'$ into sums of squares of independent variables. Proceeding as above it is seen that $D_1\Lambda^{-1}D_2 = 0$.

(vi) The necessary and sufficient condition that a linear function lx' is distributed independently of a quadratic form xDx' which is a χ^2 is that

$$1\Lambda^{-1}D = 0$$

This follows from (iv), since the quadratic forms $xl'lx'$ and xDx' are independently distributed:

$$l'1\Lambda^{-1}D = 0 \qquad \text{or} \qquad 1\Lambda^{-1}D = 0$$

(vii) The necessary and sufficient conditions in (v) and (vi) are true under more general conditions. For instance, it is not necessary to assume that the quadratic forms are distributed as χ^2. This has been assumed to obtain simpler proofs of the results. This assumption is not stringent because by using (iv) we can always test whether some given quadratic forms are distributed as χ^2 or not. If they are, then questions of independence arise; otherwise the results are not important.

(viii) The distribution of the quadratic form $x\Lambda x'$ when x is distributed as

$$\text{const. } e^{-\frac{1}{2}(x-\mu)\Lambda(x-\mu)'} \, dx$$

can be obtained by making the transformation,

$$x = yA$$

such that

$$x\Lambda x' = yy' \qquad A\Lambda A' = I \qquad \Lambda = A^{-1}A^{-1\prime}$$

$$E(x) = E(y)A \qquad \text{or} \qquad E(y) = \mu A^{-1}$$

The distribution of Σy_i^2 is the non-central χ^2 of 2b.5 with the value of

$$\nu^2 = (\mu A^{-1})^2 = \mu A^{-1}A^{-1\prime}\mu' = \mu\Lambda\mu',$$

and k = the number of variables.

2d   Least Squares Fundamental in Distribution Theory

2d.1   Two Theorems on Least Squares

Suppose $y_1, y_2, \cdots, y_n$ are n independent normal variates with the same variance σ^2 and

$$E(y_i) = a_{i1}\tau_1 + \cdots + a_{ik}\tau_k \qquad i = 1, 2, \cdots, n$$

where a_{ij} are elements of a specified matrix A and $\tau_1, \tau_2, \cdots, \tau_k$ are unknown parameters.

(i) If $R_0{}^2$ is the minimum value of

$$\Sigma(y_i - a_{i1}\tau_1 - \cdots - a_{ik}\tau_k)^2$$

when minimized with respect to $\tau_1, \cdots, \tau_k$, what is the distribution of $R_0{}^2$?

Let there be r independent vectors in the set

$$\boldsymbol{\alpha}_i = (a_{1i}, a_{2i}, \cdots, a_{ni}) \qquad i = 1, \cdots, k$$

Then there exist $(n - r)$ vectors $\boldsymbol{\beta}_1, \cdots, \boldsymbol{\beta}_{n-r}$, all orthogonal to $\boldsymbol{\alpha}_1, \cdots, \boldsymbol{\alpha}_k$, so that $\boldsymbol{\alpha}_i \cdot \boldsymbol{\beta}_j = 0$. The $\boldsymbol{\beta}$ vectors themselves can be chosen to satisfy the conditions $\boldsymbol{\beta}_i \cdot \boldsymbol{\beta}_i = 1$ and $\boldsymbol{\beta}_i \cdot \boldsymbol{\beta}_j = 0$. They are the vectors of the deficiency matrix considered in 1a.4. The vector y can be expressed as a linear function of $\boldsymbol{\alpha}$ and $\boldsymbol{\beta}$ (example 3 in 1a.4).

$$\mathbf{y} = c_1\boldsymbol{\alpha}_1 + \cdots + c_k\boldsymbol{\alpha}_k + d_1\boldsymbol{\beta}_1 + \cdots + d_{n-r}\boldsymbol{\beta}_{n-r}$$

$$E(\mathbf{y}) = \tau_1\boldsymbol{\alpha}_1 + \cdots + \tau_k\boldsymbol{\alpha}_k$$

Multiplying by $\boldsymbol{\beta}_i$ we find

$$\boldsymbol{\beta}_i \cdot \mathbf{y} = d_i \qquad \text{and} \qquad E(d_i) = \boldsymbol{\beta}_i \cdot E(\mathbf{y}) = 0$$

Also

$$V(d_i) = \boldsymbol{\beta}_i \cdot \boldsymbol{\beta}_i \sigma^2 = \sigma^2 \qquad \text{cov } (d_i d_j) = \boldsymbol{\beta}_i \cdot \boldsymbol{\beta}_j \sigma^2 = 0$$

Hence $d_1, \cdots, d_{n-r}$ are all distributed independently in $N(0, \sigma^2)$, in which case

$$\frac{(d_1{}^2 + \cdots + d^2{}_{n-r})}{\sigma^2}$$

is distributed as χ^2 with $(n - r)$ degrees of freedom.

If $\mathbf{c} = (c_1, \cdots, c_k)$, then

$$[\mathbf{y} - E(\mathbf{y})]^2 = (\mathbf{c} - \boldsymbol{\tau})A'A(\mathbf{c} - \boldsymbol{\tau})' + d_1{}^2 + \cdots + d^2{}_{n-r}$$

which attains the minimum value

$$R_0{}^2 = d_1{}^2 + \cdots + d^2{}_{n-r}$$

when $(\mathbf{c} - \boldsymbol{\tau}) = 0$. Hence $R_0{}^2/\sigma^2$ is a χ^2 with $(n - r)$ degrees of freedom.*

(ii) What is the distribution of

$$R_1{}^2 = \text{minimum of } \Sigma(y_i - a_{i1}\tau_1 - \cdots - a_{ik}\tau_k)^2$$

when minimized with respect to $\tau_1, \cdots, \tau_k$ subject to s *independent* conditions

$$\mathbf{f}_1 \cdot \boldsymbol{\tau} = f_{11}\tau_1 + \cdots + f_{1k}\tau_k = g_1$$

$$\mathbf{f}_2 \cdot \boldsymbol{\tau} = f_{21}\tau_1 + \cdots + f_{2k}\tau_k = g_2 \qquad (2\text{d}.1.1)$$

$$\cdot \qquad \cdot \qquad \cdots \qquad \cdot$$

$$\mathbf{f}_s \cdot \boldsymbol{\tau} = f_{s1}\tau_1 + \cdots + f_{sk}\tau_k = g_s$$

Starting with the representation

$$\mathbf{y} = c_1\boldsymbol{\alpha}_1 + \cdots + c_k\boldsymbol{\alpha}_k + d_1\boldsymbol{\beta}_1 + \cdots + d_{n-r}\boldsymbol{\beta}_{n-r}$$

and multiplying by $\boldsymbol{\alpha}_1, \cdots, \boldsymbol{\alpha}_k$, we obtain

$$\boldsymbol{\alpha}_1 \cdot \mathbf{y} = c_1\boldsymbol{\alpha}_1 \cdot \boldsymbol{\alpha}_1 + \cdots + c_k\boldsymbol{\alpha}_1 \cdot \boldsymbol{\alpha}_k$$

$$\cdot \qquad \cdot \qquad + \cdots \qquad \cdot$$

$$\boldsymbol{\alpha}_k \cdot \mathbf{y} = c_1\boldsymbol{\alpha}_1 \cdot \boldsymbol{\alpha}_k + \cdots + c_k\boldsymbol{\alpha}_k \cdot \boldsymbol{\alpha}_k$$

which may be written in the matrix notation

$$\mathbf{y}A = \mathbf{c}A'A$$

If there exists a vector $\mathbf{1}$ such that $\mathbf{1}A'A = \mathbf{p}$, then

$$E(\mathbf{c} \cdot \mathbf{p}) = E(\mathbf{c}A'A\mathbf{1}') = E(\mathbf{y}A\mathbf{1}')$$

$$= E(\mathbf{y})A\mathbf{1}' = \boldsymbol{\tau}A'A\mathbf{1}' = \boldsymbol{\tau}\mathbf{p}' = \boldsymbol{\tau} \cdot \mathbf{p}$$

$$V(\mathbf{c} \cdot \mathbf{p}) = V(\mathbf{c}A'A\mathbf{1}') = V(\mathbf{y}A\mathbf{1}') = \mathbf{1}A'A\mathbf{1}'\sigma^2 = \mathbf{p} \cdot \mathbf{1}\sigma^2$$

If $\mathbf{1}_1$ and $\mathbf{1}_2$ are two vectors such that $\mathbf{1}_1A'A = \mathbf{p}_1$ and $\mathbf{1}_2A'A = \mathbf{p}_2$, then

$$\text{cov } (\mathbf{c} \cdot \mathbf{p}_1, \mathbf{c} \cdot \mathbf{p}_2) = \mathbf{1}_1 \cdot \mathbf{p}_2\sigma^2 = \mathbf{1}_2 \cdot \mathbf{p}_1\sigma^2$$

Let $\mathbf{1}_1, \cdots, \mathbf{1}_t$ be such that

$$\mathbf{1}_1A'A = \mathbf{p}_1, \cdots, \mathbf{1}_tA'A = \mathbf{p}_t$$

and

$$z_1 = \mathbf{c} \cdot \mathbf{p}_1 - \mathbf{p}_1 \cdot \boldsymbol{\tau}, \cdots, z_t = \mathbf{c} \cdot \mathbf{p}_t - \mathbf{p}_t \cdot \boldsymbol{\tau}$$

---

* From this it follows that the expected value of the residual sum of squares is $(n - r)\sigma^2$. To prove this it is not necessary to assume that the variables are normally distributed. The result follows from the fact $V(d_i) = E(d_i^2) = \sigma^2$.

The dispersion matrix of z is

$$D\sigma^2 = \begin{pmatrix} \mathbf{p}_1 \cdot \mathbf{l}_1 & \cdots & \mathbf{p}_1 \cdot \mathbf{l}_t \\ \cdot & \cdots & \cdot \\ \mathbf{p}_t \cdot \mathbf{l}_1 & \cdots & \mathbf{p}_t \cdot \mathbf{l}_t \end{pmatrix} \sigma^2$$

in which case

$$\frac{\mathbf{z} D^{-1} \mathbf{z}'}{\sigma^2}$$

is distributed as χ^2 with t degrees of freedom. Also

$$\text{cov}\ (d_i,\ \mathbf{c} \cdot \mathbf{p}_j) = (\boldsymbol{\beta}_i \cdot \mathbf{1}_j A'A)\sigma^2 = 0$$

so that the d and z are uncorrelated. Hence

$$\frac{\mathbf{z} D^{-1} \mathbf{z}'}{\sigma^2} + \frac{d_1{}^2 + \cdots + d^2{}_{n-r}}{\sigma^2}$$

is distributed as the sum of two independent χ^2's with t and $(n - r)$ degrees of freedom which is the same as χ^2 with $(t + n - r)$ degrees of freedom.

To minimize $(\mathbf{c} - \boldsymbol{\tau})A'A(\mathbf{c} - \boldsymbol{\tau})'$ subject to the conditions (2d.1.1), we observe that the conditions (2d.1.1) could be replaced by an equivalent set of s independent linear combinations

$$\begin{aligned} \mathbf{p}_1 \cdot \boldsymbol{\tau} &= p_{11}\tau_1 & + \cdots + p_{1k}\tau_k &= G_1 \\ \cdot & \quad \cdot & \cdot & \quad \cdot \\ \mathbf{p}_t \cdot \boldsymbol{\tau} &= p_{t1}\tau_1 & + \cdots + p_{tk}\tau_k &= G_t \\ \mathbf{p}_{t+1} \cdot \boldsymbol{\tau} &= p_{(t+1)1}\tau_1 & + \cdots + p_{(t+1)k}\tau_k &= G_{t+1} \\ \cdot & \quad \cdot & \cdots \quad \cdot & \quad \cdot \\ \mathbf{p}_s \cdot \boldsymbol{\tau} &= p_{s1}\tau_1 & + \cdots + p_{sk}\tau_k &= G_s \end{aligned} \qquad (2\text{d}.1.2)$$

such that the vectors $\mathbf{p}_1, \cdots, \mathbf{p}_t$ lie in the space of vectors in the matrix $A'A$ and no linear combination of $\mathbf{p}_{t+1}, \cdots, \mathbf{p}_s$ lies in the space of $A'A$ (example 3 in 1b.1). Let $(s - t)$ be the rank of the matrix

$$(\boldsymbol{\delta}_i \cdot \mathbf{f}_j)$$

where $\boldsymbol{\delta}_1, \boldsymbol{\delta}_2, \cdots$ are vectors orthogonal to those in $A'A$ which are the same as those orthogonal to row vectors in A. The vectors $\mathbf{f}_1, \cdots, \mathbf{f}_s$ belong to the restraining conditions (2d.1.1).

The number of vectors $\mathbf{p}_1, \cdots, \mathbf{p}_t$ is obtained from the rule, $t = s$ minus the rank of $(\boldsymbol{\delta}_i \cdot \mathbf{f}_j)$.

It may be observed that (2d.1.1) is being replaced by (2d.1.2) for proving a result and not necessarily for convenience in determining the residual sum of squares which may be obtained in any way.

Using Lagrangian multipliers, we consider the function

$$(\mathbf{c} - \boldsymbol{\tau})A'A(\mathbf{c} - \boldsymbol{\tau})' + 2\{\lambda_1(\mathbf{p}_1 \cdot \boldsymbol{\tau} - G_1) + \cdots + \lambda_s(\mathbf{p}_s \cdot \boldsymbol{\tau} - G_s)\}$$

The minimizing equations are

$$(\mathbf{c} - \boldsymbol{\tau})A'A - \lambda_1\mathbf{p}_1 - \cdots - \lambda_s\mathbf{p}_s = 0$$

or

$$(\mathbf{c} - \boldsymbol{\tau})A'A - \lambda_1\mathbf{p}_1 - \cdots - \lambda_t\mathbf{p}_t = \lambda_{t+1}\mathbf{p}_{t+1} - \cdots - \lambda_s\mathbf{p}_s$$

This shows that there exists a linear combination of $\mathbf{p}_{t+1}, \cdots, \mathbf{p}_s$ which can be expressed in terms of the vectors in $A'A$, unless $\lambda_{t+1} = \lambda_{t+2} = \cdots = \lambda_s = 0$. Multiplying the minimizing equation by $(\mathbf{c} - \boldsymbol{\tau})'$, we find the optimum value of $(\mathbf{c} - \boldsymbol{\tau})A'A(\mathbf{c} - \boldsymbol{\tau})'$ to be $(\mathbf{c} - \boldsymbol{\tau}) \cdot (\lambda_1\mathbf{p}_1 + \cdots + \lambda_t\mathbf{p}_t)$. Also multiplying the minimizing equation by $\mathbf{l}_1, \cdots, \mathbf{l}_t$, defined earlier, we obtain

$$(\mathbf{c} - \boldsymbol{\tau})A'A\mathbf{l}_1' = z_1 = \lambda_1\mathbf{p}_1 \cdot \mathbf{l}_1 + \cdots + \lambda_t\mathbf{p}_t \cdot \mathbf{l}_1$$

$$\cdots \qquad \cdot \qquad \cdot \qquad \cdots \qquad \cdot$$

$$(\mathbf{c} - \boldsymbol{\tau})A'A\mathbf{l}_t' = z_t = \lambda_1\mathbf{p}_1 \cdot \mathbf{l}_t + \cdots + \lambda_t\mathbf{p}_t \cdot \mathbf{l}_t$$

which yields the solution

$$(\lambda_1, \cdots, \lambda_t) = \mathbf{z}D^{-1}$$

so that the minimum value of $(\mathbf{c} - \boldsymbol{\tau})A'A(\mathbf{c} - \boldsymbol{\tau})'$ is $\mathbf{z}D^{-1}\mathbf{z}'$. The minimum value of $[\mathbf{y} - E(\mathbf{y})]^2$ subject to the conditions (2d.1.1) is then

$$R_1{}^2 = \mathbf{z}D^{-1}\mathbf{z}' + d_1{}^2 + \cdots + d^2{}_{n-r}$$

and it is already shown that $R_1{}^2/\sigma^2$ is a χ^2 with $(n - r + t)$ degrees of freedom, where t is the number of vectors in the $\mathbf{f}$ space depending on the column vectors in the matrix A.

It also follows that the difference $R_1{}^2 - R_0{}^2$ between the conditional and the unconditional minima is distributed as $\sigma^2\chi^2$ with t degrees of freedom.

Suppose that $R_2{}^2$ is the minimum sum of squares when some more restrictive conditions are given. Using all the conditions, let u be the extra number of independent vectors which can be expressed as linear combinations of $\boldsymbol{\alpha}$; then by the above argument

$$R_2{}^2 = \sum_{i,j=1}^{t+u} \lambda^{ij}z_iz_j + d_1{}^2 + \cdots + d^2{}_{n-r}$$

where $1/\sigma^2(\lambda^{ij})$ is inverse to the variance-covariance matrix $(\lambda_{ij})\sigma^2$ for $z_1, \cdots, z_{(t+u)}$. This shows that $R_2{}^2/\sigma^2$ is distributed as χ^2 with $(n - r + t + u)$ degrees of freedom. The difference

$$R_2{}^2 - R_1{}^2 = \sum_{i,j=1}^{t+u} \lambda^{ij} z_i z_j - \sum_{i,j=1}^{t} d^{ij} z_i z_j$$

is distributed as $\sigma^2\chi^2$ with u degrees of freedom. (See 2c.2 and 2c.3 where the χ^2 is split into two independent components, $\mathbf{x}\Lambda\mathbf{x}' = \mathbf{u}D_1\mathbf{u}' + \mathbf{v}D_2\mathbf{v}'$. One of the parts may be identified with $\sum_{i,j=1}^{t} d^{ij} z_i z_j$).

Consider the special case where n sets of $(p + 1)$ variates $x_1, x_2, \cdots, x_{p+1}$ are such that the conditioned expectation and variance of x_{p+1} are as follows.

$$E(x_{p+1,i}) = \alpha + \beta_1 x_{1i} + \cdots + \beta_p x_{pi}$$

$$i = 1, 2, \cdots, n$$

$$V(x_{p+1}) = \sigma^2$$

The variate x_{p+1} for given $x_1, \cdots, x_p$ is considered to be normally distributed in the following examples. The values of $x_1, \cdots, x_p$ are taken as fixed quantities.

Example 1. The minimizing equations for β coefficients are (writing b for β)

$$b_1 S_{1i} + b_2 S_{2i} + \cdots + b_p S_{pi} = S_{(p+1)i}$$

$$i = 1, \cdots, p$$

where S_{ij} is the corrected sum of products for the ith and jth variables.

Example 2. If $(S^{ij})_p$ is the matrix reciprocal to $(S_{ij})_p$, $(i, j = 1, \cdots, p)$, then the dispersion matrix of $b_1, \cdots, b_p$ is $\sigma^2(S^{ij})_p$. [Hint: $V(S_{(p+1)i}) = S_{ii}\sigma^2$ and cov $(S_{(p+1)i}S_{(p+1)j}) = S_{ij}\sigma^2$.]

Example 3. The unconditional residual sum of squares is

$$S_{(p+1)(p+1)} - b_1 S_{(p+1)1} - \cdots - b_p S_{(p+1)p} = \frac{|S_{ij}|_{p+1}}{|S_{ij}|_p}$$

Example 4. If $\alpha = 0$, the minimum sum of squares is

$$\frac{|S_{ij} + n\bar{x}_i\bar{x}_j|_{p+1}}{|S_{ij} + n\bar{x}_i\bar{x}_j|_p}$$

where $\bar{x}_i$ is the average for the ith variable.

Example 5. The statistic

$$R_{p+1} = \frac{|S_{ij} + n\bar{x}_i\bar{x}_j|_p}{S_{ij}|_p} \cdot \frac{|S_{ij}|_{p+1}}{|S_{ij}| + n\bar{x}_i\bar{x}_j|_{p+1}}$$

has the distribution

$$B\left(\frac{n-p-1}{2}, \frac{1}{2}\right) dR_{p+1}$$

when $\alpha = 0$.

[Hint: $R_{p+1} = \chi_1^2/(\chi_1^2 + \chi_2^2)$ where χ_1^2 and χ_2^2 have $(n-p-1)$ and 1 degree of freedom, $\sigma^2\chi_1^2$ being the minimum sum of squares, and $\sigma^2\chi_2^2$ the additional value when $\alpha = 0$. Hence by (2a.9.5).]

Example 6. The joint distribution of $b_1, b_2, \cdots, b_p$ is

$$\frac{\left|S_{ij}\right|_p^{1/2}}{(2\pi\sigma^2)^{p/2}} e^{-\frac{1}{2\sigma^2}\Sigma\Sigma(b_i-\beta_i)(b_j-\beta_j)S_{ij}} db_1 \cdots db_p$$

(Hint: b_i are linear functions of x_{p+1}, and their dispersion matrix is as given in example 2.)

Example 7. The distribution of

$$B^2 = \Sigma\Sigma b_i b_j S_{ij}$$

is that of non-central χ^2 (viii in 2c.3)

$$\text{const. } e^{-B^2/2\sigma^2} B^{p-1} \sum_{s=0}^{\infty} \frac{\beta^{2s}}{s!2^{2s}} \frac{(B/\sigma)^{2s}}{\Gamma(s+p/2)} dB$$

where

$$\beta^2 = \frac{\Sigma\Sigma\beta_i\beta_j S_{ij}}{\sigma^2}$$

Example 8. Defining multiple correlation

$$R^2 = \frac{B^2}{B^2 + W^2}$$

where W^2 is the residual sum of squares which has the distribution $G[1/2\sigma^2, (n-p-1)/2]$, show that the distribution of R is

$$\frac{e^{-\beta^2/2}}{\beta\left(\frac{p}{2}, \frac{n-p-1}{2}\right)} R^{p-1}(1-R^2)^{(n-p-3)/2} {}_1F_1\left(\frac{n-1}{2}, \frac{p}{2}, \frac{\beta^2 R^2}{2}\right) dR$$

[Hint: Write the joint distribution of B^2 and W^2 and apply (2a.9.5) to each term.]

Example 9. The joint distribution of $\bar{x}_{p+1}, S_{(p+1)1}, \cdots, S_{(p+1)p}, S_{(p+1)(p+1)}$ can be derived as follows.

The distribution of $\bar{x}_{p+1}$, b_1, $\cdots$, b_p, and W^2 is the product of the distributions of $\bar{x}_{p+1}$; b_1, b_2, $\cdots$, b_p; and W^2.

$$\frac{\sqrt{n}}{\sqrt{2\pi}\sigma} e^{-\psi_1/2\sigma^2} d\bar{x}_{p+1}$$

$$\frac{|S_{ij}|_p^{\frac{1}{2}}}{(2\pi\sigma^2)^{p/2}} e^{-\psi_2/2\sigma^2} db_1 \cdots db_p$$

$$\frac{1}{(2\sigma^2)^{(n-p-1)/2}\Gamma[(n-p-1)/2]} e^{-\psi_3/2\sigma^2} (W^2)^{(n-p-3)/2} dW^2$$

where

$$\psi_1 = n(\bar{x}_{p+1} - \alpha - \beta_1\bar{x}_1 - \cdots)^2$$

$$\psi_2 = \Sigma\Sigma S_{ij}(b_i - \beta_i)(b_j - \beta_j)$$

$$\psi_3 = W^2 = S_{(p+1)(p+1)} - b_1 S_{(p+1)1} - \cdots - b_p S_{(p+1)p} = \frac{|S_{ij}|_{p+1}}{|S_{ij}|_p}$$

all adding up to

$$\psi = \Sigma(x_{(p+1)r} - \alpha - \beta_1 x_{1r} - \cdots - \beta_p x_{pr})^2$$

The connecting relation between b and $S_{(p+1)i}$ is

$$S_{(p+1)i} = b_1 S_{1i} + \cdots + b_p S_{pi}$$

Therefore

$$\frac{D(S_{(p+1)1}, S_{(p+1)2}, \cdots S_{(p+1)p})}{D(b_1, \cdots, b_p)} = |S_{ij}|_p$$

Also

$$\frac{\partial W^2}{\partial S_{(p+1)(p+1)}} = 1$$

Hence

$$d\bar{x}_{p+1}\, db_1 \cdots db_p dW^2 \sim \frac{1}{|S_{ij}|_p} d\bar{x}_{p+1} dS_{(p+1)1} \cdots dS_{(p+1)p}\, dS_{(p+1)(p+1)}$$

The joint distribution can be written

$$\text{const. } e^{-(\psi_1+\psi_2+\psi_3)/2\sigma^2} |S_{ij}|_p^{\frac{1}{2}} \left\{\frac{|S_{ij}|_{p+1}}{|S_{ij}|_p}\right\}^{(n-p-3)/2}$$

$$\times \frac{1}{|S_{ij}|_p} d\bar{x}_{p+1}\, dS_{(p+1)1} \cdots dS_{(p+1)(p+1)}$$

$$\text{const.} = \frac{\sqrt{n}}{\sqrt{2\pi}\sigma} \frac{1}{(\sqrt{2\pi}\sigma^2)^{p/2}} \frac{1}{(2\sigma^2)^{(n-p-1)/2}\Gamma\left(\dfrac{n-p-1}{2}\right)}$$

where ψ_1, ψ_2, ψ_3 can now be expressed in terms of the variables occurring in the differentials.

Example 10. Since the above distribution could be obtained by direct integration, it follows on omitting the exponentials

$$\left(\frac{1}{\sqrt{2\pi}}\right)^n \int_{\bar{x}_{p+1}, S_{(p+1)1}, \cdots S_{(p+1)(p+1)}} dx_{(p+1)1}\, dx_{(p+1)2} \cdots dx_{(p+1)n}$$

$$= \text{const.} \left\{ \frac{|\,S_{ij}\,|_{p+1}}{|\,S_{ij}\,|_p} \right\}^{(n-p-3)/2} |\,S_{ij}\,|_p^{-1/2}\, d\bar{x}_{p+1}\, dS_{(p+1)1} \cdots dS_{(p+1)(p+1)}$$

where the value of the constant is the same as in example 9 and does not involve any S_{ij}.

2d.2 Multivariate Distributions

In examples 1 to 10 of 2d.1, what has been considered is only the relative distribution of x_{p+1}, given $x_1, \cdots, x_p$, so that the distributions obtained are all relative distributions for fixed values of $x_1 \cdots x_p$. If these distributions are multiplied by the joint distribution $x_1, \cdots, x_p$ and integrated for these variables, then unconditional distributions are obtained. We shall assume that $x_1, x_2, \cdots, x_p$ follow a p-variate normal distribution.

Multiple Correlation Distribution. For instance, in example 8, the quantity

$$\beta^2 = \frac{(\Sigma\Sigma\beta_i\beta_j S_{ij})}{\sigma^2}$$

occurring in the distribution is a random variable if $x_1, \cdots, x_p$ are not fixed. Consider the variable $z = \beta_1 x_1 + \cdots + \beta_p x_p$, which is normally distributed, being a linear function of $x_1, \cdots, x_p$.

$$V(z) = \Sigma\Sigma\beta_i\beta_j\sigma_{ij} = \Sigma^2 \qquad \text{(say)}$$

where σ_{ij} is the covariance between x_i and x_j. Since $\sigma^2\beta^2 = \sum_{r=1}^{n} (z_r - \bar{z})^2$, where $z_r = \beta_1 x_{1r} + \cdots + \beta_p x_{pr}$ corresponding to the rth set, it follows that the distribution of β is (see 2b.1)

$$\text{const. } e^{-\sigma^2\beta^2/2\Sigma^2}\beta^{n-2}\, d\beta$$

The joint distribution of R and β is

$$P(R, \beta) = P(\beta)P(R \mid \beta)$$

$$= \text{const. } e^{-\sigma^2\beta^2/2\Sigma^2}\beta^{n-2}\, d\beta\, e^{-\beta^2/2}R^{p-1}(1 - R^2)^{(n-p-3)/2}$$

$$\times\, {}_1F_1\left(\frac{n-1}{2}, \frac{p}{2}, \frac{\beta^2 R^2}{2}\right) dR$$

Expanding $_1F_1$ and integrating term by term for β, we obtain the unconditional distribution of R.

$$\text{const. } R^{p-1}(1-R^2)^{(n-p-3)/2}\, dR \sum_{s=0}^{\infty} \frac{1}{s!} \frac{\Gamma\left(\dfrac{n-1}{2}+s\right)}{\Gamma\left(\dfrac{p}{2}+s\right)}$$

$$\times R^{2s} \int_0^{\infty} e^{-[(\sigma^2+\Sigma^2)/(2\Sigma^2)]\beta^2} \left(\frac{\beta^2}{2}\right)^{(n-3)/2+s} d\beta^2$$

$$= \text{const. } R^{p-1}(1-R^2)^{(n-p-3)/2} \sum_{s=0}^{\infty} \frac{\Gamma\left(\dfrac{n-1}{2}+s\right)\Gamma\left(\dfrac{n-1}{2}+s\right)}{s!\,\Gamma\left(\dfrac{p}{2}+s\right)}$$

$$\times \left(\frac{\Sigma^2}{\sigma^2+\Sigma^2} R^2\right)^s dR$$

$$= \frac{(1-\gamma^2)^{(n-1)/2}}{\beta\left(\dfrac{p}{2},\dfrac{n-p-1}{2}\right)} R^{p-1}(1-R^2)^{(n-p-3)/2}\,_2F_1\left(\frac{n-1}{2},\frac{n-1}{2},\right.$$

$$\left. \frac{p}{2},\gamma^2 R^2\right) dR \tag{2d.2.1}$$

where $\gamma^2 = \Sigma^2/(\sigma^2+\Sigma^2)$, the ratio of variance due to regression to total, is the measure of multiple correlation in the population.

Wishart's Distribution. The problem is to find the joint distribution of the corrected sum of squares and products arising out of n sets of observations from a k-variate normal population. If

$$x_{11} \quad \cdots \quad x_{k1}$$

$$\cdot \quad \cdots \quad \cdot$$

$$x_{1n} \quad \cdots \quad x_{kn}$$

represent the observations, their probability density is

$$\text{const. } e^{-\frac{1}{2}\phi} .$$

where $\phi = \Sigma\Sigma\lambda^{ij} \sum_r (x_{ir}-\mu_i)(x_{jr}-\mu_j) = \phi_1 + \phi_2$

$\phi_1 = \Sigma\Sigma\lambda^{ij}n(\bar{x}_i-\mu_i)(\bar{x}_j-\mu_j)$

$\phi_2 = \Sigma\Sigma\lambda^{ij}S_{ij}$

S_{ij} being the corrected sum of products. The joint distribution of $\bar{x}_i$ and S_{ij} is the product of

$$\text{const. } e^{-\frac{1}{2}(\phi_1 + \phi_2)} \tag{2d.2.2}$$

and

$$\int_{\text{over all } \bar{x}_i \text{ and } S_{ij}} dx_{11} \cdots dx_{kn} \tag{2d.2.3}$$

The value of (2d.2.3) is equal to

$$\text{const.} \int_{\bar{x}_1, S_{11}} dx_{11} \cdots dx_{1n} \int_{\bar{x}_2, S_{21}, S_{22}} dx_{21} \cdots dx_{2n} \cdots$$

which on repeated applications of the result in example 10 of 2d.1 reduces to

$$\text{const. } S_{11}{}^{(n-3)/2} \, d\bar{x}_1 \, dS_{11}$$

$$\times S_{11}{}^{-\frac{1}{2}} \left[\frac{\left| \begin{matrix} S_{11} & S_{12} \\ S_{12} & S_{22} \end{matrix} \right|}{S_{11}} \right]^{(n-1-3)/2} \quad d\bar{x}_2 \, dS_{21} \, dS_{22}$$

$$\times |S_{ij}|_2{}^{-\frac{1}{2}} \left\{ \frac{|S_{ij}|_3}{|S_{ij}|_2} \right\}^{(n-2-3)/2} \quad d\bar{x}_3 \, dS_{31} \, dS_{32} \, dS_{33}$$

$$\cdots$$

$$\times |S_{ij}|_{k-1}{}^{-\frac{1}{2}} \left\{ \frac{|S_{ij}|_k}{|S_{ij}|_{k-1}} \right\}^{[n-(k-1)-3]/2} \quad d\bar{x}_k \, dS_{k1} \cdots dS_{kk}$$

$$= \text{const. } [|S_{ij}|_k]^{[n-(k-1)-3]/2} \, d\bar{x}_1 \cdots d\bar{x}_k \, dS_{11} \cdots dS_{kk}$$

since all the other terms cancel out. This in conjunction with (2d.2.2) gives the distribution of $\bar{x}_1, \bar{x}_2 \cdots$

$$\text{const. } e^{-(n/2) \Sigma \Sigma \lambda^{ij} (\bar{x}_i - \mu_i)(\bar{x}_j - \mu_j)} \, d\bar{x}_1 \cdots d\bar{x}_k$$

and that of S_{ij}

$$\text{const. } e^{-\frac{1}{2} \Sigma \Sigma \lambda^{ij} S_{ij}} |S_{ij}|^{(n-k-2)/2} \, dS_{11} \cdots dS_{kk}$$

This is known as Wishart's distribution with $(n-1)$ degrees of freedom.

Example 1. For a bivariate normal distribution the joint distribution of corrected sums of squares $S_1{}^2$, $S_2{}^2$ and the correlation coefficient r is

$$\text{const. } e^{-\frac{1}{2(1-\rho^2)} \left(\frac{S_1{}^2}{\sigma_1{}^2} - \frac{2\rho r S_1 S_2}{\sigma_1 \sigma_2} + \frac{S_2{}^2}{\sigma_2{}^2} \right)} S_1{}^{n-2} S_2{}^{n-2} (1 - r^2)^{(n-4)/2} \, dS_1 \, dS_2 \, dr$$

Example 2. If $\rho = 0$, the statistic

$$t = \frac{r}{\sqrt{1 - r^2}} \sqrt{n - 2}$$

is distributed as Student's t with $(n - 2)$ degrees of freedom.

Example 3. If $\rho \neq 0$, on making the transformation

$$\zeta = \frac{S_1 S_2}{\sigma_1 \sigma_2} \qquad z = \log \frac{\sigma_2 S_1}{\sigma_1 S_2} \qquad r = r$$

and integrating for ζ and z, the distribution of r becomes

$$\text{const. } (1 - r^2)^{(n-4)/2} \frac{d^{n-2}}{d(r\rho)^{n-2}} \left\{ \frac{\cos^{-1}(-\rho r)}{\sqrt{1 - \rho^2 r^2}} \right\} dr$$

Example 4. The constant in Wishart's distribution in the special case when (λ_{ij}) is a unit matrix is

$$\frac{\left(\dfrac{n}{2}\right)^{p(n-1)/2}}{\pi^{p(p-1)/4} \displaystyle\prod_1^p \Gamma\left(\dfrac{n-k}{2}\right)}$$

(Hint: Retain the constant given in example 9 of 2d.1 in evaluating the successive integrals leading to Wishart's distribution.)

Example 5. For any (λ_{ij}), by making a suitable transformation the constant is found to be $|\lambda^{ij}|^{(n-1)/2}$ times the value in example 4.

Example 6. If S_{ij}' and S_{ij}'' are the corrected sums of products in two independent samples of sizes n_1 and n_2, then

$$S_{ij} = S_{ij}' + S_{ij}''$$

follows Wishart's distribution with $(n_1 + n_2 - 2)$ degrees of freedom.

Example 7. Show that the distribution of the correlation coefficient of a fixed set of n quantities with a random set of n independent observations from a normal population is const. $(1 - r^2)^{(n-4)/2} dr$.

If $(f_1, f_2, \cdots, f_k)$ is the fixed vector, define $p_i = (f_i - \bar{f})/\sqrt{\Sigma(f_i - f)^2}$; $(i = 1, \cdots, n)$. Make the orthogonal transformation

$$y_1 = \frac{x_1 + \cdots + x_n}{\sqrt{n}}$$

$$y_2 = p_1 x_1 + \cdots + p_n x_n$$

and the rest being suitably chosen. It is seen that the required statistic is $y_2/\sqrt{y_2{}^2 + \cdots + y_n{}^2}$ where $y_2, \cdots, y_n$ are all independently distributed. The problem is further reduced to determining the distribution of $y_2/\sqrt{y_2{}^2 + \chi^2}$ where y_2 is a normal variate and χ^2 is independently distributed with $(n-2)$ degrees of freedom.

Example 8. Find the distribution of

$$\frac{\Sigma f_i x_i}{\sqrt{\Sigma (x_i - \bar{x})^2}}$$

where $f_1, f_2, \cdots$ and $x_1, x_2, \cdots$ are as defined in example 7.

Example 9. If x and y are independently distributed stochastic variables and at least one has a normal distribution, then the distribution of the correlation coefficient is the same as in example 3 with $\rho = 0$. (Hint: The distribution in example 7 is independent of the fixed vector.)

Partial Correlation Coefficient. Let the variates $x_1, x_2, \cdots, x_{p+1}$ be such that, given $x_1, \cdots, x_{p-1}$,

$$E(x_p) = \alpha_1 + \beta_{1p}x_1 + \cdots + \beta_{(p-1)p}x_{p-1}$$

$$E(x_{p+1}) = \alpha_2 + \beta_{1(p+1)}x_1 + \cdots + \beta_{(p-1)(p+1)}x_{p-1}$$

The correlation between x_p and x_{p+1} for a given set of values of $x_1, \cdots, x_{p-1}$ is called the partial correlation between x_p and x_{p+1}. The partial correlation coefficient is estimated by correlating the residual pairs

$$x_p - a_1 - b_{1p}x_1 - \cdots$$

and

$$x_{p+1} - a_2 - b_{1(p+1)}x_1 - \cdots$$

where a and b stand for the values of α and β which minimize the residual sum of squares.

The vector $\mathbf{x}_p$ containing n values can be represented by

$$\mathbf{x}_p = a_1\mathbf{i} + b_{1p}\mathbf{x}_1 + \cdots + b_{(p-1)p}\mathbf{x}_{p-1} + e_{p1}\mathbf{y}_1 + \cdots + e_{p(n-p)}\mathbf{y}_{n-p}$$

where $\mathbf{i} = (1, 1, \cdots, 1)$ and $\mathbf{y}_1, \cdots, \mathbf{y}_{n-p}$ are mutually orthogonal vectors orthogonal to $\mathbf{i}$ and $\mathbf{x}_j$, and $e_{p1}, e_{p2} \cdots$ are suitably determined. $\mathbf{x}_{p+1}$ has a similar representation from which the following quantities can be constructed.

$$S_{pp}{}' = e_{p1}{}^2 + \cdots + e^2{}_{p(n-p)}$$

$$S'_{(p+1)(p+1)} = e^2{}_{(p+1)1} + \cdots + e^2{}_{(p+1)(n-p)}$$

$$S'_{p(p+1)} = e_{p1}e_{(p+1)1} + \cdots + e_{p(n-p)}e_{(p+1)(n-p)}$$

which supply the residual sum of squares and products. The estimated partial correlation coefficient is

$$r' = \frac{S'_{p(p+1)}}{\sqrt{S_{pp}{}'S'_{(p+1)(p+1)}}}$$

It is easy to verify that

$$E(e_{pi}) = 0 \qquad V(e_{pi}) = V(x_p) = \sigma_1{}^2$$

$$E(e_{(p+1)i}) = 0 \qquad V(e_{(p+1)i}) = V(x_{p+1}) = \sigma_2{}^2$$

$$\text{cov } (e_{pi}e_{(p+1)i}) = \rho\sigma_1\sigma_2$$

where ρ is the partial correlation coefficient.

If x_p and x_{p+1} for a given $x_1, \cdots, x_{p-1}$ are normally distributed, then e_{pi} and e_{p+i} can be regarded as observations from a bivariate population with correlation ρ, and the distribution of r' is the same as that derived above with $(n-1)$ replaced by $(n-p) = (n-1) - (p-1)$, corresponding to $(p-1)$ eliminated variables.

Distribution of T, D^2, etc. Consider the following n sets of observations:

$$
\begin{array}{ccc}
x_{11} & \cdots & x_{p1} \\
x_{12} & \cdots & x_{p2} \\
x_{1n} & \cdots & x_{pn}
\end{array}
$$

having the joint distribution

$$\text{const. } e^{-\frac{1}{2}\Sigma[(x_{1i}-\mu)^2 + x_{2i}{}^2 + \cdots + x_{pi}{}^2]}\, dx_{11} \cdots dx_{pn}$$

Defining

$$R_s = \frac{|S_{ij} + n\bar{x}_i\bar{x}_j|_{s-1}}{|S_{ij}|_{s-1}} \div \frac{|S_{ij} + n\bar{x}_i\bar{x}_j|_s}{|S_{ij}|_s}$$

we find from example 5 in 2d.1 that the distribution of R_s for $s \neq 1$ is

$$B\left(\frac{n-s}{2}, \frac{1}{2}\right) dR_s$$

Considering the variables in the order $x_p, \cdots, x_2$, the joint distribution of $R_p, R_{p-1}, \cdots, R_2$ is

$$B\left(\frac{n-2}{2}, \frac{1}{2}\right) dR_2 B\left(\frac{n-3}{2}, \frac{1}{2}\right) dR_3 \cdots B\left(\frac{n-p}{2}, \frac{1}{2}\right) dR_p$$

and that of R_1 is as shown in (2b.2.4).

$$e^{-n\mu^2/2} \sum_0^\infty \frac{1}{r!}\left(\frac{n\mu^2}{2}\right)^r B\left(\frac{n-1}{2}, r+\frac{1}{2}\right) dR_1$$

The joint distribution of $R_1, R_2, \cdots, R_t$ is

$$e^{-n\mu^2/2} \sum_{r=0}^{\infty} \frac{1}{r!} \left(\frac{n\mu^2}{2}\right)^r B\left(\frac{n-1}{2}, r+\frac{1}{2}\right) dR_1 B\left(\frac{n-2}{2}, \frac{1}{2}\right)$$

$$dR_2 \cdots B\left(\frac{n-t}{2}, \frac{1}{2}\right) dR_t$$

Using the result (2a.9.8) for each term, we find the distribution of

$$S_t = R_1 R_2 \cdots R_t = \frac{|S_{ij}|_t}{|S_{ij} + n\bar{x}_i\bar{x}_j|_t}$$

is

$$e^{-n\mu^2/2} \Sigma \frac{1}{r!} \left(\frac{n\mu^2}{2}\right)^r B\left(\frac{n-t}{2}, r+\frac{t}{2}\right) dS$$

$$= \text{const. } S_t^{(n-t-2)/2} (1 - S_t)^{(t-2)/2} {}_1F_1\left(\frac{n}{2}, \frac{t}{2}, \frac{(1-S_t)n\mu^2}{2}\right) dS_t \quad (2\text{d}.2.4)$$

Similarly, the distribution of

$$R = R_{t+1} \cdots R_p = \frac{|S_{ij} + n\bar{x}_i\bar{x}_j|_t |S_{ij}|_p}{|S_{ij} + n\bar{x}_i\bar{x}_j|_p |S_{ij}|_t}$$

is

$$B\left(\frac{n-p}{2}, \frac{p-t}{2}\right) dR \quad (2\text{d}.2.5)$$

and is independent of S_t since $R_1, \cdots, R_p$ are independent.

In proving Wishart's distribution it was shown that the joint distribution of the means $\bar{x}_1, \cdots, \bar{x}_p$ and the corrected sum of products, S_{ij}, is

$$\text{const. } e^{-\frac{1}{2}\Sigma(n\bar{x}_i^2 + S_{ii}) + n\bar{x}_1\mu} |S_{ij}|^{(n-1)/2 - (p+1)/2} \Pi d\bar{x}_i \Pi dS_{ij}$$

The joint distribution of S_t and R could be directly derived from the above expression. Hence we obtain the following lemma.

Lemma. If the variables $z_1, \cdots, z_k$ and $c_{ij}, (i, j = 1, \cdots, k)$, have the probability density

$$\text{const. } e^{-\frac{1}{2}\Sigma(z_i^2 + c_{ii}) + fz_1} |c_{ij}|^{q/2 - (k+1)/2}$$

then the statistic

$$S_t = \frac{|c_{ij}|_t}{|c_{ij} + z_i z_j|_t}$$

has the probability density

$$e^{-f^2/2} \Sigma \frac{1}{r!} \left(\frac{f^2}{2}\right)^r B\left(\frac{q-t+1}{2}, \frac{t}{2} + r\right) dS_t \quad (2\text{d}.2.6)$$

and

$$R = \frac{|\, c_{ij} + z_i z_j\,|_t}{|\, c_{ij}\,|_t} \div \frac{|\, c_{ij} + z_i z_j\,|_k}{|\, c_{ij}\,|_k}$$

has the probability density independent of S_t

$$B\left(\frac{q - k + 1}{2}, \frac{k - t}{2}\right) dR \qquad (2d.2.7)$$

Example 1.   Show that the statistic

$$S_t = \frac{|\, S_{ij}\,|_t}{|\, S_{ij} + n\bar{x}_i \bar{x}_j\,|_t}$$

is invariant under linear transformations of the variables $x_1, \cdots, x_t$. (Hint: If L is the transformation matrix $|\, S_{ij}'\,| = |\, L\,|\,|\, S_{ij}\,|\,|\, L'\,|$).

Applications of the Lemma.   (i) Consider a sample of size n from a p-variate normal distribution

$$\text{const. } e^{-\frac{1}{2}(\mathbf{x} - \boldsymbol{\mu})\Lambda(\mathbf{x} - \boldsymbol{\mu})'}\, d\mathbf{x}$$

To find the distribution of S_p we first make a linear transformation $\mathbf{x} = \mathbf{y}L$ such that

$$(\mathbf{x} - \boldsymbol{\mu})\Lambda(\mathbf{x} - \boldsymbol{\mu})' \sim (y_1 - \mu)^2 + y_2{}^2 + \cdots + y_p{}^2$$

where $\mu = \boldsymbol{\mu}\Lambda\boldsymbol{\mu}'$. Since S_p is invariant under linear transformations, it has the distribution (2d.2.4) with $\mu = \boldsymbol{\mu}\Lambda\boldsymbol{\mu}'$. Suppose that the mean value of every linear function

$$a_1 x_1 + a_2 x_2 + \cdots + a_p x_p$$

uncorrelated with $x_1, x_2, \cdots, x_t$ is zero; then we can make a linear transformation of the type

$$
\begin{aligned}
y_1 &= a_{11}x_1 & + \cdots + a_{1t}x_t \\
&\ \ \vdots & \vdots \qquad\quad \vdots \\
y_t &= a_{t1}x_1 & + \cdots + a_{tt}x_t \\[1em]
y_{t+1} &= a_{(t+1)1}x_1 + \cdots + a_{(t+1)p}x_p \\
&\ \ \vdots \qquad\quad \vdots \qquad\qquad \vdots \\
y_p &= a_{p1}x_1 & + \cdots + a_{pp}x_p
\end{aligned}
$$

such that $y_1, \cdots, y_p$ are uncorrelated.   Since S_t and R are invariant under the above transformation, it follows that R has the distribution (2d.2.5) under the assumption that any linear function uncorrelated with $x_1, \cdots, x_t$ has zero mean value.

(ii) Suppose that two samples of sizes n_1 and n_2 are available from two p-variate normal populations having the same dispersion matrix. Let

$d_i = \bar{x}_{i1} - \bar{x}_{i2} =$ Difference in mean values for the ith variable in the sample.

$\delta_i = \mu_{i1} - \mu_{i2} =$ Difference in mean values for the ith variable in the population.

The dispersion matrix of $\mathbf{d}$ is $1/c = [(1/n_1) + (1/n_2)]$ times that of $\mathbf{x}$, so that the probability density of $\mathbf{d}$ is

$$\text{const. } e^{-c/2(\mathbf{d}-\mathbf{\delta})\Lambda(\mathbf{d}-\mathbf{\delta})'}$$

The $p(p+1)/2$ quantities

$$S_{ij} = S_{ij}' + S_{ij}''$$

where S_{ij}' and S_{ij}'' are the corrected sums of products in the first and second samples, are distributed in Wishart's distribution with $(n_1 - 1) + (n_2 - 1)$ degrees of freedom. Hence the statistic

$$S_p = \frac{|S_{ij}|_p}{|S_{ij} + cd_id_j|_p}$$

is distributed as in (2d.2.6) with $q = (n_1 + n_2 - 2)$, $t = p$, $f^2 = c\mathbf{\delta}\Lambda\mathbf{\delta}'$.

If all linear functions uncorrelated with $x_1, \cdots, x_t$ have no difference in mean values between the two populations, then, by making a transformation similar to that used in (i) above, it can be shown that

$$R = \frac{|S_{ij} + cd_id_j|_t}{|S_{ij}|_t} \div \frac{|S_{ij} + cd_id_j|_p}{|S_{ij}|_p}$$

is distributed as in (2d.2.7) with $q = (n_1 + n_2 - 2)$, $k = p$, $t = t$.

The distribution of Mahalanobis' D^2, connected with S_p by the relation

$$S_p = \frac{1}{1 + \dfrac{c}{n_1 + n_2 - 2}D_p^2} \qquad D_p^2 = \Sigma\Sigma s^{ij}d_id_j$$

where (s^{ij}) is the matrix reciprocal to $(s_{ij}) = (S_{ij}/(n_1 + n_2 - 2))$ or that of Hotelling's T defined by

$$S_p = \frac{1}{1 + T_p}$$

can be deduced from that of S. When $\delta_1 = \delta_2 = \cdots = 0$ the distribution of S_p is

$$B\left(\frac{n_1 + n_2 - p - 1}{2}, \frac{p}{2}\right) dS_p$$

or that of $(1 - S_p)/S_p = T$ is

$$\text{const. } \frac{T_p^{(p/2)-1}}{(1 + T_p)^{(n_1+n_2-1)/2}} \, dT_p$$

which means that

$$\frac{n_1 + n_2 - p - 1}{p} T_p \qquad \text{or} \qquad \frac{n_1 + n_2 - p - 1}{p} \frac{c}{n_1 + n_2 - 2} D_p^2$$

is distributed as a variance ratio with p and $(n_1 + n_2 - p - 1)$ degrees of freedom. Similarly, when the conditions under which the distribution of R is derived hold, the statistic

$$U = \frac{n_1 + n_2 - p - 1}{p - t}\left(\frac{1}{R} - 1\right) = \frac{n_1 + n_2 - p - 1}{p - t}\left(\frac{1 + T_p}{1 + T_t} - 1\right)$$

is distributed as the variance ratio with $(p - t)$ and $(n_1 + n_2 - p - 1)$ degrees of freedom.

References

Bose, R. C., and S. N. Roy (1938). The distribution of Studentised D^2-statistic. *Sankhyā*, **4**, 337.

Cochran, W. G. (1935). The distribution of quadratic forms in a normal system, with applications to the analysis of covariance. *Proc. Camb. Phil. Soc.*, **30**, 178.

Fisher, R. A. (1915). Frequency distribution of the values of the correlation coefficient in samples from an indefinitely large population. *Biom.*, **10**, 507.

Fisher, R. A. (1924). The distribution of the partial correlation coefficient. *Metron.*, **3**, 329.

Fisher, R. A. (1928). The general sampling distribution of the multiple correlation coefficient. *Proc. Roy. Soc.* **A**, **121**, 654.

Hotelling, H. (1931). The generalization of 'Student's' ratio. *Ann. Math. Stats.*, **2**, 360.

Hsu, P. L. (1938). Notes on Hotelling's generalized T. *Ann. Math. Stats.*, **9**, 231.

Nair, U. S. (1949). Allahabad Science Congress, Presidential Address.

Nandi, H. K. (1949). A note on conditional tests of significance. *Bull. Cal. Math. Soc.*, **41**, 121.

Pearson, K. (1934). Editor, Tables of the incomplete gamma function. Cambridge University Press.

Pearson, K. (1934). Editor, Tables of the incomplete beta function. Cambridge University Press.

Rao, C. R. (1946). Tests with discriminant functions in multivariate analysis. *Sankhyā*, **7**, 407.

Rao, C. R. (1949). On some problems arising out of discrimination with multiple characters. *Sankhyā*, **9**, 343.

Romanovsky, V. (1925). On the moments of the hypergeometric series. *Biom.*, **17**, 57.

Wishart, J. (1928). The generalised product moment distribution in samples from a normal multi-variate population. *Biom.*, **20A**, 32.

CHAPTER 3

The Theory of Linear Estimation
and Tests of Hypotheses

3a   Linear Estimation

3a.1   Observational Equations

Let $y_1, \cdots, y_n$ be n independent stochastic variables with a common unknown variance σ^2 and having as expectations linear functions of k unknown parameters $\tau_1, \cdots, \tau_k$, the expectation of y_i being

$$E(y_i) = a_{i1}\tau_1 + \cdots + a_{ik}\tau_k \qquad i = 1, \cdots, n \qquad (3a.1.1)$$

where the compounding coefficients a_{ij} are known. Let the rank of the matrix (a_{ij}) or the number of independent linear functions on the right side of the equations (3a.1.1) be r. The quantities n giving the number of observations, k the number of unknown parameters and r the rank of the matrix (a_{ij}) can be quite general and need not satisfy any equality or inequality relationships. Equations such as (3a.1.1) are called the *observational equations*. Nothing need be assumed at this stage about the actual distribution of the stochastic variables.

3a.2   Best Unbiased Estimates

A linear function $p_1\tau_1 + \cdots + p_k\tau_k$ where the p coefficients are known is called a linear parametric function. This parametric function is said to be estimable if there exists a linear function $b_1y_1 + \cdots + b_ny_n$ of the observations such that

$$E(b_1y_1 + \cdots + b_ny_n) = p_1\tau_1 + \cdots + p_k\tau_k$$

A function $b_1y_1 + \cdots + b_ny_n$ satisfying the above condition is called an unbiased estimate of $p_1\tau_1 + \cdots + p_k\tau_k$. If no such linear function exists, the parametric function is said to be non-estimable.

An unbiased estimate with the minimum possible variance is said to be the *best unbiased estimate*. The mathematical discussion of arriving at an estimate with the minimum possible variance out of a large class of unbiased estimates is known as the theory of linear estimation, which was originally considered by Gauss and later explicitly formulated by Markoff (1912).

3a.3 The Necessary and Sufficient Condition for the Existence of an Unbiased Estimate

If $b_1 y_1 + \cdots + b_n y_n$ is an unbiased estimate of $p_1 \tau_1 + \cdots + p_k \tau_k$, then

$$E(b_1 y_1 + \cdots + b_n y_n) = p_1 \tau_1 + \cdots + p_k \tau_k \qquad (3a.3.1)$$

Using the expected value of y from the equations (3a.1.1) and equating the coefficients of τ on both sides, the following equations are obtained:

$$p_i = b_1 a_{1i} + \cdots + b_n a_{ni} \qquad i = 1, \cdots, k \qquad (3a.3.2)$$

This means that the set of equations (3a.3.2) treating b as unknown is soluble. Also, if the equations (3a.3.2) are soluble, then (3a.3.1) holds. The necessary and sufficient condition for the estimability of the parametric function $p_1 \tau_1 + \cdots + p_k \tau_k$ is that the set of equations (3a.3.2) is soluble, the condition for which is given in 1a.5. The vector $\mathbf{p} = (p_1, \cdots, p_k)$ must depend on the row vectors in (a_{ij}).

3a.4 Normal Equations

If the solution of (3a.3.2) is unique, then there is only one unbiased estimate and that is the best possible. In general there will be a multiplicity of solutions, and the one for which the variance is the least has to be chosen. The variance of $b_1 y_1 + \cdots + b_n y_n$ is $(b_1^2 + \cdots + b_n^2)\sigma^2$. The problem, then, reduces to minimizing $(b_1^2 + \cdots + b_n^2)$ subject to the conditions (3a.3.2). To obtain the restricted minimum we need to consider the expression

$$\sum_{i=1}^{n} b_i^2 + 2 \sum_{j=1}^{k} \lambda_j (p_j - b_1 a_{1j} - \cdots - b_n a_{nj})$$

where $\lambda_1, \cdots, \lambda_k$ are Lagrangian multipliers and to differentiate with respect to $b_1, \cdots, b_n$. The minimizing equations are

$$b_j = \lambda_1 a_{j1} + \cdots + \lambda_k a_{jk} \qquad j = 1, \cdots, n \qquad (3a.4.1)$$

On eliminating b in (3a.3.2) with the use of (3a.4.1), the equations giving λ are obtained

$$p_i = (\boldsymbol{\alpha}_1 \cdot \boldsymbol{\alpha}_i)\lambda_1 + \cdots + (\boldsymbol{\alpha}_k \cdot \boldsymbol{\alpha}_i)\lambda_k \qquad i = 1, \cdots, k \qquad (3a.4.2)$$

where $\boldsymbol{\alpha}_i$ is the vector $(a_{1i}, a_{2i}, \cdots, a_{ni})$ and $\boldsymbol{\alpha}_i \cdot \boldsymbol{\alpha}_j$ is the vector product $a_{1i} a_{1j} + \cdots + a_{ni} a_{nj}$. It is enough to get a single set of $(\lambda_1, \cdots, \lambda_k)$ satisfying (3a.4.2) for substitution in (3a.4.1) to obtain the b coefficients, since these are unique * so long as $\lambda_1, \cdots, \lambda_k$ satisfy (3a.4.2). The best estimate is

$$b_1 y_1 + \cdots + b_n y_n = (\boldsymbol{\alpha}_1 \cdot \mathbf{y})\lambda_1 + \cdots + (\boldsymbol{\alpha}_k \cdot \mathbf{y})\lambda_k \qquad (3a.4.3)$$

where $\mathbf{y} = (y_1, \cdots, y_n)$ and $\boldsymbol{\alpha}_i \cdot \mathbf{y} = a_{1i} y_1 + \cdots + a_{ni} y_n$. The condition of unbiasedness gives

$$\lambda_1 E(\boldsymbol{\alpha}_1 \cdot \mathbf{y}) + \lambda_2 E(\boldsymbol{\alpha}_2 \cdot \mathbf{y}) + \cdots = p_1 \tau_1 + p_2 \tau_2 + \cdots$$

This shows that if the observational equations (3a.1.1) are replaced by

$$E(\boldsymbol{\alpha}_i \cdot \mathbf{y}) = E(Q_i) = (\boldsymbol{\alpha}_1 \cdot \boldsymbol{\alpha}_i)\tau_1 + \cdots + (\boldsymbol{\alpha}_k \cdot \boldsymbol{\alpha}_i)\tau_k \qquad (3a.4.4)$$

$$i = 1, \cdots, k$$

then any linear function of $Q_1, \cdots, Q_k$, unbiased for a parametric function $p_1 \tau_1 + \cdots + p_k \tau_k$, is unique as a function of $y_1, \cdots, y_n$ and is also the best estimate. The equations (3a.4.4) so constructed are called the normal equations.

3a.5 Linear Functions with Zero Expectations

If $c_1 y_1 + \cdots + c_n y_n$ is a linear function whose expectation is zero, then

$$c_1 a_{1j} + \cdots + c_n a_{nj} = 0 \qquad j = 1, \cdots, k \qquad (3a.5.1)$$

Since the rank of (a_{ij}) is r, there are $(n - r)$ independent sets $(c_1, \cdots, c_n)$ which satisfy the equations (3a.5.1) (see 1a.4), which shows that there are $(n - r)$ independent linear functions of the variables whose expectations are identically zero.

If $b_1 y_1 + \cdots + b_n y_n$ is the best estimate of a parametric function, then

$$b_i = \sum_{j=1}^{k} \lambda_j a_{ij}$$

$$\sum_{1}^{n} b_i c_i = \sum_j \lambda_j \sum_i c_i a_{ij} = 0 \qquad (3a.5.2)$$

Equation (3a.5.2) shows that the best estimates of parametric functions are uncorrelated with linear functions whose expectations are zero. The number of independent parametric functions that can be estimated is r, the rank of the matrix (a_{ij}), and their best estimates are uncorrelated with the $(n - r)$ linear functions whose expectations are zero.

---

* If $\lambda'_1, \cdots, \lambda'_k$ is another solution leading to $b'_1, \cdots, b'_n$, then, defining $\lambda_i - \lambda'_i = d_i$ and $b_i - b'_i = c_i$, we have

$$0 = (\boldsymbol{\alpha}_1 \cdot \boldsymbol{\alpha}_i)d_1 + \cdots + (\boldsymbol{\alpha}_k \cdot \boldsymbol{\alpha}_i)d_k \qquad i = 1, \cdots, k$$
$$c_j = d_1 a_{j1} + \cdots + d_k a_{jk}$$

from which it follows that $\Sigma c_j^2 = 0$. Hence $c_1 = c_2 = \cdots = c_n = 0$.

3a.6 Standard Errors of Estimates and Intrinsic Properties of Normal Equations

Since $Q_i = (\alpha_i \cdot y)$, it follows that

$$V(Q_i) = (\alpha_i \cdot \alpha_i)\sigma^2$$

$$\text{cov } (Q_iQ_j) = (\alpha_i \cdot \alpha_j)\sigma^2 \tag{3a.6.1}$$

Hence the variance of Q_i is σ^2 times the coefficient of τ_i in the ith normal equation, and the covariance of Q_i, Q_j is σ^2 times the coefficient of τ_i in the jth normal equation or of τ_j in the ith normal equation. If the best estimate of $p_1\tau_1 + \cdots + p_k\tau_k$ is given by $l_1Q_1 + \cdots + l_kQ_k$, then

$$p_i = (\alpha_1 \cdot \alpha_i)l_1 + \cdots + (\alpha_k \cdot \alpha_i)l_k \qquad i = 1, 2, \cdots, k \tag{3a.6.2}$$

Using (3a.6.1),

$$V(l_1Q_1 + \cdots + l_kQ_k) = \sigma^2 \Sigma\Sigma l_il_j(\alpha_i \cdot \alpha_j)$$

$$= \sigma^2 \Sigma l_i \Sigma l_j(\alpha_i \cdot \alpha_j)$$

$$= \sigma^2 \Sigma l_ip_i \tag{3a.6.3}$$

by virtue of (3a.6.2). Similarly the covariance of Σl_iQ_i, Σm_iQ_i, the best estimates of $\Sigma p_i\tau_i$ and $\Sigma q_i\tau_i$, is given by

$$\sigma^2 \Sigma l_iq_i = \sigma^2 \Sigma m_ip_i \tag{3a.6.4}$$

The formulae (3a.6.3) and (3a.6.4) supply an easy method of evaluating the variances and covariances of the best estimates. Only the compounding coefficients of $Q_1, \cdots, Q_k$ need be determined for the application of these formulae.

If in the first equation the coefficient of τ_1 is reduced to unity,

$$\frac{E(Q_1)}{(\alpha_1 \cdot \alpha_1)} = \tau_1 + \frac{(\alpha_2 \cdot \alpha_1)}{(\alpha_1 \cdot \alpha_1)} \tau_2 + \cdots + \frac{(\alpha_k \cdot \alpha_1)}{(\alpha_1 \cdot \alpha_1)} \tau_k$$

and τ_1 is eliminated from the rest of the equations by the method of sweep out (see 1a.3), then

$$E(Q_i') = E\left\{ Q_i - \frac{(\alpha_i \cdot \alpha_1)}{(\alpha_1 \cdot \alpha_1)} Q_1 \right\} = \sum_{j=2}^{k} \left\{ \alpha_j \cdot \alpha_i - \frac{(\alpha_i \cdot \alpha_1)(\alpha_j \cdot \alpha_1)}{(\alpha_1 \cdot \alpha_1)} \right\} \tau_i$$

$$i = 2, \cdots, k$$

These become normal equations for the estimation of parametric functions involving $\tau_2, \cdots, \tau_k$. Also

$$V(Q_i') = V\left\{Q_i - \frac{\alpha_i \cdot \alpha_1}{\alpha_1 \cdot \alpha_1} Q_1\right\}$$

$$= \sigma^2 \left\{\alpha_i \cdot \alpha_i - \frac{(\alpha_i \cdot \alpha_1)(\alpha_i \cdot \alpha_1)}{\alpha_1 \cdot \alpha_1}\right\}$$

$$= \sigma^2 \times \text{the coefficient of } \tau_i \text{ in the equation for } Q_i'$$

Similarly

$$\text{cov }(Q_i'Q_j') = \sigma^2 \times \text{the coefficient of } \tau_i \text{ in the equation for } Q_j'$$

$$= \sigma^2 \times \text{the coefficient of } \tau_j \text{ in the equation for } Q_i'$$

These properties may be termed "the intrinsic properties" of normal equations. From this it follows that, if the best estimates of $r_2\tau_2 + \cdots + r_k\tau_k$ and $s_2\tau_2 + \cdots + s_k\tau_k$ are $f_2Q_2' + \cdots + f_kQ_k'$ and $g_2Q_2' + \cdots + g_kQ_k'$, then

$$V(f_2Q_2' + \cdots + f_kQ_k') = (f_2r_2 + \cdots + f_kr_k)\sigma^2 \qquad (3a.6.5)$$

$$\text{cov }(\Sigma f_iQ_i', \Sigma g_iQ_i') = (f_2s_2 + \cdots + f_ks_k)\sigma^2$$
$$= (g_2r_2 + \cdots + g_kr_k)\sigma^2 \qquad (3a.6.6)$$

These properties hold good when the parameters are successively eliminated by the method of sweep out.

3a.7 Principle of Substitution

Some amount of simplification can be effected in the computational methods of the foregoing analysis by adopting the principle of substitution or fitting of constants. Let $t_1, \cdots, t_k$ be a solution of the equations

$$Q_i = (\alpha_1 \cdot \alpha_i)t_1 + \cdots + (\alpha_k \cdot \alpha_i)t_k \qquad i = 1, 2, \cdots, k \quad (3a.7.1)$$

If an estimable parametric function $p_1\tau_1 + \cdots + p_k\tau_k$ is estimated by $c_1Q_1 + \cdots + c_kQ_k$, then

$$\Sigma p_i\tau_i \equiv \Sigma c_i\{(\alpha_1 \cdot \alpha_i)\tau_1 + \cdots + (\alpha_k \cdot \alpha_i)\tau_k\} \qquad (3a.7.2)$$

Substituting t for τ in (3a.7.2),

$$\Sigma p_it_i = \Sigma c_i\{(\alpha_1 \cdot \alpha_i)t_1 + \cdots + (\alpha_k \cdot \alpha_i)t_k\}$$
$$= c_1Q_1 + \cdots + c_kQ_k$$

by virtue of the equations (3a.7.1). This shows that the best estimate of an estimable parametric function is obtained by substituting for the parameters $\tau_1, \cdots, \tau_k$ any *solution* of the equations (3a.7.1). The solution for t_i will be the best estimate of τ_i only when τ_i is estimable. The equations (3a.7.1) can be obtained formally by minimizing the sum of squares

$$\tfrac{1}{2}\Sigma(y_i - a_{i1}t_1 - \cdots - a_{ik}t_k)^2$$

with respect to $t_1, \cdots, t_k$.

If $\Sigma n_i\tau_i$ is non-estimable and $\Sigma n_i t_i$ is homogeneous in y, then $E(\Sigma n_i t_i) \neq \Sigma n_i\tau_i$, for otherwise it contradicts the assumption of non-estimability. Also, the result of substituting a solution in an estimable parametric function leads to a homogeneous function of the observations. Hence the necessary and sufficient conditions for $\Sigma n_i t_i$ to be the best estimate of $\Sigma n_i\tau_i$ is that (*a*) $\Sigma n_i t_i$ is homogeneous in $y_1, \cdots, y_n$ and (*b*) $E(\Sigma n_i t_i) = \Sigma n_i\tau_i$. Also, if the result of substituting two different solutions in $\Sigma n_i\tau_i$ leads to two different values, then $\Sigma n_i\tau_i$ is non-estimable. This supplies a sufficient condition for non-estimability.

The set of normal equations are consistent in the sense that there always exist solutions $t_1, \cdots, t_k$ satisfying them. To prove this it is sufficient to show that, if there exist quantities $d_1, \cdots, d_k$ such that $\Sigma d_i(\alpha_i \cdot \alpha_j) = 0$ for all j, then $\Sigma d_i Q_i = 0$. Now

$$V(\Sigma d_i Q_i) = \sigma^2\Sigma d_j\Sigma d_i(\alpha_i \cdot \alpha_j) = 0$$

which shows that the variance of a homogeneous function of stochastic variables is identically zero. This is not possible unless the compounding coefficients identically vanish, in which case $\Sigma d_i Q_i = 0$.

Since a single solution is sufficient for the purpose of substitution, we may add a set of consistent, convenient, or conventionally chosen equations to the normal equations and solve them. In many practical situations the normal equations have unique solutions, in which case all parametric functions are estimable.

This aspect of normal equations is not properly brought out in literature. Unnecessary restrictions * have been imposed on the rank of the observational equations to make all the unknown quantities estimable, in which case the normal equations have a unique solution. The above treatment covers the most general case.

---

* This generalization was first noted by R. C. Bose, who developed a special method for estimating an assigned parametric function. The author (Rao, 1945) has shown that even when all the restrictions are withdrawn the least square technique of deriving normal equations and substituting the solution in a parametric function works. The principle of least squares in estimation and derivation of statistical tests is thus valid under very general conditions.

3a.8 Observational Equations with Linear Restrictions on Parameters

Sometimes it may be known that the parameters $\tau_1, \cdots, \tau_k$ in the observational equations (3a.1.1) satisfy some linear restrictions:

$$g_i = r_{i1}\tau_1 + \cdots + r_{ik}\tau_k \qquad i = 1, \cdots, m \qquad (3a.8.1)$$

In this situation two courses are open. It may be possible to eliminate some of the τ parameters in the observational equations with the help of equations (3a.8.1) and obtain a different set of observational equations with fewer τ parameters having no restrictions. The theory developed above will then be applicable. Another method is to derive the normal equations by minimizing

$$\tfrac{1}{2}\Sigma(y_i - a_{i1}\tau_1 - \cdots - a_{ik}\tau_k)^2$$

subject to the restrictions (3a.8.1). Introducing Lagrangian parameters $l_1, \cdots, l_m$, the normal equations $(m + k)$ in number are

$$Q_i = (\alpha_1 \cdot \alpha_i)t_1 + \cdots + (\alpha_k \cdot \alpha_i)t_k + l_1 r_{1i} + \cdots + l_m r_{mi}$$

$$i = 1, \cdots, k \qquad (3a.8.2)$$

and

$$g_j = r_{j1}t_1 + \cdots + r_{jk}t_k \qquad j = 1, \cdots, m$$

The best estimate of any estimable parametric function $p_1\tau_1 + \cdots + p_k\tau_k$ is simply $p_1 t_1 + \cdots + p_k t_k$, where $t_1, \cdots, t_k$ are chosen to satisfy equations (3a.8.2).

If the best estimate of $p_1\tau_1 + \cdots + p_k\tau_k$ is obtained as $c_1 Q_1 + \cdots + c_k Q_k + d_1 g_1 + \cdots + d_m g_m$, then its variance is simply $(p_1 c_1 + \cdots + p_k c_k)\sigma^2$ as before. Similar expressions hold good for the covariances. The intrinsic properties considered in 3a.6 are also true. Equations (3a.8.2) are always soluble. Also, the best estimates of parametric functions are uncorrelated with the linear functions having zero expectations and with the estimates of the parametric functions on the right-hand side of equations (3a.8.1).

3a.9 Observational Equations with Correlated Variables

In the setup of (3a.1.1) it was assumed that $y_1, \cdots, y_n$ are independent stochastic variables having a common variance σ^2. This condition can be relaxed by assuming that the dispersion matrix is of the form $\sigma^2\Lambda$ where the elements of Λ are all known and σ^2 is an unknown multiplier. The observational equations may be written

$$E(\mathbf{y}) = \tau A'$$

where $A = (a_{ij})$. The condition of unbiasedness of an estimate $\mathbf{b}\mathbf{y}'$ of $\mathbf{p}\boldsymbol{\tau}'$ is the same as (3a.3.2)

$$\mathbf{p} = \mathbf{b}A \tag{3a.9.1}$$

The variance of $\mathbf{b}\mathbf{y}'$ is proportional to $\mathbf{b}\Lambda\mathbf{b}'$. Minimizing this expression, the best estimate is found to be

$$\mathbf{m}A'\Lambda^{-1}\mathbf{y}' \tag{3a.9.2}$$

where

$$\mathbf{p} = \mathbf{m}A'\Lambda^{-1}A$$

This shows that, if $\mathbf{p}\boldsymbol{\tau}'$ is estimable, the estimate is given by $\mathbf{p}\mathbf{t}'$ where $\mathbf{t}$ satisfies the equation

$$\mathbf{y}\Lambda^{-1}A = \mathbf{t}A'\Lambda^{-1}A \tag{3a.9.3}$$

which is similar to (3a.4.4). With the new definition $\mathbf{Q} = \mathbf{y}\Lambda^{-1}A$ the results of 3a.5, 3a.6, 3a.7, and 3a.8 hold good in the correlated case also. The equation (3a.9.3) can be obtained by minimizing the expression

$$\tfrac{1}{2}\Sigma\Sigma\lambda^{ij}(y_i - a_{i1}\tau_1 - \cdots - a_{ik}\tau_k)(y_j - a_{j1}\tau_1 - \cdots - a_{jk}\tau_k)$$

where $(\lambda^{ij}) = \Lambda^{-1}$. If the τ parameters are subject to some restrictions, then the above expression is minimized subject to these restrictions.

3b   Tests of Linear Hypotheses

3b.1   Nature of Linear Hypotheses

The data on which tests of significance are based consist of n independent observations $y_1, \cdots, y_n$ with a common variance σ^2 and having expectations *

$$E(y_i) = a_{i1}\tau_1 + \cdots + a_{ik}\tau_k \qquad i = 1, \cdots, n \tag{3b.1.1}$$

where a_{ij} are known and τ_i are unknown parameters except that they may be known to satisfy a set of s restrictions, R_0.

$$r_{11}\tau_1 + \cdots + r_{1k}\tau_k = \gamma_1$$

$$R_0: \qquad \cdot \qquad \cdots \qquad \cdot \qquad \cdot \tag{3b.1.2}$$

$$r_{s1}\tau_1 + \cdots + r_{sk}\tau_k = \gamma_s$$

These linear restrictions can be assumed to be independent, for, if not, they can be replaced by an independent set.

* If $E(y_i) = a_{i0} + a_{i1}\tau_1 + \cdots + a_{ik}\tau_k$, then $(y_i - a_{i0})$ can be considered to be the stochastic variable.

A linear hypothesis H_0 specifies the values of one or more linear functions of parameters.

$$h_{11}\tau_1 + \cdots + h_{1k}\tau_k = \theta_1$$

$$H_0: \qquad \cdot \qquad \cdots \qquad \cdot \qquad \cdot \qquad\qquad (3b.1.3)$$

$$h_{m1}\tau_1 + \cdots + h_{mk}\tau_k = \theta_m$$

As in R_0, the linear functions in H_0 can be assumed to be independent. Also, if some linear combination of the functions in H_0 can be expressed in terms of the conditions in R_0, then they can be immediately verified. To start with, H_0 may be replaced by a set of equations, no combination of which belongs to R_0 (example 3 in 1b.1). Let H_0 in (3b.1.3) be such a set.

3b.2   Test for H_0

If the hypothesis H_0 is to be tested, it is necessary that all vectors $\mathbf{h}_1, \cdots, \mathbf{h}_m$ in H_0 must belong to the vector space generated by the vectors

$$\mathbf{a}_1 = (a_{11}, \cdots, a_{1k})$$

$$\cdot \qquad\qquad \cdot$$

$$\mathbf{a}_n = (a_{n1}, \cdots, a_{nk})$$

$$\mathbf{r}_1 = (r_{11}, \cdots, r_{1k})$$

$$\cdot \qquad\qquad \cdot$$

$$\mathbf{r}_s = (r_{s1}, \cdots, r_{sk})$$

This is the condition for estimability of the parametric functions in H_0. Let

(i) $\sigma^2 \chi^2_{R_0 + H_0}$ be the minimum value of $\Sigma(y_i - a_{i1}\tau_1 - \cdots - a_{ik}\tau_k)^2$ when τ_i are subject to the conditions R_0 and H_0,

(ii) $\sigma^2 \chi_{R_0}^2$ be the minimum value of $\Sigma(y_i - a_{i1}\tau_1 - \cdots - a_{ik}\tau_k)^2$ when τ_i are subject to the conditions R_0 only, and

(iii) $y_1, y_2, \cdots$ are all normally distributed.

It is shown in 2d.1 that $\chi_{R_0}^2$ is distributed as χ^2 with $(n - r + t)$ degrees of freedom where r is the rank of the space of $\mathbf{a}_1, \cdots, \mathbf{a}_n$ and t is the number of independent vectors in the space of $\mathbf{r}_1, \cdots, \mathbf{r}_s$ which lie entirely in the space of $\mathbf{a}_1, \cdots, \mathbf{a}_n$. When both R_0 and H_0 are considered, there are $(t + m)$ independent vectors in the space of $\mathbf{r}_1, \cdots,$ $\mathbf{r}_s, \mathbf{h}_1, \cdots, \mathbf{h}_m$ which can be expressed in terms of $\mathbf{a}_1, \cdots, \mathbf{a}_n$. Therefore

$\chi^2_{R_0+H_0}$ is distributed as χ^2 with $(n - r + t + m)$ degrees of freedom. Hence, as shown in 2d.1,

$$\chi^2_{H_0 \mid R_0} = \chi^2_{R_0+H_0} - \chi_{R_0}{}^2$$

is also a χ^2 with m degrees of freedom, the distribution being valid only when the hyopthesis H_0 is true. If σ^2 is known, then the χ^2 distribution can be used to test H_0. On the other hand, the ratio

$$F = \frac{\chi^2_{H_0 \mid R_0}}{m} \div \frac{\chi_{R_0}{}^2}{n - r + t}$$

is independent of σ^2 and is distributed as a variance ratio with m and $(n - r + t)$ degrees of freedom. Hence the hypothesis H_0 can be tested, using the F distribution when σ^2 is unknown.

3b.3   Test for H_0 When R_0 Is Not True

In problems of the nature posed in 3b.1 it is often desirable not to take on trust the given restrictions but to test for them if possible. In this case all parametric functions in R_0 must be estimable. If the restrictions are true and are estimable, then $\chi_{R_0}{}^2$ is distributed as χ^2 with $(n - r + s)$ degrees of freedom. On the other hand, the unconditional minimum value $\chi_E{}^2$ of $(1/\sigma^2)\Sigma(y_i - a_{i1}\tau_1 - \cdots - a_{ik}\tau_k)^2$ is distributed as χ^2 with $(n - r)$ degrees of freedom. Hence a test for R_0 is provided by the variance ratio

$$\frac{\chi_{R_0}{}^2 - \chi_E{}^2}{s} \div \frac{\chi_E{}^2}{n - r}$$

based on s and $(n - r)$ degrees of freedom. If this is significant, then R_0 cannot be used in testing for H_0. In such a case all parametric functions in H_0 must be directly estimable from the observational equations (3b.1.1). The statistic $\chi_{H_0}{}^2$, the minimum value of $(1/\sigma^2)\Sigma(y_i - a_{i1}\tau_1 - \cdots - a_{ik}\tau_k)^2$ subject to H_0, is distributed as χ^2 with $(n - r + m)$ degrees of freedom. The test for H_0 when R_0 is not true is provided by the variance ratio

$$\frac{\chi_{H_0}{}^2 - \chi_E{}^2}{m} \div \frac{\chi_E{}^2}{n - r}$$

based on m and $(n - r)$ degrees of freedom.

Example 1.   Expressing the restrictions (3a.8.1) in the matrix form $\mathbf{g} = \tau R$, show that the condition for the estimability of a parametric function $\mathbf{p}\tau'$ is that there exist vectors $\mathbf{b}$ and $\mathbf{c}$ such that

$$\mathbf{p} = \mathbf{b}A + \mathbf{c}R$$

Example 2. The best estimate of $\mathbf{p\tau'}$ is given by $\lambda Q' + \mathbf{cg'}$ where $Q = \mathbf{y}A'$ and λ, $\mathbf{c}$ are such that

$$\lambda A'A + \mathbf{c}R = \mathbf{p}$$

$$\lambda R' = \mathbf{0}$$

Hence deduce the principle of least squares given in 3a.8.

Example 3. Show that the minimum value of

$$\Sigma(y - a_{i1}\tau_1 - a_{i2}\tau_2 - \cdots)^2$$

is $\Sigma y^2 - t_1 Q_1 - t_2 Q_2 - \cdots -$, where t_1, t_2, $\cdots$ and Q_1, Q_2, $\cdots$ are as in (3a.7.1).

Example 4. The minimum value of the expression in example 3 when the τ parameters are subject to the relations (3a.8.1) is

$$\Sigma y^2 - t_1 Q_1 - t_2 Q_2 - \cdots - l_1 g_1 - l_2 g_2 - \cdots$$

where t_i, Q_j, l_k are as in (3a.8.2).

Example 5. Let z_1, z_2, $\cdots$, z_m be the estimates of parametric functions in (3b.1.3) with the dispersion matrix $\sigma^2 D$. If $\mathbf{c} = (c_1, c_2, \cdots)$ is a vector of arbitrary constants, then a linear compound of the m deviations from the hypothetical values in (3b.1.3) is

$$\mathbf{c}(\mathbf{z} - \boldsymbol{\theta})' = c_1(z_1 - \theta_1) + c_2(z_2 - \theta_2) + \cdots + c_m(z_m - \theta_m)$$

with its variance $\sigma^2 \mathbf{c}D\mathbf{c}'$. Show that the maximum value of the ratio $\{\mathbf{c}(\mathbf{z} - \boldsymbol{\theta})\}^2/\sigma^2 \mathbf{c}D\mathbf{c}'$ is $(\mathbf{z} - \boldsymbol{\theta})D^{-1}(\mathbf{z} - \boldsymbol{\theta})'/\sigma^2$.

Example 6. Show that $\chi^2_{H_0|R_0}$ defined in 3b.2 is $(\mathbf{z} - \boldsymbol{\theta})D^{-1}(\mathbf{z} - \boldsymbol{\theta})'/\sigma^2$, the expression derived in example 5. (Hint: Follow the method of 2d.1.)

3c The Combination of Weighted Observations

3c.1 Transformation to Unweighted Observations

The general theory of least squares as discussed above can be extended to observations having unequal variance but with known ratios. The variances σ_1^2, $\cdots$, σ_n^2 of y_1, $\cdots$, y_n can be expressed as $w_1^2\sigma^2$, $\cdots$, $w_n^2\sigma^2$ where w_i are known quantities and σ^2 is an unknown parameter. The problem is reduced to the unweighted case by replacing y_i by z_i where

$$z_i = \frac{y_i}{w_i}$$

in which case

$$E(z_i) = \frac{a_{i1}}{w_i}\tau_1 + \cdots + \frac{a_{ik}}{w_i}\tau_k \qquad (3c.1.1)$$

The general theory is applicable when the observational equations are considered as in (3c.1.1).

3c.2 An Example of Weighted Observations

Consider the observational equations

$$E(y_i) = \tau x_i \qquad V(y_i) = x_i^2 \sigma^2$$

where the x_i are known but σ^2 is unknown. The transformed equations are

$$E(z_i) = E\left(\frac{y_i}{x_i}\right) = \tau \qquad V(z_i) = \sigma^2$$

The normal equation is

$$E(Q) = n\tau$$

where $Q = \Sigma z_i$. The best estimate of τ is

$$\frac{Q}{n} = \bar{z} \qquad V\left(\frac{Q}{n}\right) = \frac{\sigma^2}{n}$$

For testing whether $\tau = \xi$, an assigned quantity, the following analysis of sum of squares is needed.

$$\Sigma(z_i - \xi)^2 = n(\bar{z} - \xi)^2 + \Sigma(z_i - \bar{z})^2$$

$$\chi_{H_0}^2 = (\chi_{H_0}^2 - \chi_E^2) + \chi_E^2$$

In the following data are considered the variables y_i, the dry weight of paddy, and x_i, the green weight obtained from 25 samples. It is desired to test whether the conversion factor from green to dry is $\frac{3}{4}$. The mean weight of dry paddy increases with the increase in green weight and so also the variance. The constancy of coefficient of variation is a plausible hypothesis, and therefore the method developed above is applicable.

$$n = 25 \qquad \Sigma\left(\frac{y_i}{x_i}\right) = \Sigma(z_i) = 17.300 \qquad \bar{z} = 0.692 \qquad \Sigma z_i^2 = 11.9716$$

$$\Sigma z_i^2 - n\bar{z}^2 = 0.2952$$

$$n(\bar{z} - \xi)^2 = (0.692 - 0.75)^2 \times 25 = 0.0841$$

TABLE 3c.2α.   Test for a Given Value of τ

	D.F.	Sum of Squares (S.S.)	Mean Square (M.S.)	F Statistic
Due to hypothesis	1	$n(\bar{z} - \xi)^2 = 0.0841$	0.0841	6.837
Residual	$n - 1$	$\min \Sigma(z_i - \tau)^2 = \Sigma z_i^2$ $- n\bar{z}^2 = 0.2952$	0.0123	

$$F = \frac{0.0841}{1} \div \frac{0.2952}{24} = 6.837$$

The ratio 6.837 with 1 and 24 degrees of freedom is significant at the 5% level, so we reject the hypothesis that the conversion factor is ¾.

3d Tests of Hypotheses with a Single Degree of Freedom

3d.1 Student's t Test

Situations arise in which there is a single series of observations and it is desired to test whether the mean in the population is an assigned quantity μ_0. If n is the size of the sample and $\bar{x}$ the mean, the variance ratio appropriate to test the above hypothesis is

$$F = \frac{n(\bar{x} - \mu_0)^2}{(\Sigma x_i^2 - n\bar{x}^2)/(n - 1)}$$

with 1 and $(n - 1)$ degrees of freedom. When the sum of squares in the numerator has a single degree of freedom as above, tables * have been constructed for the statistic

$$t = \frac{\sqrt{n}(\bar{x} - \mu_0)}{\sqrt{(\Sigma x_i^2 - n\bar{x}^2)/(n - 1)}}$$

This statistic is also useful in testing whether the true mean value is above or below the hypothetical quantity μ_0. This test was first proposed by Student,† who demonstrated that an exact test of significance is possible when the standard deviation is unknown. This epoch-making discovery is the starting point of the exact sampling theory as developed by R. A. Fisher.

3d.2 Asymmetry of Right and Left Femora

The mean difference (right femur − left femur) in length between the right and left femora of 36 skeletons of a certain series is found to be 2.0234; the corrected sum of squares of these 36 differences is 418.6875. The estimated variance on 35 degrees of freedom is

$$\frac{418.6875}{35} = 11.9625$$

---

* See Table III in "Statistical Tables for Biological, Agricultural, and Medical Research," by R. A. Fisher and F. Yates.

† This is the pen name under which W. S. Gosset wrote. The reader is referred to Student's (1908) original paper where this test was first derived.

If the right and left femora are of equal length on the average, then the observed mean is a chance deviation from the true value, zero. The value of

$$t = \frac{2.0234}{\sqrt{11.9625}} \sqrt{36} = 3.5193$$

is significant at the 5% level so that on the basis of this test the lengths of the right and left femora cannot be considered equal on the average. Actually the probability of a tabulated t value corresponds to the probability that the absolute value of t (irrespective of sign) exceeds the tabulated value. If it is known a priori that the alternative hypothesis is that the right femur is longer than the left or if the purpose of the test is to discriminate only the asymmetry due to the bigger length of the right femur, then the sign of t is important. The hypothesis of equality is rejected in favor of the suggested alternative only when t exceeds the upper 5% value of t which corresponds to the 10% tabulated value of t. If the alternative hypothesis is that the left femur has a greater length, then $(-t)$ should exceed the 10% tabulated value for significance. In the above example t certainly exceeds the upper 5% value of t, showing that the data are in agreement with the suggested alternative that the right femur is longer than the left. If the suggested alternative is the other way, the null hypothesis could not be rejected on the basis of the test utilizing the lower 5% value of t. In any problem the decision to use a two-sided or a one-sided test should be taken in advance before the analysis is undertaken considering the situation arising out of the problem at hand.

These tests are useful in situations where the mean values of two series are to be compared, but the observations are such that there is a one-to-one correspondence between a member of one series and a member of the other. In the above example two measurements belong to the same skeleton. The 36 pairs of measurements give rise to 36 differences which can now be treated as a single series in which the mean is expected to be zero.

On the other hand, the two series may not have any correspondence; for instance, no two measurements are made on the same skeleton, in which case the method of analysis of variance applied to groups (see 3e.1) has to be used. In the second test the variation due to skeletons has also to be taken into account, and therefore the precision of the comparison decreases and such a small difference as the above may go undetected, even in a large sample. The variance of femur length is about 400, in which case the variance for difference in means of two independent series of 36 is

$$400(\tfrac{1}{36} + \tfrac{1}{36}) = 22.22$$

whereas the corresponding variance for the correlated series is 11.9625 $\div$ 36 = 0.33, which admits a more precise assessment of asymmetry. This aspect should be kept in view while conducting any investigation. When two measurements are to be compared, it may be designed to obtain two correlated series of measurements. The higher the correlation, the greater is the advantage. The association should be positive; otherwise the test based on correlated pairs becomes less efficient.

3e Analysis of Variance

3e.1 One-Way Classification

Let there be k samples of sizes $n_1, \cdots, n_k$ from k populations with unknown means $\mu_1, \cdots, \mu_k$ and with a common unknown variance σ^2. The hypothesis which may be desired to be tested is

$$\mu_1 = \mu_2 = \cdots = \mu_k$$

The observational equations $n_1 + \cdots + n_k$ in number are given below

	First Sample				kth Sample	
	Observed Variable	Expectation			Observed Variable	Expectation
	x_{11}	μ_1	$\cdots$		x_{k1}	μ_k
	$\cdot$	$\cdot$	$\cdots$		$\cdot$	$\cdot$
	x_{1n_1}	μ_1	$\cdots$		x_{kn_k}	μ_k
Total	T_1		$\cdots$		T_k	

The minimum value of $\Sigma\Sigma(x_{ij} - \mu_i)^2$ subject to the condition of the hypothesis is

$$\Sigma\Sigma x_{ij}{}^2 - \frac{(\Sigma\Sigma x_{ij})^2}{n} \qquad n = n_1 + \cdots + n_k \qquad (3e.1.1)$$

which is the total corrected sum of squares of all the observations. The minimum value of $\Sigma\Sigma(x_{ij} - \mu_i)^2$ without any restrictions is

$$\sum_i \left\{ \sum_j x_{ij}{}^2 - \frac{\left(\sum_j x_{ij}\right)^2}{n_i} \right\} \qquad (3e.1.2)$$

The sum of squares due to deviation from the hypothesis

$$(3e.1.1) - (3e.1.2) = \frac{T_1{}^2}{n_1} + \cdots + \frac{T_k{}^2}{n_k} - \frac{T^2}{n} \qquad (3e.1.3)$$

$$T = T_1 + \cdots + T_k$$

is obtained from the totals for the samples only. This has $(k - 1)$ degrees of freedom. It is easier to calculate the expressions (3e.1.1) and (3e.1.3) in practice and derive the expression (3e.1.2) by subtraction. The scheme of computation is set out below.

TABLE 3e.1α.   Analysis of Variance, One-Way Classification

	D.F.	S.S.
Deviation from hypothesis or between samples	$k - 1$	$\Sigma \dfrac{T_i^2}{n_i} - \dfrac{T^2}{n}$
Residual	*	*
Total	$n - 1$	$\Sigma\Sigma x_{ij}^2 - \dfrac{T^2}{n}$

The quantities marked by * are obtained by subtraction. The F statistic is constructed using the mean squares derived from the above table.

The following data relate to the head breadths of 142 skulls belonging to three series. Can the mean head breadth be considered the same in the three series?

Series	Sample Size	Head Breadth Total	Head Breadth Mean
1	83	11,277	135.87
2	51	7,049	138.22
3	8	1,102	137.75
Total	142	19,428	136.817

The sum of squares between series is

$11,277 \times 135.87 + 7,049 \times 138.22$

$\qquad\qquad + 1,102 \times 137.75 - 19,428 \times 136.817 = 238.59$

The total sum of squares is found to be 4616.64. The analysis of variance is set out in Table 3e.1β.

TABLE 3e.1β.   Analysis of Variance

	D.F.	S.S.	M.S.	F
Between series	2	238.59	119.29	3.79
Residual	139	4378.05	31.50	
Total	141	4616.64		

The variance ratio 3.79 with 2 and 139 degrees of freedom is significant at the 5% level so that the mean values cannot be considered equal in all the series.

When between series has 1 degree of freedom the square root of F can be referred to the t distribution with degrees of freedom of the residual. If the two series can be distinguished as the first and the second, then t can be given the same sign as the difference between the averages of the first and second series. Then as in 3d.1 it is possible to test whether the mean of the first series significantly exceeds the other, and vice versa.

3e.2   Two-Way Classification with a Single Observation in a Cell

Let there be pq observations, each of which can be specified in terms of the categories of two classes. The observations may be set out in the following tabular form.

Class A	Class B			Total
	B_1	B_2 $\cdots$	B_p	
A_1	x_{11}	x_{12} $\cdots$	x_{1p}	$x_1.$
A_2	x_{21}	x_{22} $\cdots$	x_{2p}	$x_2.$
.	.	. $\cdots$	.	.
A_q	x_{q1}	x_{q2} $\cdots$	x_{qp}	$x_q.$
Total	$x._1$	$x._2$	$x._p$	$x..$

The observational equations are known to be

$$E(x_{ij}) = \alpha_i + \beta_j \qquad V(x_{ij}) = \sigma^2 \qquad (3e.2.1)$$

The α and β parameters may be called the effects of the categories in the A and B classes. When only a single observation is present in each cell, it is not possible to test whether the additive setup assumed in (3e.2.1) is correct. If, however, this can be taken to be true, two hypotheses which may be tested from these data are

$$\alpha_1 = \alpha_2 = \cdots = \alpha_q$$
$$\beta_1 = \beta_2 = \cdots = \beta_p$$
$$(3e.2.2)$$

It is easy to see that the rank of the matrix of equations (3e.2.1) is $(p + q - 1)$ so that not all parametric functions can be estimated. As a matter of fact, the individual parameters α_i and β_j are not estimable. But the differences of α_i or β_j which are relevant to the hypotheses (3e.2.2) to be tested are estimable. The residual sum of squares is the minimum value of $\Sigma\Sigma(x_{ij} - \alpha_i - \beta_j)^2$ with $pq - (p + q - 1)$ degrees of freedom. This is obtained as

$$\Sigma\Sigma(x_{ij} - \bar{x}_{i\cdot} - \bar{x}_{\cdot j} + \bar{x}_{\cdot\cdot})^2 \qquad (3e.2.3)$$

The minimum value of the sum of squares $\Sigma\Sigma(x_{ij} - \alpha_i - \beta_j)^2$ subject to the restriction $\alpha_1 = \cdots = \alpha_q$ is

$$\Sigma\Sigma(x_{ij} - \bar{x}_{i\cdot} - \bar{x}_{\cdot j} + \bar{x}_{\cdot\cdot}) + \frac{1}{p}\Sigma x_{i\cdot}^2 - \frac{1}{pq}x_{\cdot\cdot}^2 \qquad (3e.2.4)$$

with $(pq - p)$ degrees of freedom. The sum of squares between the categories of class A, obtained by subtraction, is

$$\frac{1}{p}\Sigma x_{i\cdot}^2 - \frac{1}{pq}x_{\cdot\cdot}^2 \qquad (3e.2.5)$$

with $(q - 1)$ degrees of freedom. The sum of squares due to the categories of class B is similarly

$$\frac{1}{q}\Sigma x_{\cdot i}^2 - \frac{1}{pq}x_{\cdot\cdot}^2 \qquad (3e.2.6)$$

with $(p - 1)$ degrees of freedom. The expressions (3e.2.5) and (3e.2.6) are easy to compute, and the expression (3e.2.3) can be deduced from the equality

$$\Sigma\Sigma x_{ij}^2 - \frac{x_{\cdot\cdot}^2}{n}$$

= the sum of the expressions (3e.2.3), (3e.2.5), and (3e.2.6)

The scheme of computation is presented below.

TABLE 3e.2α. Analysis of Variance, Two-Way Classification

	D.F.	S.S.
Between A classes	$q - 1$	$\frac{1}{p}\Sigma x_{i\cdot}^2 - \frac{1}{pq}x_{\cdot\cdot}^2$
Between B classes	$p - 1$	$\frac{1}{q}\Sigma x_{\cdot i}^2 - \frac{1}{pq}x_{\cdot\cdot}^2$
Residual	$(p - 1)(q - 1)$	*
Total	$pq - 1$	$\Sigma\Sigma x_{ij}^2 - \frac{1}{pq}x_{\cdot\cdot}^2$

* Obtained by subtraction.

The analysis is similar for more complex classifications. The numerical methods of the analysis are given in 3g.3.

3e.3 Two-Way Classification with Multiple but Equal Numbers in Cells

In the last section it was shown that the differences in class effects can be tested when the effects due to the classes are known to be additive. This can, however, be tested when each cell contains more than one observation. If there are n observations in the (i, j)th cell, they may be represented by

$$x_{ij1}, x_{ij2}, \cdots, x_{ijn}$$

with a total x_{ij} and mean $\bar{x}_{ij}$. The observational equations are

$$E(x_{ijk}) = \alpha_{ij} \qquad V(x_{ijk}) = \sigma^2$$

The hypothesis to be tested is

$$\alpha_{ij} = \alpha_i + \beta_j$$

If this is not true, there is said to be *interaction*, in which case the test of significance for the class effects cannot be properly interpreted. Differences in A classes might be tested for each B class. The magnitudes of these will depend on the nature of the B class considered. The residual sum of squares with $pq(n-1)$ degrees of freedom is

$$\min \Sigma\Sigma\Sigma(x_{ijk} - \alpha_{ij})^2 = \sum_i \sum_j \sum_k (x_{ijk} - \bar{x}_{ij})^2$$

treating α_{ij} as free parameters. The sums of squares due to the interaction and the A or B classes are derivable as in 3e.2 by considering the totals x_{ij} in each cell as single observations and dividing the final expressions of sums of squares by n to reduce to the scale of the original observations. By considering the obvious identity relations, the scheme of computation is given in Table 3e.3α.

TABLE 3e.3α.   Analysis of Variance, Two-Way Classification

	D.F.	S.S.
Between A classes	$q - 1$	$\dfrac{1}{n}\dfrac{1}{p}\sum_1^q x_i.^2 - \dfrac{1}{npq} x..^2$
Between B classes	$p - 1$	$\dfrac{1}{n}\dfrac{1}{q}\sum_1^p x._i{}^2 - \dfrac{1}{npq} x..^2$
Interaction	$(p-1)(q-1)$	*
Between pq cells	$pq - 1$	$\dfrac{1}{n}\Sigma\Sigma x_{ij}{}^2 - \dfrac{1}{npq} x..^2$
Residual	$pq(n-1)$	*
Total	$npq - 1$	$\Sigma\Sigma\Sigma x_{ijk}{}^2 - \dfrac{1}{npq} x..^2$

The sum of squares indicated by * are to be filled in by subtraction. If the interaction is significant when tested against the residual, it may be necessary to test for differences in A classes for every B class, or vice versa. The sum of squares with $(q - 1)$ degrees of freedom due to A classes for the jth class of B is

$$\frac{1}{n} \sum_{i=1}^{q} x_{ij}^2 - \frac{1}{nq} x_{\cdot j}^2$$

The mean square corresponding to this is tested against the residual mean square.

If the interaction is not significant, the first two entries of Table 3e.3α can be tested against the residual mean square or the interaction mean square, whichever is greater. This is to guard against any bias due to small effects of interaction which could not be detected by the test but which is indicated when the interaction mean square exceeds the error. When both the mean squares are of the same magnitude, a common estimate can be obtained by adding the degrees of freedom and the sum of squares corresponding to interaction and error.

3e.4   Two-Way Classification with Unequal Numbers in Cells

The following notation is used.

x_{ij} = the total of all observations in the (i, j)th cell.

$\bar{x}_{ij}$ = mean in the (i, j)th cell.

$x_{\cdot j} = \sum_{i} x_{ij}$ (total for the jth column).

$x_{i\cdot} = \sum_{j} x_{ij}$ (total for the ith row).

$x_{\cdot\cdot}$ = total of all observations.

$\bar{x}_{\cdot\cdot}$ = mean of all observations.

n_{ij}, $n_{\cdot j}$, $n_{i\cdot}$, and $n_{\cdot\cdot}$ are the numbers of observations for the (i, j)th cell, jth column, ith row, and all the cells, respectively.

The data in Table 3e.4α present the mean values and totals of nasal height of skulls excavated from three different strata by three observers. It is desired to test for the stratum and observer differences.

In problems of this nature it is convenient to set up the figures as in Table 3e.4α for the computation of the various sums of squares. The analysis is carried out in three stages. The total sum of squares with 309 degrees of freedom is found to be 5398.4206. For further calculations the entries in the above table are sufficient.

A. **The Computation of Between–Cell Sum of Squares.** The between-cell sum of squares with $pq - 1 = 8$ degrees of freedom is $\Sigma\Sigma x_{ij}\bar{x}_{ij} - x_{\cdot\cdot}\bar{x}_{\cdot\cdot} = 931.5204$.

TABLE 3e.4α. Mean Values and Totals

| Observer | Strata | | | $x_i.$ | $\bar{x}_i.$ |
	S_1	S_2	S_3		
O_1 $\quad x_{11}$ $\quad \bar{x}_{11}$ $\quad n_{11}$	1,071.00 51.00 (21)	1,572.48 49.14 (32)	913.50 50.75 (18)	3,556.98 (71)	50.098
O_2	1,966.86 46.83 (42)	2,315.40 45.40 (51)	1,721.52 47.82 (36)	6,003.78 (129)	46.541
O_3	1,219.00 48.76 (25)	2,091.60 46.48 (45)	1,849.20 46.23 (40)	5,159.80 (110)	46.907
$x._j$ $\bar{x}._j$	4,256.86 48.373 (88)	5,979.48 46.715 (128)	4,484.22 47.704 (94)	14,720.56 $= x..$ (310)	47.4857 $= \bar{x}..$

B. The Computation of the Interaction Sum of Squares.

When there are only two classes for A or B, the computation of the interaction sum of squares is very simple.

TABLE 3e.4β. Mean Values in Cells and Weights

	B_1	B_2		B_p	
A_1 A_2	$\bar{x}_{11}$ $\bar{x}_{21}$	$\bar{x}_{12}$ $\bar{x}_{22}$	$\cdots$ $\cdots$	$\bar{x}_{1p}$ $\bar{x}_{2p}$	
Difference	y_1	y_2	$\cdots$	y_p	
Weights	$\dfrac{n_{11}n_{21}}{n_{11}+n_{21}}$	$\dfrac{n_{12}n_{22}}{n_{12}+n_{22}}$	$\cdots$	$\dfrac{n_{1p}n_{2p}}{n_{1p}+n_{2p}}$	
					Total
	$= w_1$	$= w_2$		$= w_p$	Σw_i
Difference × Weight	$w_1 y_1$	$w_2 y_2$	$\cdots$	$w_p y_p$	$\Sigma w_i y_i$
(Difference)^2 × Weight	$w_1 y_1^2$	$w_2 y_2^2$	$\cdots$	$w_p y_p^2$	$\Sigma w_i y_i^2$

Note: For obtaining wy^2, we need to multiply wy by y.

The interaction sum of squares with $(2 - 1)(p - 1)$ degrees of freedom is

$$\Sigma w_i y_i{}^2 - \frac{(\Sigma w_i y_i)^2}{\Sigma w_i}$$

In the general case, for any number of A and B classes the absence of interaction means that

$$\alpha_{ij} + \alpha_{i'j'} - \alpha_{i'j} - \alpha_{ij'} = 0$$

for all $i \neq i'$, $j \neq j'$, where α_{ij} is the expected value in the (i, j)th cell. The best estimate of this tetrad difference is

$$\bar{x}_{ij} + \bar{x}_{i'j'} - \bar{x}_{i'j} - \bar{x}_{ij'}$$

To obtain the sum of squares due to interaction we can directly consider these functions and derive the suitable sum of squares.

There are $(p - 1)(q - 1)$ such independent functions whose variances and covariances can be easily written down. Consider, for instance, a 3×3 table with the mean values

$$
\begin{array}{ccc}
\bar{x}_{11} & \bar{x}_{12} & \bar{x}_{13} \\
\bar{x}_{21} & \bar{x}_{22} & \bar{x}_{23} \\
\bar{x}_{31} & \bar{x}_{32} & \bar{x}_{33}
\end{array}
$$

The following four functions indicated by the tetrad differences may be taken

$$y_1 = +\bar{x}_{11} + \bar{x}_{22} - \bar{x}_{21} - \bar{x}_{12} \qquad\qquad = \quad 0.43$$

$$y_2 = \quad -\bar{x}_{22} \quad + \bar{x}_{12} + \bar{x}_{23} - \bar{x}_{13} \qquad = \quad 0.81$$

$$y_3 = \quad -\bar{x}_{22} + \bar{x}_{21} \qquad\qquad + \bar{x}_{32} - \bar{x}_{31} \quad = -0.85$$

$$y_4 = \quad +\bar{x}_{22} \qquad - \bar{x}_{23} \quad - \bar{x}_{32} \quad + \bar{x}_{33} = -2.67$$

If $\sigma^2(a_{ij})$ is the covariance matrix of y_1, y_2, y_3, y_4, then

$$a_{11} = \frac{1}{n_{11}} + \frac{1}{n_{22}} + \frac{1}{n_{21}} + \frac{1}{n_{12}} = 0.122286$$

$$a_{12} = -\frac{1}{n_{22}} - \frac{1}{n_{12}} \qquad = -0.050858$$

$$a_{13} = -\frac{1}{n_{22}} - \frac{1}{n_{21}} \qquad = -0.043417$$

$$a_{14} = \frac{1}{n_{22}} \qquad\qquad = 0.019608$$

$$a_{22} = \frac{1}{n_{22}} + \frac{1}{n_{12}} + \frac{1}{n_{23}} + \frac{1}{n_{13}} = 0.134192$$

$$a_{23} = \frac{1}{n_{22}} \qquad\qquad = 0.019608$$

$$a_{24} = -\frac{1}{n_{22}} - \frac{1}{n_{23}} \qquad = -0.047386$$

$$a_{33} = \frac{1}{n_{22}} + \frac{1}{n_{21}} + \frac{1}{n_{32}} + \frac{1}{n_{31}} = 0.105639$$

$$a_{34} = -\frac{1}{n_{22}} - \frac{1}{n_{32}} \qquad = -0.041830$$

$$a_{44} = \frac{1}{n_{22}} + \frac{1}{n_{23}} + \frac{1}{n_{32}} + \frac{1}{n_{33}} = 0.094608$$

Table 3e.4γ contains the required computations. The matrix a_{ij} is written with an extended column of y and reduced by the method of pivotal condensation (1d.1).

The elements below the diagonal are omitted because the matrix is symmetrical at each stage. It is sometimes necessary to retain a large number of decimal places to obtain sufficient accuracy in the final value. More examples illustrating this computational scheme are given in Chapter 7.

The last pivotal value with the sign changed, 125.5049, is the sum of squares for interaction. An alternative way of calculating the interaction sum of squares is by fitting constants by the method of least squares. We need to find the minimum value of

$$\Sigma\Sigma n_{ij}(\bar{x}_{ij} - \alpha_i - \beta_j)^2$$

If a_i and b_j are the optimum values, then the minimum value is

$$\Sigma\Sigma \frac{x_{ij}^2}{n_{ij}} - \Sigma a_i x_i. - \Sigma b_j x._j$$

TABLE 3e.4γ. Method of Pivotal Condensation for Interaction Sum of Squares

Matrix a_{ij}				Value of y
0.122286	−0.050858	−0.043417	0.019608	0.43
	0.134192	0.019608	−0.047386	0.81
		0.105639	−0.041830	− 0.85
			0.094608	− 2.67
				0
1	−0.415894	−0.355045	0.160345	3.516347
	0.113040	0.001551	−0.039231	0.988834
		0.090224	−0.034868	− 0.697331
			0.091464	− 2.738949
				− 1.512029
	1	0.013721	−0.347054	8.747647
		0.090203	−0.034330	− 0.710899
			0.077849	− 2.395770
				− 10.162000
		1	−0.380586	− 7.881102
			0.064783	− 2.666328
				− 15.764667
			1	− 41.15783
				−125.504944

The optimum values are obtained from the equations

a_1	a_2	a_3	b_1	b_2	b_3	Marginal Total
71	·	·	21	32	18	= 3556.98
·	129	·	42	51	36	= 6003.78
·	·	110	25	45	40	= 5159.80
21	42	25	88	·	·	= 4256.86
32	51	45	·	128	·	= 5979.48
18	36	40	·	·	94	= 4484.22

The method of writing down these equations is very simple. Start with any marginal total, say 3556.98, based on 71 observations distributed in the B classes as 21, 32, and 18. This gives the first equation. There are six marginal totals corresponding to A and B classes, giving rise to six equations.

The method of solution is also simple. First reduce the first three equations by making the coefficients of a_1, a_2, a_3 equal to unity. The value of b_3 can be assumed to be zero so that the column corresponding to b_3 (the last constant) may be omitted.

a_1	a_2	a_3	b_1	b_2	Marginal Value
1	.	.	0.295775	0.450704	50.098310
.	1	.	0.325581	0.395349	46.540930
.	.	1	0.227273	0.409091	46.907272

Subtracting from the fourth row of the original equations 21 (first row above) + 42 (second row above) + 25 (third row above), and similarly from the fifth row subtracting 32 (first row) + 51 (second row) + 45 (third row), we obtain

.	.	.	62.432498	−36.296717	77.394630
.	.	.	−36.296717	64.844662	−108.080590

which give simultaneous equations in b_1, b_2 with solutions

$$b_1 = 0.559250 \qquad b_2 = -1.170335 \qquad b_3 = 0$$

Substituting them in the first three reduced equations with unit coefficients for a_1, a_2, a_3, we find the values of a_1, a_2, a_3 to be

$$a_1 = 50.460372 \qquad a_2 = 46.821539 \qquad a_3 = 47.258943$$

The minimum sum of squares is then computed:

Uncorrected between-cell sum of squares

$$-a_1(3556.98) - a_2(6003.78) - \cdots$$

$$-b_1(4256.86) - b_2(5979.48) - \cdots$$

$$= 125.4490$$

The method of solving the above equations is quite general. First, omit one b if the number of b classes is greater than or equal to that of a, and reduce the coefficients of a to unity in the first set and eliminate a from the latter set. The resulting equations contain b only, which may be directly solved. Also, the last equation may be omitted or it may be retained as a check, since the column sums should be zero. The a coefficients can be obtained by substitution for b in the first set of reduced equations.   The value 125.4490 for interaction sum of squares agrees with that obtained earlier only to three significant figures.   This is the order of accuracy expected in computations of this nature unless, of course, the calculations are carried to a large number of decimal places.   This is unnecessary because the data, to start with, may not be so accurate, in which case there is a limit to the number of significant figures in any computed value.   Even in the above case the number of decimal places retained could be reduced, but it is a good arithmetical discipline to assume that the original figures are absolutely correct and carry out the computations to as many decimal places as can be conveniently retained.   In this particular case the average of the two values is 125.4769, which is used in Table 3e.4ε.   In general, the first method needs the reduction of a matrix of $[(p-1)(q-1)+1]$th order; the second leads to a solution of simultaneous equations of order $(p+q-1)$.   The latter method may be relatively simpler when p and q exceed 3.

C. The Computation of Main Effects.   If the interaction is significant, then the problem reduces to testing the differences in each row or in each column of the two-way table.   On the other hand, when the interaction is not significant, the main effects may be tested by considering all the table entries.

As shown above, the interaction sum of squares is the minimum value of $\Sigma\Sigma n_{ij}(\bar{x}_{ij}-\alpha_i-\beta_j)^2$ when minimized with respect to α and β.   If now this quantity is minimized with the further restriction that $\alpha_1 = \cdots = \alpha_q$, it is easily seen that the minimum value is

$$\left\{\Sigma\Sigma\left(\frac{x_{ij}{}^2}{n_{ij}}\right)-\frac{x..^2}{n..}\right\}-\left\{\Sigma\left(\frac{x._i{}^2}{n._i}\right)-\frac{x..^2}{n..}\right\}$$

This can be recognized as the total sum of squares between the pq cells minus the sum of squares between the B classes, ignoring the classification due to A.   If the interaction sum of squares is subtracted from this, the valid sum of squares for testing the differences in A classes is obtained.   The scheme of computation is shown in Table 3e.4δ.

TABLE 3e.4δ.   Sum of Squares for A Classes

	D.F.	S.S.
Between B classes ignoring A	$p-1$	$\Sigma x._i\bar{x}._i - x..\bar{x}..$
Interaction	$(p-1)(q-1)$	(As obtained in stage B)
Between A classes	$q-1$	*
Total between cells	$pq-1$	$\Sigma\Sigma x_{ij}\bar{x}_{ij} - x..\bar{x}..$

* Obtained by subtraction.

Similarly, the valid sum of squares between B classes is obtained. The mean squares obtained from each of these sums of squares can be tested against the residual or the interaction mean square, whichever is greater. This completes the analysis.

The final analysis of variance is given in Table 3e.4ε.

TABLE 3e.4ε. Complete Analysis of Variance for the Two-Way Data

	D.F.	S.S.	M.S.	M.S.	S.S.	D.F.	
Strata, ignoring observers	2	147.6319	73.8159	317.0758	634.1516	2	Observers, ignoring strata
Interaction	4	125.4769	31.3692		125.4769	4	Interaction
Observers	2	658.4116 *	329.2058	85.9459	171.8919 *	2	Strata
Between cells	8	931.5204			931.5204	8	
Within cells	301	4466.9002 *	14.8402				
Total	309	5398.4206					

* Obtained by subtraction.

The variance ratio for interaction is

$$\frac{31.3692}{14.8402} = 2.11$$

which with 4 and 301 degrees of freedom is not significant. The interaction mean square is greater than the within-cell mean square and is therefore used in testing for observer and stratum differences. The variance ratio for observers is

$$\frac{329.2058}{31.3692} = 10.49$$

which with 2 and 4 degrees of freedom is significant at the 5% level. The variance ratio for strata is

$$\frac{85.9459}{31.3692} = 2.74$$

which with 2 and 4 degrees of freedom is not significant.

Thus the discrepancy in the mean values can be traced to observer differences. Probably the observers used different techniques of measuring nasal height.

The calculations become very simple when the unequal cell numbers are proportionate so that

$$n_{ij} = \frac{n_{\cdot i} n_{\cdot j}}{n_{\cdot \cdot}}$$

In this case the main effects of A and B can be calculated in the usual manner from the marginal totals. Thus the sum of squares due to A is

$$\Sigma \frac{x_i \cdot^2}{n_i \cdot} - \frac{x \cdot \cdot^2}{n \cdot \cdot}$$

The interaction sum of squares is obtained by subtracting the sum of squares due to A and B from the total for the pq cells.

Suppose that we ignore the observers and look for stratum differences. The analysis will then be in the nature of

	D.F.	M.S.	Ratio
Between strata	2	73.8159	4.31
Within strata	307	17.1035	

which gives a significant ratio of 4.31, leading to the conclusion that three different groups of people inhabited the three different strata. A closer analysis reveals that observer differences are also important so that some caution is necessary in combining the results of the three different investigators.

3f   The Theory of Statistical Regression

3f.1   The Concept of Regression

The theory of regression is concerned with the derivation of the relationship between a set of variables $x_1, \cdots, x_p$ and the mean value of another variable y observable with them. The variables $x_1, \cdots, x_p$ are called concomitant variables, and y the dependent variable. The equation

$$m = R(x_1, \cdots, x_p)$$

giving m the mean value of y for given x, as a function of x, is called the regression equation of y on $x_1, \cdots, x_p$. It is customary to write the above equation as

$$Y = R(x_1, \cdots, x_p)$$

Various uses of the regression are discussed below with suitable examples.

3f.2 Prediction of Cranial Capacity

One of the uses of the regression equation is for the prediction of the dependent variate for a given set of concomitant variates. For instance, a skull may be broken so that the actual cranial capacity cannot be determined. In such a case the capacity may be predictable if at least some external measurements are available. This requires the construction of the regression equation between the cranial capacity and the observed set of external measurements on complete skulls.

The Regression Equation. Three important measurements from which the cranial capacity (C) may be predicted are the glabella-occipital length (L), the maximum parietal breadth (B), and the basio-bregmatic height (H'). Since the magnitude to be estimated is a volume, it is appropriate to set up a regression formula of the type

$$C = \alpha' L^{\beta_1} B^{\beta_2} H'^{\beta_3}$$

where α', β_1, β_2, and β_3 are the constants to be estimated. By transforming the variables to

$$y = \log_{10} C \qquad x_1 = \log_{10} L \qquad x_2 = \log_{10} B \qquad x_3 = \log_{10} H'$$

the formula can be written

$$y = \alpha + \beta_1 x_1 + \beta_2 x_2 + \beta_3 x_3$$

where $\alpha = \log_{10} \alpha'$. From this equation the constants are estimated by the method of least squares.

Estimation of the Constants. Using the measurements on the 86 male skulls from the Farringdon Street series (Hooke, 1926), we find the mean values

$$\bar{y} = 3.1685 \qquad \bar{x}_1 = 2.2752 \qquad \bar{x}_2 = 2.1523 \qquad \bar{x}_3 = 2.1128$$

The corrected sums of the products matrix (S_{ij}) for x_1, x_2, x_3 is

0.01875	0.00848	0.00684
0.00848	0.02904	0.00878
0.00684	0.00878	0.02886

The corrected sums of products of y with x_1, x_2, and x_3 are, respectively,

$$Q_1 = 0.03030 \qquad Q_2 = 0.04410 \qquad Q_3 = 0.03629$$

The reciprocal of the matrix (S_{ij}) denoted by (C_{ij}) * is obtained by the method of 1d.1.

$$
\begin{array}{rrr}
64.21 & -15.57 & -10.49 \\
-15.57 & 41.71 & -9.00 \\
-10.49 & -9.00 & 39.88
\end{array}
$$

The estimates of the parameters are

$$b_1 = \quad 64.21Q_1 - 15.57Q_2 - 10.49Q_3 = 0.878$$

$$b_2 = -15.57Q_1 + 41.71Q_2 - 9.00Q_3 = 1.041$$

$$b_3 = -10.49Q_1 - 9.00Q_2 + 39.88Q_3 = 0.733$$

$$a = \bar{y} - b_1\bar{x}_1 - b_2\bar{x}_2 - b_3\bar{x}_3 = -2.618$$

The formula for the prediction of cranial capacity † is

$$C = 0.00241 L^{0.878} B^{1.041} H'^{0.733}$$

Since the estimate of β_i is $C_{1i}Q_1 + C_{2i}Q_2 + C_{3i}Q_3$, it follows from (3a.6.5) and (3a.6.6) that

$$V(b_i) = C_{ii}\sigma^2 \quad \text{and} \quad \operatorname{cov}(b_i b_j) = C_{ij}\sigma^2$$

where C_{ij} are elements of the above matrix.

Tests of Hypotheses. Having estimated these constants, it is relevant to examine how far the concomitant variables are helpful in prediction. If these variables are of no use, then the prediction formula does not depend on them so that $\beta_1 = \beta_2 = \beta_3 = 0$. This hypothesis may be tested from the above data.

The residual sum of squares with $(n - 4)$ degrees of freedom is the minimum value of

$$\Sigma(y_i - \alpha - \beta_1 x_{1i} - \beta_2 x_{2i} - \beta_3 x_{3i})^2$$

which is

$$(\Sigma y^2 - n\bar{y}^2) - b_1 Q_1 - b_2 Q_2 - b_3 Q_3$$

$$= 0.12692 - 0.878(0.03030) - 1.041(0.04410) - 0.733(0.03629)$$

$$= 0.12692 - 0.09911 = 0.02781$$

---

* To be consistent with the matrix notation the reciprocal (S_{ij}) should be written (S^{ij}). In statistical literature this is already known as the C matrix with the elements C_{ij}.

† The capacity of the Farringdon Street series skulls was determined by tight packing with mustard seed and weighing in the manner described by Macdonell (1904). The formula is applicable only for predicting capacity determined in this way.

If the hypothesis $\beta_1 = \beta_2 = \beta_3 = 0$ is true, then the minimum value of $\Sigma(y_i - \alpha)^2$ is $\Sigma y_i^2 - n\bar{y}^2 = 0.12692$, which is the total sum of squares with $(n - 1)$ degrees of freedom. The reduction in the above sum of squares is due to regression. The analysis of the sum of squares is shown in Table 3f.2α.

TABLE 3f.2α. Test of the Hypothesis $\beta_1 = \beta_2 = \beta_3 = 0$

	D.F.	S.S.	M.S.	F
Regression	3	0.09911	0.033037	97.41
Residual	82	0.02781	0.0003391	
Total	85	0.12692		

The variance ratio 97.41 with 3 and 82 degrees of freedom is significant at the 1% level, which shows that the variables considered above are useful in prediction.

It may now be examined whether the three linear dimensions appear to the same degree in the prediction formula. From the estimates it is seen that the index b_2 for maximum parietal breadth is higher than the others. This means that a given ratio of increase in breadth counts more for capacity than the corresponding increase in length or height. The hypothesis relevant to examine this point is

$$\beta_1 = \beta_2 = \beta_3 = \beta \qquad \text{(say)}$$

The minimum value of $\Sigma\{y_i - \alpha - \beta(x_{1i} + x_{2i} + x_{3i})\}^2$ has to be found out. The normal equation giving the estimate of β is

$$\{S_{11} + S_{22} + S_{33} + 2(S_{12} + S_{23} + S_{31})\}b = Q = (Q_1 + Q_2 + Q_3)$$

$$0.12485b = 0.11069$$

$$b = 0.8866$$

The minimum value with $(n - 2)$ degrees of freedom is

$$(\Sigma y_i^2 - n\bar{y}^2) - bQ = 0.12692 - 0.09814 = 0.02878$$

TABLE 3f.2β. Test of the Hypothesis $\beta_1 = \beta_2 = \beta_3$

	D.F.	S.S.	M.S.	F
Deviation from equality	2	0.00097	0.000485	1.430
Residual	82	0.02781	0.0003391	
Total	84	0.02878		

The ratio is not significant, so there is no evidence from the data to conclude that β_1, β_2, β_3 are different. The differences, if any, are likely to be small, and a large collection of measurements may be necessary before anything definite can be said about this. Evolutionists believe that the breadth is increasing relatively more than any other magnitude on the skull. If this is true it is of interest to examine how far the cranial capacity is influenced by the breadth.

So far as the problem of prediction is concerned, the formula

$$C = 0.002342(LBH')^{0.8866}$$

obtained by assuming $\beta_1 = \beta_2 = \beta_3$, may be as useful as the formula derived without assuming that these are equal. The variance of the estimate b of β is $\sigma'^2/\Sigma\Sigma S_{ij}$ where σ'^2 is the estimate based on 84 degrees of freedom with the corresponding sum of squares given in Table 3f.2β.

A simple formula of the type $C = \alpha'LBH'$ is sometimes used for predicting the cranial capacity. A test of the adequacy of such a formula is equivalent to testing the hypothesis

$$\beta_1 = \beta_2 = \beta_3 = 1$$

The minimum value of $\Sigma(y_i - \alpha - \beta_1 x_{1i} - \beta_2 x_{2i} - \beta_3 x_{3i})^2$, assuming this to be true, is

$$(\Sigma y_i^2 - n\bar{y}^2) + S_{11} + S_{22} + S_{33} + 2(S_{12} + S_{23} + S_{31})$$

$$-2(Q_1 + Q_2 + Q_3) = 0.03039$$

which has $(n - 1)$ degrees of freedom. The residual has $(n - 4)$ degrees of freedom so that the difference with 3 degrees of freedom is due to deviation from the hypothesis.

TABLE 3f.2γ.   Test of the Hypothesis $\beta_1 = \beta_2 = \beta_3 = 1$

	D.F.	S.S.	M.S.	F
Deviation from				
$\beta_1 = \beta_2 = \beta_3 = 1$	3	0.00258	0.00086	2.544 •
Residual	82	0.02781	0.0003391	
Total	85	0.03039		

The ratio 2.544 with 3 and 82 degrees of freedom is just below the 5% significance level. It would be of interest to examine this point with more adequate material.

In Table 3f.2γ the sum of squares due to deviation from the hypothesis could be directly calculated from the formula, providing a compound measure of the deviations of the estimates b_1, b_2, b_3 from the expected values 1, 1, 1.

$$\Sigma\Sigma S_{ij}(b_i - 1)(b_j - 1)$$

$$= (b_1 - 1)\{S_{11}(b_1 - 1) + S_{12}(b_2 - 1) + S_{13}(b_3 - 1)\} + \cdots$$

$$= (b_1 - 1)(Q_1 - S_{11} - S_{12} - S_{13}) + \cdots$$

$$= b_1 Q_1 + b_2 Q_2 + b_3 Q_3 - 2(Q_1 + Q_2 + Q_3) + \Sigma\Sigma S_{ij}$$

$$= 0.09911 - 2(0.11069) + 0.12485$$

$$= 0.00258$$

which is the same as that given in Table 3f.2γ.

Having found evidence that the β coefficients differ individually from unity, it is of some interest to examine whether the indices add up to 3 while distributing unequally among the three dimensions used. This requires the test of the hypothesis $\beta_1 + \beta_2 + \beta_3 = 3$. The best estimate of the deviation is $b_1 + b_2 + b_3 - 3 = 2.652 - 3 = -0.348$.

$$V(b_1 + b_2 + b_3 - 3) = (\Sigma\Sigma C_{ij})\sigma^2 = 75.68\sigma^2$$

The ratio with 1 and 82 degrees of freedom is

$$\frac{(0.348)^2}{75.68} \times \frac{1}{0.0003391} = 4.72$$

which is significant at the 5% level. This shows that the number of dimensions of the prediction formula is not 3.

It is often desirable to test whether the inclusion of an extra variable increases the accuracy of prediction. For instance, in the above example we can test whether H' is necessary when L and B have already been considered. This is equivalent to testing whether $\beta_3 = 0$. The estimate $b_3 = 0.733$ has the variance $C_{33}\sigma^2$. The ratio with 1 and 82 degrees of freedom is

$$\frac{b_3{}^2}{C_{33}\sigma^2} = \frac{(0.733)^2}{39.88} \times \frac{1}{0.0003391}$$

$$= \frac{0.01347}{0.0003391} = 39.72$$

where for σ^2 the estimate based on 82 degrees of freedom is used. This is significant at the 1% level, showing that H' is also relevant.

If b_3 were not significant, the sum of squares due to b_3

$$\frac{b_3{}^2}{C_{33}} = 0.01347$$

could be added to the residual sum of squares 0.02781 to obtain a sum 0.04128 based on 83 degrees of freedom, giving the estimate of $\sigma^2 = 0.0004973$.

If b_3 is declared to be zero, the best estimates of b_1 and b_2 have to be revised, starting with the equation

$$y = \alpha + \beta_1 x_1 + \beta_2 x_2$$

It is, however, not necessary to start afresh. The C matrix

$$
\begin{array}{ccc}
64.21 & -15.57 & -10.49 \\
-15.57 & 41.71 & -9.00 \\
-10.49 & -9.00 & 39.88
\end{array}
$$

is reduced by the method of pivotal condensation, starting from the last row and using C_{33} as the pivot.

$$
\begin{bmatrix}
64.21 - \dfrac{(10.49)^2}{39.88} & -15.57 - \dfrac{(9.00)(10.49)}{39.88} \\[3ex]
-15.57 - \dfrac{(9.00)(10.49)}{39.88} & 41.71 - \dfrac{(9.00)^2}{39.88}
\end{bmatrix}
$$

$$
= \begin{bmatrix}
61.45 & -17.94 \\
-17.94 & 39.68
\end{bmatrix}
$$

which gives the reduced C matrix for the evaluation of b_1 and b_2.

$$b_1 = 61.45 Q_1 - 17.94 Q_2 \quad = \quad 1.071$$

$$b_2 = -17.94 Q_1 + 39.68 Q_2 = \quad 1.206$$

$$a = \bar{y} - b_1 \bar{x}_1 - b_2 \bar{x}_2 \quad = -1.864$$

The residual sum of squares is

$$\Sigma(y - \bar{y})^2 - b_1 Q_1 - b_2 Q_2 = 0.0004973$$

which agrees with the value obtained by adding the sum of squares due to b_3 to the residual, thus providing a check on the calculation of b_1 and b_2. The variance-covariance matrix of b_1, b_2 is σ^2 times the new C matrix.

If more variables are omitted, the method of pivotal condensation has to be carried further. The reduced matrix at each stage gives the

C matrix appropriate to the retained variables. It would avoid some confusion if the C matrix could be written in the order in which the variables are eliminated before attempting the method of pivotal condensation. Thus if x_1, x_2, x_3, x_4 are the original variables and if x_2 and x_4 are to be eliminated, we may write the C matrix as

$$C_{22} \quad C_{24} \quad C_{21} \quad C_{23}$$

$$C_{42} \quad C_{44} \quad C_{41} \quad C_{43}$$

$$C_{12} \quad C_{14} \quad C_{11} \quad C_{13}$$

$$C_{32} \quad C_{34} \quad C_{31} \quad C_{33}$$

which is obtained by bringing the second and fourth *rows* and *columns* to the first two positions. Now this matrix can be reduced by the method of forward pivotal condensation.

If the order in which the variables are to be included in the regression equation is assigned, the successive regression equations can be obtained by following the computational method of Table 7b.6β in Chapter 7.

The Use of the Formula for Predicting the Capacity of a Single Skull.

A skull with $L = 198.5$, $B = 147$, $H' = 131$, i.e., $x_1 = 2.298$, $x_2 = 2.167$, $x_3 = 2.117$, will have the estimated log capacity

$$Y = \bar{y} + b_1(x_1 - \bar{x}_1) + b_2(x_2 - \bar{x}_2) + b_3(x_3 - \bar{x}_3)$$

$$= 3.2069$$

$$C = \text{antilog } 3.2069 = 1610$$

$$V(Y) = \left\{ \frac{\sigma^2}{n} + \Sigma\Sigma(x_i - \bar{x}_i)(x_j - \bar{x}_j) \text{ cov } b_i b_j \right\}$$

$$= \frac{\sigma^2}{n} + \sigma^2 \Sigma\Sigma(x_i - \bar{x}_i)(x_j - \bar{x}_j)C_{ij}$$

$$= \sigma^2(0.04187) = 0.0003391(0.04187) = 0.0001420$$

The estimated value of σ^2 is obtained from the residual line in Table 3f.2α.

$$V(C) = C^2 V(y) \qquad \text{approximately} \; *$$

$$= 195.2$$

* A general method of obtaining the variances of transformed variables is given in 5e.1.

It is seen that in the above formula for variance of the estimated value (Y) the precision of the estimate depends on the closeness of x_1, x_2, x_3 to the averages $\bar{x}_1$, $\bar{x}_2$, $\bar{x}_3$ realized in the sample used to construct the prediction formula.   In fact, the variance is least, equal to σ^2/n, for the estimate when the measurements on the specimen coincide with the average values.   The accuracy of prediction diminishes as x_1, x_2, x_3 depart more and more from the average values, and the prediction may become completely unreliable if x_1, x_2, x_3 fall outside the range of values observed in the sample.

For prediction with a single variable the regression equation is

$$Y = a + b(x - \bar{x})$$

and

$$V(Y) = \left\{ \frac{1}{n} + \frac{(x - \bar{x})^2}{S_{11}} \right\} \sigma^2$$

where S_{11} is the corrected sum of squares for x in the observed sample. As before, accuracy is higher for prediction near the mean.   The formula also depends on S_{11}, the scatter of x in the sample; the larger the scatter, the higher is the precision of the estimate for any x.   Therefore, in choosing the sample for the construction of the prediction formula, the values of x at the extremities of its range should be observed if a best prediction formula is to be constructed.   This is, no doubt, a theoretically sound policy which can be carried out with advantage when it is known for certain that the regression equation is of the linear form. In fact, data collected in such a manner are not suitable for judging whether the regression is linear or not, and there is no reason to believe that linearity of regression is universal.   The biometric experience is that the regressions are very nearly linear, deviations from linearity being detectable only in large samples.   If this is so, the regression line fitted to the data is only an approximation to the true regression function, and the data should allow a closest possible fit of the straight line to the ideal curve.   The best plan for this is to choose x from all over its range or, preferably, to choose x at random so that different values of x may occur with their own probability and exert their influence in the determination of the straight-line fit.

The Use of the Formula in Estimating the Mean Capacity.   The formula can also be used to estimate the mean cranial capacity of a series of skulls.   For this purpose two methods are available.   We may estimate the cranial capacity of individual skulls and calculate the mean of these estimates, or we may apply the formula directly to the mean values of L, B, H' for the series.   It is of interest to know whether these two methods give the same results.   For this purpose estimates were made of the mean cranial capacity of an additional 29 male skulls of the Farringdon Street series for which measurements of L, B, H' but not of C were available.

For these 29 skulls the mean of L is 191.1, of B is 143.1, and of H' is 129.0.

Applying the formula $C = 0.00241L^{0.878}B^{1.041}H'^{0.733}$ to these mean values, we estimate the mean of C to be 1498.3. If we estimate C for the 29 skulls individually and take the mean of the 29 estimates, we get an estimate of the mean value of C equal to 1498.2.

The same estimates were calculated for the 22 male skulls of the Moorfields series (Hooke, 1926) for which all four measurements were available. For these 22 skulls the mean of L is 189.5, of B is 142.5, and of H' is 128.8, giving an estimate of the mean of C equal to 1479.0. If we estimate C for the 22 skulls individually and calculate the mean, we get an estimate of the mean of C equal to 1480.0. Thus it appears that the two methods give very nearly the same estimates.

Are Only Small Skulls Preserved? A point of some interest is that, whereas the mean value of C for the Farringdon Street series as calculated from 86 measured values is 1481.3, the mean value of C as estimated by our formula from the 29 skulls for which measurements of L, B, H' but not of C are available is 1498.3.

Again, for the Moorfields series the mean of L is 189.2 based on 44 measurements, of B is 143.0 based on 46 measurements, and of H' is 129.8 based on 34 measurements. Applying our formula to these mean values (as we may do with some confidence as shown above), we obtain an estimate of the mean of C equal to 1490.7. The mean of C as calculated from 22 measured values is only 1473.8.

The above results suggest that those skulls which are damaged to such an extent that the cranial capacity cannot be measured are on the whole larger than those that remain intact.

This raises a serious issue. Are not the published mean values of cranial capacities gross underestimates? Can a suitable method be suggested to correct these values? One way would be to use the samples providing observations on C, L, B, and H' for merely constructing the prediction formula. As observed earlier, the prediction formula, provided the nature of the regression function used is appropriate, could be obtained from samples providing observations on all the measurements although the samples are not drawn at random from the population. For instance, if only small skulls are preserved, the measurements obtained are not strictly random from the population of skulls. Such material is being used just to establish a relationship. Having obtained this formula, the mean values of L, B, H' obtained from all the available measurements may be substituted to obtain an estimate of the mean capacity. This value will be higher than the average of the available measurements of the cranial capacity but less than the predicted value on the basis of mean L, B, H' from skulls providing these measurements only.

The extent of underestimation depends on the proportion of the disintegration of the large skulls. This may vary from series to series, and hence for a proper comparison of the mean capacities the correction indicated above may have to be applied.

3f.3   Test for the Equality of Regression Equations

It is very often necessary to test whether regression functions constructed from two series are the same. Thus if the formulae for the prediction of the cranial capacity from a different series is

$$y = a' + b_1'x_1 + b_2'x_2 + b_3'x_3$$

two types of hypotheses may be tested whether, in the expectation,

(i) $a = a'$ $b_1 = b_1'$ $b_2 = b_2'$ $b_3 = b_3'$

(ii) $b_1 = b_1'$ $b_2 = b_2'$ $b_3 = b_3'$ irrespective of whether a equals a' or not

If the former is true, then the whole regression function is the same in both series; if the latter is true, the regression functions are the same apart from a change in the constant. These two hypotheses are relevant because many problems arise where a prediction formula constructed from one series may have to be used for a specimen from an entirely different series. An extreme and rather ambitious case of such a use is the prediction of stature of prehistoric men from the length of fossil femur by using a formula connecting the stature of modern man with the length of his long bones (K. Pearson, 1898). Some sort of justification for such a procedure will be available if the first hypothesis is proved to be correct in analogous situations. We first deal with the test procedures when the prediction formulae are available for both the series.

Let the derived quantities for the second series be:

Sample size: n'

Mean values: $\bar{x}_1'$, $\bar{x}_2'$, $\bar{x}_3'$ and $\bar{y}'$

Corrected sums of products:

$$\Sigma(x_{ir}' - \bar{x}_i')(x_{jr}' - \bar{x}_j') = S_{ij}'$$

$$\Sigma(x_{ir}' - \bar{x}_i')(y_r' - \bar{y}') = Q_i'$$

These are sufficient to determine the regression function.

$$y = a' + b_1'x_1 + b_2'x_2 + b_3'x_3$$

The residual sum of squares

$$R_0{}^2 = \Sigma(y_r' - \bar{y}')^2 - b_1'Q_1' - b_2'Q_2' - b_3'Q_3' \quad \text{(for the second sample)}$$

$$+ \Sigma(y_r - \bar{y})^2 - b_1Q_1 - b_2Q_2 - b_3Q_3 \quad \text{(for the first sample)}$$

has $(n' - 4) + (n - 4) = (n + n' - 8)$ degrees of freedom.

We now throw the two samples together and consider them as a single sample of size $(n + n')$ and determine the regression line and residual sum of squares by using the above formula. The necessary quantities can be computed from those already available:

Sample size: $n + n'$

Mean values: $\dfrac{(n\bar{x}_i + n'\bar{x}_i')}{(n + n')} = \bar{x}_i''$

Corrected sums of products:

$$S_{ij}'' = S_{ij} + S_{ij}' + \frac{nn'}{n + n'}(\bar{x}_i - \bar{x}_i')(\bar{x}_j - \bar{x}_j')$$

$$Q_i'' = Q_i + Q_i' + \frac{nn'}{n + n'}(\bar{x}_i - \bar{x}_i')(\bar{y} - \bar{y}')$$

If b_1'', $b_2'' \cdots$ are the regression coefficients, then the residual sum of squares $R_1{}^2$ with $(n + n' - 4)$ degrees of freedom is

$$\Sigma(y_r' - \bar{y}')^2 + \Sigma(y_r - \bar{y})^2 + \frac{nn'}{n + n'}(\bar{y} - \bar{y}')^2$$

$$-b_1''Q_1'' - b_2''Q_2'' - b_3''Q_3''$$

We can set up the analysis of variance table.

TABLE 3f.3α.   Analysis of Variance for Testing Equality of Regression Coefficients

Residual Due to	D.F.	S.S.
Deviation from hypothesis	4	*
Separate regressions	$n + n' - 8$	$R_0{}^2$
Common regression	$n + n' - 4$	$R_1{}^2$

* Obtained by subtraction.

The significance of the ratio of mean square due to deviation from hypothesis to residual due to separate regressions is tested.

If the object is to test for the equality of the b coefficients only, we calculate the quantities

$$Q_i''' = Q_i + Q_i' \qquad S_{ij}''' = S_{ij} + S_{ij}'$$

and obtain the constants b_1''', b_2''', b_3''' from the equations

$$Q_i''' = b_1'''S_{1i}''' + b_2 S_{2i}''' + b_3 S_{3i}''' \quad i = 1, 2, 3$$

and find the residual sum of squares R_2^2 with $(n + n' - 5)$ degrees of freedom.

$$R_2^2 = \Sigma(y_r - \bar{y})^2 + \Sigma(y_r' - \bar{y}')^2 - b_1'''Q_1''' - b_2'''Q_2''' - b_3 Q_3'''$$

The test depends on the variance ratio

$$\frac{R_2^2 - R_0^2}{3} \div \frac{R_0^2}{n + n' - 8}$$

with 3 and $(n + n' - 8)$ degrees of freedom.

In biological data it is often found that the mutual correlations and variabilities of measurements are approximately the same for all allied series, in which case the coefficients b_1, b_2, b_3 in the regression formula will not differ much. On the other hand the mean values differ to some extent from series to series, in which case the equality of the constant term means that the expected value of

$$y - \beta_1 x_1 - \beta_2 x_2 - \beta_3 x_3$$

is the same for both the series. This leads us to consider a different problem whether $\alpha = \alpha'$ when $\beta_1 = \beta_1'$, $\beta_2 = \beta_2'$, $\cdots$. A test for this can be immediately obtained from the sums of squares calculated above. The suitable statistic is the variance ratio

$$\frac{R_1^2 - R_2^2}{1} \div \frac{R_2^2}{n + n' - 5}$$

with 1 and $(n + n' - 5)$ degrees of freedom. If the above hypothesis is true, then the difference in the mean value of y could be completely explained by differences in the other variables x_1, x_2, x_3. This problem is considered more fully in Chapter 7 (7b.6). It appears that when a sufficient number of measurements is considered the extra difference contributed by any other measurement independent of the set already considered is negligibly small. In such situations the equality of the dispersion matrix in both series is sufficient to ensure the equality of the regression functions as a whole. A good deal of caution is necessary when the prediction formula based on one or two variables is so used. Such a statistical adventure undertaken by Karl Pearson in predicting the stature of prehistoric men is, however, justifiable if we agree with the last statement of his article (K. Pearson, 1898).

"No scientific investigation is final; it merely represents the most probable conclusion which can be drawn from the data at the disposal of the writer. A wider range of facts, or more refined analysis, experiment, and observation will lead to new formulae and new theories. This is the essence of scientific progress."

3f.4 The Test for an Assigned Regression Function

In 3f.2 it was assumed that the regression function for log capacity is linear in the logarithms of length, breadth, and height. If, at least, for some·given sets of values of the independent variables multiple observations on the dependent variable have been observed, the validity of such an assumption can be tested.

In Table 3f.4α are given the mean values of nasal index of people living in various parts of India together with the mean annual temperature and relative humidity of the places.

TABLE 3f.4α. Nasal Index of the Inhabitants and the Temperature and Humidity of the Region

Region	Sample Size (n)	Nasal Index		Temperature		Relative Humidity	
		Mean $(\bar{y})$	Total $(n\bar{y})$	Mean Annual $(\bar{l})$	Total $(n\bar{l})$	Mean Annual $(\bar{h})$	Total $(n\bar{h})$
Assam	36	83.0	2,988.0	72.6	2,613.6	85	3,060
Orissa	40	80.4	3,216.0	80.3	3,212.0	69	2,760
Bihar	30	80.1	2,403.0	74.8	2,244.0	88	2,640
Malabar	45	77.0	3,465.0	80.2	3,609.0	81	3,645
Bombay	26	76.2	1,981.2	77.6	2,017.6	66	1,716
Madras	35	75.9	2,656.5	81.8	2,863.0	76	2,660
Punjab	28	71.4	1,999.2	76.4	2,139.2	63	1,764
United Province	32	80.8	2,585.6	77.2	2,470.4	69	2,208
Andhra	41	76.8	3,148.8	80.3	3,292.3	69	2,829
Ceylon	31	80.3	2,490.0	80.2	2,486.2	82	2,542
Total	344		26,933.3		26,947.3		25,824
Mean		78.294		78.335		75.070	

The corrected total sum of squares for nasal index has been found to be 11,140.209 with $(344 - 1)$ degrees of freedom.

If no assumption is made about the regression of nasal index on temperature and relative humidity, the analysis of variance between and within groups is obtained as in Table 3f.4β.

TABLE 3f.4β.   Analysis of Variance for Nasal Index

	D.F.	S.S.		M.S.
Between groups	9	$\Sigma(\bar{y})(n\bar{y}) - \dfrac{\Sigma n\bar{y}}{\Sigma n}\Sigma n\bar{y} =$	3,169.900	352.21
Within groups	334	*	7,970.309	23.863
Total	343		11,140.209	

* Obtained by subtraction.

The mean square for between groups is very large, indicating real differences in nasal index. Can these differences be explained by a regression of nasal index (y) on temperature (t) and relative humidity (h) of the form

$$y = \alpha + \beta_1 t + \beta_2 h$$

The normal equations leading to the estimates b_1, b_2 of β_1, β_2 are

$$Q_1 = b_1 S_{11} + b_2 S_{12}$$

$$Q_2 = b_1 S_{12} + b_2 S_{22}$$

where $Q_1 = \Sigma(n\bar{y}\bar{t}) - \dfrac{(\Sigma n\bar{t})(\Sigma n\bar{y})}{\Sigma n} = -1{,}072.40$

$$Q_2 = \Sigma(n\bar{y}\bar{h}) - \dfrac{(\Sigma n\bar{h})(\Sigma n\bar{y})}{\Sigma n} = 4{,}586.57$$

$$S_{12} = \Sigma(n\bar{t}\bar{h}) - \dfrac{(\Sigma n\bar{t})(\Sigma n\bar{h})}{\Sigma n} = -2{,}334.91$$

$$S_{11} = \Sigma(n\bar{t}\bar{t}) - \dfrac{(\Sigma n\bar{t})(\Sigma n\bar{t})}{\Sigma n} = 2{,}721.06$$

$$S_{22} = \Sigma(n\bar{h}\bar{h}) - \dfrac{(\Sigma n\bar{h})(\Sigma n\bar{h})}{\Sigma n} = 22{,}042.32$$

Solving the above equations, b_1 and b_2 are obtained as

$$b_1 = -0.237113 \qquad b_2 = 0.182963$$

With these values the regression analysis can be set up as in Table 3f.4γ.

TABLE 3f.4γ. Regression Analysis

	D.F.	S.S.	M.S.
Due to regression	2	$b_1Q_1 + b_2Q_2 =$ 1,093.45	546.72
Residual about regression	341	* 10,046.759	29.463
Total	343	11,140.209	

* Obtained by subtraction.

If the hypothesis concerning the regression is true, then the mean squares obtained from "Within groups" of Table 3f.4β and "Residual about regression" of Table 3f.4γ will be of the same magnitude. A significant difference would disprove the hypothesis.

TABLE 3f.4δ. Test for the Specified Regression Function

	D.F.	S.S.	M.S.	F
Deviation from specified regression	7	2,076.450 *	296.636	12.4
Within groups	334	7,970.309	23.863	
Residual about regression	341	10,046.759		

* Obtained by subtraction.

The ratio 12.4 with 7 and 334 degrees of freedom is significant at the 1% level, so that the regression of nasal index on temperature and relative humidity cannot be considered linear. It is also seen from Table 3f.4γ that the variance ratio 2.34 with 2 and 341 degrees of freedom is significant, but this does not mean that nasal index depends entirely on weather conditions of the place in which the individuals live. The observed differences may be more complex than can be explained by weather differences, or the nature of dependence on weather may itself be very complicated. Unless such a relationship is discovered and found to fit well, some caution is necessary before concluding that the shape of the nose is determined by temperature, humidity, etc.

In some cases, as in the distribution of heights of father and daughter, it may be desired to test whether the regression of one variable on the other is linear. For the purposes of such a test the range of the independent variable has to be divided into a suitable number of class intervals and the variance of the dependent variable analyzed into between and within classes. To get an estimate of within variation it is necessary that at least some of the classes contain more than one observation. The regression analysis can be done without the use of the class intervals, or if the data are already grouped the midpoint of the class interval is taken as the value of the independent variable for each observation of the dependent variable in that class. The final test can be carried out as in Table 3f.4δ.

3g   The General Problem of Least Squares with Two Sets of Parameters

3g.1   Concomitant Variables

Suppose that the growth rates of groups of animals receiving different diets are to be compared. The observed differences in growth rates can be attributed to diet only if all the animals treated are similar in some observable aspects such as age, initial weight, parentage, etc., which influence the growth rate. In fact, if the groups of animals receiving different diet differ in these aspects, it is desirable to compare the growth rates after eliminating these differences.

However, it may be noted that no bias is introduced in the experiment if the animals which might differ in these aspects are assigned at random to the groups to be treated differently. This procedure enhances the residual variation calculable from the differences in the growth rates of animals receiving the same treatment and thus decreases the efficiency of the experiment.

If the magnitudes of these additional variables are known, it is possible to eliminate the differences caused by them independently of the treatments both from within and between groups and to test for the pure effects of the treatments with greater efficiency. The computational technique relating to this process is known as the adjustment for concomitant variation.

For significant reduction in the residual variation it must be known that the effects under study are influenced by the concomitant variables. This is important in experimental studies where due consideration is to be given to the cost and time involved in recording the concomitant variables. This can be tested as shown in the example considered in 3g.3.

On the other hand, the concomitant variables chosen must not have been influenced by the treatments under consideration. Sometimes, in assessing the differences in yields of plants treated differently, concomitant variables such as the number of branches or the quantity of straw are chosen. These will be valid only when variations in them produce corresponding variation in the yield of plants treated alike.

3g.2 Adjustment for Concomitant Variation

Assuming the regression of y on the concomitant variables $x_1, \cdots, x_k$ to be linear, the observational equations containing the parameters $\tau_1, \cdots, \tau_m$ under consideration and the regression coefficients $\beta_1, \cdots, \beta_k$ can be written

$$E(y_i) = a_{i1}\tau_1 + \cdots + a_{im}\tau_m + \beta_1 x_{1i} + \cdots + \beta_k x_{ki} * \quad (3g.2.1)$$

The normal equations giving the best estimates of parametric functions are

$$Q_j^{(0)} = (\alpha_1 \cdot \alpha_j)t_1 + \cdots + (\mathbf{x}_1 \cdot \alpha_j)b_1 + \cdots \quad j = 1, \cdots, m \quad (3g.2.2)$$

and

$$P_{0s} = (\alpha_1 \cdot \mathbf{x}_s)t_1 + \cdots + (\mathbf{x}_1 \cdot \mathbf{x}_s)b_1 + \cdots \quad s = 1, \cdots, k \quad (3g.2.3)$$

where $Q_j^{(0)} = (\alpha_j \cdot \mathbf{y})$ and $P_{0s} = (\mathbf{x}_s \cdot \mathbf{y})$. To solve them let us construct the equations

$$Q_j^{(0)} = (\alpha_1 \cdot \alpha_j)t_1^{(0)} + \cdots + (\alpha_m \cdot \alpha_j)t_m^{(0)} \quad j = 1, \cdots, m$$

and

$$Q_j^{(s)} = (\alpha_1 \cdot \alpha_j)t_1^{(s)} + \cdots + (\alpha_m \cdot \alpha_j)t_m^{(s)}$$

$$j = 1, \cdots, m \quad s = 1, \cdots, k$$

where $Q_j^{(s)}$ is the same function as $Q_j^{(0)}$ with the variable y replaced by the sth concomitant variable x_s. Multiplying the equations in (3g.2.2) by $t_1^{(1)}, t_2^{(1)}, \cdots, t_m^{(1)}$ and subtracting their total from the first equation in (3g.2.3), we obtain

$$E_{01} = P_{01} - t_1^{(1)}Q_1^{(0)} - \cdots - t_m^{(1)}Q_m^{(0)}$$

$$= b_1(P_{11} - t_1^{(1)}Q_1^{(1)} - \cdots - t_m^{(1)}Q_m^{(1)}) + b_2(P_{12} - t_1^{(1)}Q_1^{(2)} -$$

$$\cdots t_m^{(1)}Q_m^{(2)}) + \cdots$$

$$= b_1 E_{11} + b_2 E_{12} + \cdots + b_k E_{1k}$$

Similarly, the equations

$$E_{0j} = b_1 E_{j1} + b_2 E_{j2} + \cdots + b_k E_{jk} \quad j = 2, \cdots, k \quad (3g.2.4)$$

* The regression can be of the type $\beta_1 f_1 + \beta_2 f_2 + \cdots + \beta_k f_k$ where $f_1, \cdots, f_k$ are functions of the concomitant variables, in which case $f_1, \cdots, f_k$ will be treated as separate variables. Thus, if the regression is polynomial in one variable $\beta_1 x + \beta_2 x^2 + \cdots$, the functions $x, x^2, \cdots$ are considered as separate variables.

are obtained. In the above equations

$$E_{ij} = P_{ij} - t_1^{(i)}Q_1^{(j)} - \cdots - t_m^{(i)}Q_m^{(j)} =$$

$$P_{ij} - t_1^{(j)}Q_1^{(i)} - \cdots - t_m^{(j)}Q_m^{(i)}$$

$$i, j = 0, 1, \cdots, k$$

and

$$P_{ij} = \mathbf{x}_i \cdot \mathbf{x}_j$$

These are the residual sums of products, the residuals being obtained from the observational equations for any two variables with the same matrix of equations but different sets of parameters. Having obtained the values of $b_1, \cdots, b_k$ satisfying equations (3g.2.4), the solution for t_i is given by

$$t_i = t_i^{(0)} - b_1 t_i^{(1)} - \cdots - b_k t_i^{(k)}$$

This completes the estimation of the parametric functions. The residual sum of squares for the observational equations (3g.2.1) is

$$\Sigma y^2 - \Sigma t_j Q_j^{(0)} - \Sigma b_s P_{0s} = (\Sigma y^2 - \Sigma t_j^{(0)} Q_j^{(0)}) - \Sigma b_s E_{0s}$$

$$= E_{00} - \Sigma b_s E_{0s}$$

which is a function of the residual sum of squares and products.

There are two types of hypotheses to be tested in the above problem.

Do the concomitant variables increase the efficiency of comparisons? The hypothesis to be tested is $\beta_1 = \cdots = \beta_k = 0$. If this is true the residual sum of squares is E_{00}, which differs from the pure residual $E_{00} - b_1 E_{01} - \cdots$ by $b_1 E_{01} + b_2 E_{02} + \cdots$ which has k degrees of freedom. The mean square of this is compared with the mean square for the pure residual.

Is there any additional advantage in considering x_k in conjunction with $x_1, \cdots, x_{k-1}$? The hypothesis to be tested is $\beta_k = 0$. Omitting b_k in the equations (3g.2.4), let the solutions be $b_1', \cdots, b'_{k-1}$ so that the residual sum of squares is

$$E_{00} - b_1' E_{01} - \cdots - b'_{k-1} E_{0k-1}$$

The pure residual is $E_{00} - b_1 E_{01} - \cdots - b_k E_{0k}$. Their difference with 1 degree of freedom supplies the valid sum of squares for testing the above hypothesis. Similarly, we can test whether two or more variables are useful in conjunction with others.

If the hypothesis to be tested is specified by some linear restrictions on $\tau_1, \tau_2, \cdots$, then the residual sum of squares has to be obtained subject to these restrictions. If E_{ij}' represents the residual sum of products under these restrictions, then the residual sum of squares is

$$E_{00}' - b_1''E_{01}' - \cdots - b_k''E_{0k}'$$

where b_1'', $\cdots$, b_k'' are the solutions of

$$E_{01}' = b_1''E_{11}' + \cdots + b_k''E_{1k}'$$

$$\cdot \qquad \cdot \qquad \cdots \qquad \cdot$$

$$E_{0k}' = b_1''E_{k1}' + \cdots + b_k''E_{kk}'$$

The sum of squares for testing the above hypothesis is

$$E_{00}' - b_1''E_{01}' - \cdots - b_k''E_{0k}' - \text{pure residual sum of squares}$$

The degrees of freedom will be equal to the degrees of freedom of the hypothesis. The mean square corresponding to this can be tested against the pure residual. This completes the formal theory. The method is further explained in the illustration considered in 3g.3.

3g.3 An Illustrative Example

The following data relate to the initial weights and the growth rates of 30 pigs classified according to pen, sex, and type of food given.

TABLE 3g.3α. Data for Analysis (Wishart, 1938).

Pen	Treat-ment	Sex	Initial Weight (w)	Growth Rate in Pounds per Week (g)
	A	G	48	9.94
	B	G	48	10.00
I	C	G	48	9.75
	C	H	48	9.11
	B	H	39	8.51
	A	H	38	9.52
	B	G	32	9.24
	C	G	28	8.66
II	A	G	32	9.48
	C	H	37	8.50
	A	H	35	8.21
	B	H	38	9.95
	C	G	33	7.63
	A	G	35	9.32
III	B	G	41	9.34
	B	H	46	8.43
	C	H	42	8.90
	A	H	41	9.32

TABLE 3g.3α. Data for Analysis—*Continued*

Pen	Treat-ment	Sex	Initial Weight (w)	Growth Rate in Pounds per Week (g)
	C	G	50	10.37
	A	H	48	10.56
IV	B	G	46	9.68
	A	G	46	10.98
	B	H	40	8.86
	C	H	42	9.51
	B	G	37	9.67
	A	G	32	8.82
V	C	G	30	8.57
	B	H	40	9.20
	C	H	40	8.76
	A	H	43	10.42

The problem is to study the effect of food after eliminating the initial weight.

The first step in the analysis is to analyze the sum of squares of both the dependent and independent variables and also the sum of products. The analysis of the sum of products is done in the same manner as the analysis of the sum of squares by adopting the rule that the square of a variable in the latter is replaced by the product of the variables involved in the former.

The total sums of squares and products are

$$\left. \begin{aligned} \Sigma g^2 - \bar{g}\Sigma g &= 16.6068 \\ \Sigma wg - \bar{w}\Sigma g &= 78.979 \\ \Sigma w^2 - \bar{w}\Sigma w &= 1108.70 \end{aligned} \right\} 29 \text{ D.F.}$$

If w_i and g_i denote the totals of 6 observations for the ith pen, then the sums of squares and products for pens are

$$\left. \begin{aligned} \tfrac{1}{6}\Sigma g_i^2 - \bar{g}\Sigma g &= 4.8518 \\ \tfrac{1}{6}\Sigma g_i w_i - \bar{g}\Sigma w &= 39.905 \\ \tfrac{1}{6}\Sigma w_i^2 - \bar{w}\Sigma w &= 605.87 \end{aligned} \right\} 4 \text{ D.F.}$$

Similarly, the sums of squares and products for food and sex can be obtained.

If w_{ij} and g_{ij} denote the total of 5 observations for the ith type of food and jth sex, then the sums of squares and products for the joint effects of food and sex are

$$\tfrac{1}{5}\Sigma\Sigma g_{ij}^2 - \bar{g}\Sigma g = 3.2422$$
$$\tfrac{1}{5}\Sigma\Sigma g_{ij}w_{ij} - \bar{g}\Sigma w = -0.885 \Big\} \ 5 \ \text{D.F.}$$
$$\tfrac{1}{5}\Sigma\Sigma w_{ij}^2 - \bar{w}\Sigma w = 59.90$$

If from these the corresponding expressions due to food (2 D.F.) and sex (1 D.F.) are subtracted, the expressions for food $\times$ sex interaction are obtained. Table 3g.3β gives the whole analysis. The error line is obtained by subtraction from the total.

TABLE 3g.3β. Analysis of Variance and Covariance

	D.F.	g^2	wg	w^2
Pen	4	4.9607	40.324	605.87
Food	2	2.3242	− 0.171	5.40
Sex	1	0.4538	− 4.813	32.03
Food $\times$ Sex	2	0.4642	4.099	22.47
Error	20	8.4039	39.540	442.93
		$= E_{00}$	$= E_{01}$	$= E_{11}$
Total	29	16.6068	78.979	1108.70

There is only one regression constant to be estimated.

$$E_{11}b = E_{01}$$
$$442.93b = 39.540$$
$$b = 0.089269$$

TABLE 3g.3γ. Test for Regression from Error Line Above

	D.F.	S.S.	M.S.	F
Regression	1	$bE_{01} = 3.5297$	3.5297	13.76
Residual	19	$E_{00} - bE_{01} = 4.8742$	0.2565	
Total	20	$E_{00} = 8.4039$		

The ratio is significant at the 1% level so that the comparisons can be made more efficient by eliminating the concomitant variations.

If the hypothesis specifies that there are no differences in food, then the residual sums of squares and products are obtained by adding the rows corresponding to food and error:

$$E_{00}' = 10.7281 \qquad E_{01}' = 39.369 \qquad E_{11}' = 448.33$$

The new regression coefficient is

$$b''E_{11}' = E_{01}'$$

$$b'' = 0.087813$$

The residual sum of squares when the hypothesis is true is

$$E_{00}' - b''E_{01}' = 7.2710 \quad \text{with 21 D.F.}$$

TABLE 3g.3δ. Test for Differences in Food, Eliminating
the Effects of Initial Weight

	D.F.	S.S.	M.S.	F
Food	2	* $= 2.3968$	1.1984	4.67
Residual	19	$E_{00} - bE_{01} = 4.8742$	0.2565	
Food + Error	21	$E_{00}' - b''E_{01}' = 7.2710$		

* Obtained by subtraction.

The ratio is significant at the 5% level. To test for food without adjustment for concomitant variation, we have to construct the ratio with 2 and 20 degrees of freedom.

$$F = \left(\frac{2.3242}{2}\right)\left(\frac{20}{8.4039}\right) = 2.76$$

which is not significant at the 5% level. The quantities used above are taken from the analysis of variance table (Table 3g.3β). The differences caused by food could be detected when the concomitant variation is eliminated. Similarly, any other effect such as sex or interaction can be tested.

3g.4 A Problem of Inheritance in Man

The methods of analysis of variance and regression are of great value in studying the problems of inheritance. Some aspects of Boas' data * analyzed by Fisher and Gray (1937), are given in this section for illustrating the methods.

The data consist of measurements on Sicilian children and some of their parents. The first step in problems of this nature is to obtain the measurements on children corrected for age. The measurement (m) on any character can be represented by

$$m = f_i + bA + E$$

* The data are published in *Materials for the study in inheritance* (New York, Columbia University Press, 1928).

where f_i is a constant for the ith fraternity, A the age of the child, b the regression coefficient, and E the deviation from expectation. From the above formulation the covariance between A and m can be analyzed into between and within fraternities. If the latter is denoted by E_{01} and the sum of squares for A within fraternities by E_{11}, then the best estimate of b is E_{01}/E_{11}. The measurement corrected for age will be $y = m - AE_{01}/E_{11}$.

In the above data the measurements of all the children were used in calculating the regression coefficient. For studying the problems of inheritance only 752 children whose parents had been also measured were considered. The sum of the corrected statures for these children is 1505, and their sum of squares 3,304,643 mm². The total corrected sum of squares for 751 degrees of freedom is

$$3{,}304{,}643 - \frac{(1505)^2}{752} = 3{,}304{,}643 - 3012$$

$$= 3{,}301{,}631 \text{ mm}^2$$

The children belonged to 337 different fraternities and 235 different combinations of parental heights. The sum of squares between fraternities with 336 degrees of freedom can be split up into between fraternities with the same parental statures (102 D.F.) and between combinations of parental heights (234 D.F.). The sum of squares between fraternities is obtained by the usual formula for between groups. To derive the sum of squares between 235 different combinations of parental heights, all the children belonging to any combination are considered as forming a group and the between group sum of squares is calculated. The sum of squares between fraternities of the same parental heights is obtained by subtracting the latter sum of squares from the former.

The analysis of variance is given in Table 3g.4α.

TABLE 3g.4α. Analysis of Variance, Stature

	D.F.	S.S.	M.S.
Within fraternities	415	1,272,150	3065
Between fraternities with the same parental height	102	406,257	3983
Between combinations of parental height	234	1,623,224	
Total	751	3,301,631	

The mean square for between fraternities with the same parental height is greater, though not significantly, than that for within fraternities, indicating that parents of the same height were not identical genetically. Whether the former mean square is significantly different from the latter or not, it supplies the valid estimate of error for testing any hypothesis concerning the regression of child's stature on those of parents.

In order to test not only for linear regression on the two parents independently but also for theoretically possible deviations due to bias in dominance, the formula chosen was of the form

$$y = a + b_1 x_1 + b_2 x_2 + b_3 x_3$$

where x_1 and x_2 stand for the heights of the father and mother and x_3 for the product of $x_1 x_2$.

The method of solving for a, b_1, b_2, b_3 is the same as that considered in detail in 3f.2. The matrix (C_{ij}) giving the variances and covariances of the estimates b_1, b_2, b_3, written in millionths, is

$$
\begin{array}{ccc}
0.384227 & -0.041917 & -0.0074896 \\
-0.041917 & 0.438083 & -0.0052768 \\
-0.0074896 & -0.0052768 & 0.0117165
\end{array}
$$

The values of the coefficients are

$$b_1 = 0.02618850 \qquad b_2 = 0.3420271 \qquad b_3 = 0.0008596738$$

The sum of squares due to regression (3 D.F.) is 526,452. To test the adequacy of the regression formula chosen, the mean square for deviation from regression is to be compared with the mean square for between fraternities of like parents.

TABLE 3g.4β. Test for the Adequacy of Regression

	D.F.	S.S.	M.S.	F
Regression	3	526,452		
Deviation from regression	231	1,096,772	4748	1.2057
Between combinations of parental heights	234	1,623,224		
Between fraternities of like parents	102	406,257	3983	

The ratio for deviation from regression is not significant so that there is no evidence against the inadequacy of the regression formula. The mean square for deviation from regression supplies the valid estimate of error for testing any hypothesis concerning the regression coefficients.

The sum of squares for b_3 alone is

$$\frac{b_3{}^2}{C_{33}} = 6308$$

The sum of squares for regression (2 D.F.) when b_3 is not considered is obtained by subtracting this quantity from the total sum of squares due to regression (3 D.F.). The test for the regression coefficients is given in Table 3g.4γ.

TABLE 3g.4γ.   Tests for the Regression Coefficients

	D.F.	S.S.	M.S.	F
Due to b_3	1	6,308	6,308	1.3286
Linear regression	2	520,144	260,072	5.4775
Regression	3	526,452		
Deviation from regression	231	1,096,772	4,748	

The ratio for linear regression is significant. Since b_3 is positive, there is an indication of negative bias in dominance, i.e., "a situation in which the heterozygotes more nearly, or more frequently, resemble the smaller rather than the larger of the corresponding homozygotes." The ratio for b_3, though greater than unity, is not large enough to establish the existence of negative bias in dominance.

The actual regression formula is derived as

$$y = 1.684225 + 0.2690299(x_1 - \bar{x}_1) + 0.3483146(x_2 - \bar{x}_2)$$
$$+ 0.0008596738(x_1 - \bar{x}_1)(x_2 - \bar{x}_2) *$$

The sex difference in selection is

$$b_2 - b_1 - (\bar{x}_2 - \bar{x}_1)b_3 = 0.0792847$$

with standard error 0.06559 so that the difference in regression in favor of the mother, though large, is not significant.

References

AITKEN, A. C. (1935). On least squares and linear combination of observations. *Proc. Roy. Soc. Edin.*, **55**, 42.

FISHER, R. A. (1948). Statistical methods for research workers. Oliver & Boyd. Tenth edition.

FISHER, R. A. (1924). On a distribution yielding the error functions of several well-known statistics. *Proc. Int. Math. Congress*, Toronto, p. 805.

* The coefficients b_1 or b_2 are changed because of using the deviations from the mean in the product term.

FISHER, R. A., and H. GRAY (1937).   Inheritance in man: Boas' data studied by the method of analysis of variance. *Ann. Eugen. London,* **8,** 74.

HOOKE, B. G. E. (1926).   A third study of the English skull with special reference to the Farringdon Street crania. *Biom.,* **18,** 1.

KOLODZIECZYK, St. (1935).   On an important class of statistical hypotheses. *Biom.,* **27,** 161.

MACDONELL, W. R. (1904).   A study of the variation and the correlation of the human skull with special reference to English crania. *Biom.,* **3,** 19.

MARKOFF, A. A. (1904).   Calculus of probability. Russian Edition.

MÜNTER, A. H. (1936).   A study of the long bones of the arms and legs in man with special reference to Anglo-Saxon skeletons. *Biom.,* **28,** 258.

PEARSON, K. (1898).   Mathematical contributions to the theory of evolution. V. On reconstruction of stature of prehistoric men. *Philos. Trans. Roy. Soc.,* A, **192,** 169.

RAO, C. R. (1945).   Generalisation of Markoff's theorem and tests of linear hypotheses. *Sankhyā,* **7,** 9.

RAO, C. R. (1945).   Markoff's theorem with linear restrictions on parameters. *Sankhyā,* **7,** 16.

RAO, C. R. (1946).   On the linear combination of observations and the general theory of least squares. *Sankhyā,* **7,** 237.

"STUDENT" (W. S. GOSSET) (1908).   On the probable error of a mean. *Biom.,* **6,** 1.

WISHART, J. (1938).   Growth rate determination in nutrition studies with the bacon pig and their analysis. *Biom.,* **30,** 16.

CHAPTER 4

The General Theory of Estimation and the Method of Maximum Likelihood

4a Best Unbiased Estimates

4a.1 Estimation by Minimizing the Variance

In Chapter 3 problems were considered in which the class of estimates of parametric functions was restricted to linear functions of observations only. Nothing, however, was assumed about the actual distribution functions of these variables, except that their expectations are linear functions of unknown parameters and have a common unknown variance. It is of interest to examine the methods of obtaining the estimates with the minimum possible variance by considering the totality of unbiased estimates. This method of estimation is not necessarily the best. The general problem is that of deriving a function $t = f(y_1, \cdots, y_n)$ of the observations $y_1, \cdots, y_n$ such that with respect to any other function t' the probabilities satisfy the relationship

$$P(\theta - \lambda_1 < t < \theta + \lambda_2) \not< P(\theta - \lambda_1 < t' < \theta + \lambda_2) \quad (4a.1.1)$$

for all possible λ_1 and λ_2 in an interval $(0, \lambda)$. The choice of the interval may be fixed by other considerations, depending on the frequency and the magnitude of departure of the estimate from the true value allowable in a problem. If the condition (4a.1.1) is satisfied for all λ, then a necessary condition is

$$E(t - \theta)^2 \not> E(t' - \theta)^2$$

where E stands for expectation. If, further, it is assumed that the estimate should be unbiased, then it follows that

$$V(t) \not> V(t')$$

where V stands for variance.

129

As no simple solution satisfying the postulate (4a.1.1) exists, the inevitable arbitrariness of the postulates of unbiasedness and minimum variance needs no emphasis. The only justification for choosing the estimate with the minimum possible variance from the class of unbiased estimates is that a necessary condition for (4a.1.1) to hold for all λ, with the further requirement $E(t) = \theta$, is ensured. The condition of unbiasedness is particularly defective in that many biased estimates with smaller variances lose their claim as estimating functions. There are, however, numerous examples where a slightly biased estimate is preferred to an unbiased estimate with a greater variance. Until a unified solution of the problem of estimation is set forth, an estimating function has to be subjected to a critical examination as to its bias, variance, and frequency for a given amount of departure from the true value before utilizing it. The theory of confidence intervals as developed by J. Neyman is a great advance toward such a unified theory.

There is one important aspect which favors unbiased estimates. In biometric investigations it is often necessary to combine the evidence supplied by various sources. Often the evidence is in the nature of an estimate, probably with a standard error attached to it. For instance, two geneticists may be determining the proportion of albino mice produced under certain types of mating. One gives a proportion $p_1 \pm \epsilon_1$, and the other $p_2 \pm \epsilon_2$. If the estimates are unbiased, then a combined unbiased estimate may be reached, and with the accumulation of more and more evidence the true value can be approached through a series of unbiased estimates. On the other hand, if biased estimates are published *without any indication as to the nature of the bias involved*, nothing definite can be said about the combined estimate. The bias may exceed the standard error at some stage, and ultimately the combined estimate may not be near the true value.

4a.2 The Information Limit to Variance: A Single Parameter

Let $\phi(x_1, \cdots, x_n, \theta)$ be the probability density of the observations x_1, $\cdots$, x_n, and $t(x_1, \cdots, x_n)$ be an unbiased estimate of $\psi(\theta)$, a function of θ, the parameter occurring in the probability density. Then

$$\int t\phi \, dv = \psi(\theta) \qquad (4a.2.1)$$

where dv stands for the product of differential elements $dx_1, \cdots, dx_n$, and a single integral sign stands for the multiple integral. It may be noted that when the variables are discrete the integral sign can be replaced by the summation symbol. If the limits of integration do not involve θ, then differentiation under the integral sign yields

$$\int t \frac{d\phi}{d\theta} \, dv = \frac{d\psi}{d\theta}$$

if the above integral exists, which shows that the covariance between t and $(1/\phi)(d\phi/d\theta)$ is $(d\psi/d\theta)$. Since the square of the covariance is not greater than the product of the variances of the two variables, the following relationships (using V and C for variance and covariance) are true.

$$V(t) V \left(\frac{1}{\phi} \frac{d\phi}{d\theta} \right) \nleq \left\{ C \left(t, \frac{1}{\phi} \frac{d\phi}{d\theta} \right) \right\}^2$$

$$V(t) \nleq \frac{(d\psi/d\theta)^2}{I} \qquad (4a.2.2)$$

where

$$I = V \left(\frac{1}{\phi} \frac{d\phi}{d\theta} \right) = E \left[-\frac{d^2 \log \phi}{d\theta^2} \right]$$

The quantity I is the information on θ supplied by a sample of n observations as defined by R. A. Fisher. This gives the following theorem.

Theorem. The variance of any unbiased estimate of $\psi(\theta)$, a function of the unknown parameter θ, is not less than $[\psi'(\theta)]^2/I$, which is defined independently of any method of estimation. The conditions to be satisfied are that the range of the stochastic variable is independent of θ and the probability density admits differentiation under the integral sign.

If $\psi(\theta) = \theta$, then this limit is $1/I$. We shall call $[\psi'(\theta)]^2/I$ the information limit to variance for the estimation of $\psi(\theta)$. This is not, however, the *minimum attainable* in any particular distribution. An unbiased estimate of $\psi(\theta)$ with the minimum attainable variance will be called a *best unbiased estimate*. It is incorrect to conclude that an estimate is *inefficient* if its variance is not equal to $[\psi'(\theta)]^2/I$ unless it is ascertained that this minimum is attainable. In fact, it is shown later that there exists a more exact expression for the minimum possible variance.

As a corollary to the above theorem, it follows that the minimum value of

$$E(T - \theta)^2$$

for the set of statistics T with expectation $\psi(\theta)$ is

$$[\theta - \psi(\theta)]^2 + \frac{[\psi'(\theta)]^2}{I(\theta)}$$

Thus if $b(\theta)$ is the bias in the estimate T of θ, then

$$\psi(\theta) = \theta + b(\theta)$$

in which case

$$E(T - \theta)^2 \geq \{b(\theta)\}^2 + \frac{[1 + b'(\theta)]^2}{I(\theta)}$$

4a.3   Distributions Admitting Estimates with the Information Limit to Variance

The relationship (4a.2.2) may be written as

$$\int [t - \psi(\theta)]^2 \phi \, dv \times \int \left(\frac{1}{\phi}\frac{d\phi}{d\theta}\right)^2 \phi \, dv \nless \left\{\int [t - \psi(\theta)]\frac{1}{\phi}\frac{d\phi}{d\theta}\phi \, dv\right\}^2$$

It is known from Schwarz's inequality that the equality is attained only when

$$t - \psi(\theta) = \lambda \frac{1}{\phi}\frac{d\phi}{d\theta}$$

where λ is a constant depending only on θ. The solution of this differential equation is

$$\log \phi = \int \left\{\frac{t}{\lambda} - \frac{\psi(\theta)}{\lambda}\right\} d\theta = A + t\Theta_1 + \Theta_2$$

where Θ_1 and Θ_2 are functions of θ, and A is independent of θ. Hence

$$\phi = \phi_1 \exp\left(t\Theta_1 + \Theta_2\right) \tag{4a.3.1}$$

where ϕ_1 is only a function of the observations. Also if

$$\phi = \phi_1 \exp\left(t\Theta_1 + \Theta_2\right)$$

then

$$\int \phi \, dv = \int \phi_1 \exp\left(t\Theta_1 + \Theta_2\right) dv = 1$$

$$\therefore \int \phi_1 \exp\left(t\Theta_1\right) dv = \exp\left(-\Theta_2\right)$$

On differentiating with respect to Θ_1 twice,

$$\int \phi_1 t \exp\left(t\Theta_1\right) dv = -\frac{d\Theta_2}{d\Theta_1}\exp\left(-\Theta_2\right)$$

$$\int \phi_1 t^2 \exp\left(t\Theta_1\right) dv = \left\{-\frac{d^2\Theta_2}{d\Theta_1^2} + \left(\frac{d\Theta_2}{d\Theta_1}\right)^2\right\}\exp\left(-\Theta_2\right)$$

Hence

$$E(t) = -\frac{d\Theta_2}{d\Theta_1} \quad \text{and} \quad V(t) = -\frac{d^2\Theta_2}{d\Theta_1^2} \qquad (4a.3.2)$$

The information limit for the estimation of $-d\Theta_2/d\Theta_1$ is

$$\left\{\frac{d}{d\theta}\frac{d\Theta_2}{d\Theta_1}\right\}^2 \div \left\{-\frac{d^2\Theta_2}{d\Theta_1^2}\left(\frac{d\Theta_1}{d\theta}\right)^2\right\} = -\frac{d^2\Theta_2}{d\Theta_1^2}$$

which is the same as that derived in (4a.3.2) so that the information limit is attainable.

Hence the necessary and sufficient condition that a distribution admits the estimation of a suitably chosen function of the parameter with variance equal to the information limit is that

$$\phi = \phi_1 \exp(t\Theta_1 + \Theta_2)$$

where ϕ_1 and t are functions of the observations only and Θ_1 and Θ_2 are functions of θ only. The parametric function to be estimated is

$$-\frac{d\Theta_2}{d\Theta_1} = -\frac{d\Theta_2}{d\theta}\frac{d\theta}{d\Theta_1}$$

and the variance of the estimate is

$$-\frac{d^2\Theta_2}{d\Theta_1^2} = \left(\frac{d\Theta_1}{d\theta}\right)^{-1}\frac{d}{d\theta}\left(-\frac{d\Theta_2}{d\Theta_1}\right)$$

For any estimate t which has the minimum variance (4a.2.2),

$$t - \psi(\theta) = \lambda\frac{1}{\phi}\frac{d\phi}{d\theta}$$

$$V[t - \psi(\theta)] = \lambda^2 I = \frac{[\psi'(\theta)]^2}{I}$$

so that $\lambda^2 = [\psi'(\theta)]^2/I^2$, which is a unique function of θ. This shows that t is unique as the best unbiased estimate of $\psi(\theta)$.

Example 1. Let $x_1, \cdots, x_n$ be n independent observations from the normal population

$$\frac{1}{\sigma\sqrt{2\pi}}e^{-(x-\mu)^2/2\sigma^2}\,dx$$

If $n\bar{x} = x_1 + \cdots + x_n$, then

$$\phi = \frac{1}{(\sigma\sqrt{2\pi})^n} e^{-[n(\bar{x}-\mu)^2 + \Sigma(x_i-\bar{x})^2]/2\sigma^2}$$

$$= \phi_1 e^{(2\mu n\bar{x} - n\mu^2)/2\sigma^2}$$

where

$$\phi_1 = \frac{1}{(\sigma\sqrt{2\pi})^n} e^{-\Sigma x_i^2/2\sigma^2}$$

which is independent of μ. Thus ϕ can be expressed in the form (4a.3.1), which means that $\bar{x}$ is the estimate of

$$-\frac{d(-n\mu^2/2\sigma^2)}{d(n\mu/\sigma^2)} = \mu$$

and has the minimum variance (4a.2.2).

Example 2. Consider n independent observations from the population

$$\frac{\alpha^p}{\Gamma(p)} e^{-\alpha x} x^{p-1} \, dx$$

$$\phi = \frac{\alpha^{np}}{\{\Gamma(p)\}^n} e^{-\alpha \Sigma x_i} \Pi(x_i)^{p-1}$$

$$= \phi_1 e^{-p\alpha n y + np \log \alpha}$$

where ϕ_1 is independent of α and $y = (\Sigma x_i)/pn$, so that the minimum variance (4a.2.2) is attained for the estimate y of

$$-\frac{d(np \log \alpha)}{d\alpha} \div \frac{d(-p\alpha n)}{d\alpha} = \frac{1}{\alpha}$$

$$V(y) = \left\{\frac{d}{d\alpha}(-p\alpha n)\right\}^{-1} \frac{d}{d\alpha}\left(\frac{1}{\alpha}\right) = \frac{1}{pn\alpha^2}$$

Also

$$\phi = \phi_1 e^{n(p-1)z - n \log \Gamma(p)}$$

where ϕ_1 is independent of p and $z = (1/n) \log (\Pi x_i)$, so that the minimum variance (4a.2.2) is attained for the estimate z of

$$\frac{d \log \Gamma(p)}{dp} \div \frac{d(p-1)}{dp} = \frac{d \log \Gamma(p)}{dp}$$

Example 3. The chance of obtaining r successes in n independent trials with probability π for success in a trial is

$$\phi = \binom{n}{r} \pi^r (1 - \pi)^{n-r}$$

$$\frac{d \log \phi}{d\pi} = \frac{r - n\pi}{\pi(1 - \pi)}$$

$$I = \frac{V(r - n\pi)}{\pi^2(1 - \pi)^2} = \frac{n}{\pi(1 - \pi)}$$

$$E\left(\frac{r}{n}\right) = \pi \quad \text{and} \quad V\left(\frac{r}{n}\right) = \frac{\pi(1 - \pi)}{n} = \frac{1}{I}$$

This shows that r/n as the estimate of π has the minimum variance (4a.2.2).

Example 4. The chance of n independent observations from a Poisson distribution is

$$\phi = e^{-n\mu} \frac{\mu^{x_1}}{x_1!} \cdots \frac{\mu^{x_n}}{x_n!}$$

$$\frac{1}{\phi} \frac{d\phi}{d\mu} = -n + \frac{x_1}{\mu} + \cdots + \frac{x_n}{\mu}$$

$$I = V\left(\frac{1}{\phi} \frac{d\phi}{d\mu}\right) = \frac{1}{\mu^2} V(x_1 + \cdots + x_n) = \frac{n\mu}{\mu^2} = \frac{n}{\mu}$$

The estimate $\bar{x}$ of μ has the variance $\mu/n = 1/I$ so that the minimum variance (4a.2.2) is attained.

4a.4 Sufficient Statistics and Unbiased Estimates

A statistic T is said to be sufficient for the parameter θ if, with respect to any other statistic T', the joint probability density $P(T, T')$ of T and T' is of the form

$$P(T, T') = P_1(T, \theta)P_2(T' \mid T)$$

where $P_1(T, \theta)$ is the probability density for T, and $P_2(T' \mid T)$, the relative probability density of T' given T, is independent of θ. From this definition it can be shown that the necessary and sufficient condition for ϕ to admit a sufficient statistic is

$$\phi = \Phi(T, \theta)\phi_1(x_1, \cdots, x_n) \tag{4a.4.1}$$

where ϕ_1 as a relative probability density given T is independent of θ, and T is a function of x only. The statistic T is said to be sufficient for θ.

In fact, any function of T having one-to-one correspondence * with T will be sufficient for θ.

Theorem. If an unbiased estimate and a sufficient statistic exist for $\psi(\theta)$, the best unbiased estimate of $\psi(\theta)$ is an explicit function of the sufficient statistic.

The statement does not imply that there exists a function of the sufficient statistic which attains the minimum variance (4a.2.2). But the best unbiased estimates have to be sought from the functions of the sufficient statistic only.

If t is unbiased for $\psi(\theta)$, then

$$\psi(\theta) = \int t\phi \, dv = \int t\Phi(T, \theta)\phi_1 \, dv$$

Integration over the surfaces of the constant T gives

$$\psi(\theta) = \int f(T)\Phi(T, \theta) \, dT \qquad (4a.4.2)$$

which shows that there exists a function $f(T)$, of the sufficient statistic T, which is unbiased for $\psi(\theta)$. Also

$$\int [t - \psi(\theta)]^2 \phi \, dv = \int [t - f(T)]^2 \phi \, dv + \int [f(T) - \psi(\theta)]^2 \Phi(T, \theta) \, dT$$

since the product term vanishes in virtue of (4a.4.2). Hence

$$\int [t - \psi(\theta)]^2 \phi \, dv \geq \int [f(T) - \psi(\theta)]^2 \Phi(T, \theta) \, dT$$

i.e.,
$$V(t) \geq V[f(T)]$$

which proves the theorem. Thus, when a sufficient statistic exists, we need only search for the best estimates among functions of the sufficient statistic. If there exists a unique function of T unbiased for $\psi(\theta)$, then this is necessarily the best. But, if more than one function of T is unbiased for $\psi(\theta)$, then the one with the least variance has to be chosen. This leads to the corollary.

Corollary. If a function $F(T)$ of the sufficient statistic T is unbiased for $\psi(\theta)$ and is also unique, then this is the best unbiased estimate.

---

* It can be verified that $\bar{x}$ is a sufficient statistic for μ, the mean of a normal distribution. But $\bar{x}^2$ is not sufficient for μ for the condition (4a·4·1) is no longer true. The statement, generally made, that any function of a sufficient statistic is also sufficient is not true.

Example 1.   The minimum variance unbiased estimate is unique. {Hint: If T_1 and T_2 are two such estimates, then $V[(T_1 + T_2)/2] \not> V(T_1)$. This shows that the correlation between T_1 and T_2 is unity.}

Example 2.   If T_1 and T_2 are two unbiased estimates of a parameter with variances σ_1^2, σ_2^2 and correlation ρ, what is the best unbiased linear combination of T_1 and T_2 and what is the variance of such a compound?

We have to minimize

$$l_1^2\sigma_1^2 + 2\rho l_1 l_2 \sigma_1 \sigma_2 + l_2^2 \sigma_2^2$$

subject to the condition $l_1 + l_2 = 1$. This gives, in one step,

$$l_1(\sigma_1^2 - \rho\sigma_1\sigma_2) = l_2(\sigma_2^2 - \rho\sigma_1\sigma_2)$$

giving the ratio between l_1 and l_2.

Example 3.   Suppose that T_1 in the above example is an unbiased minimum variance estimate and T_2 any other unbiased estimate with variance σ^2/e where $V(T_1) = \sigma^2$. Then the correlation between T_1 and T_2 is $\sqrt{e}$.

The best linear compound of T_1, T_2 has the coefficients l_1 and l_2 satisfying the condition

$$l_1(e - \rho\sqrt{e}) = l_2(1 - \rho\sqrt{e})$$

Express the condition that the variance of the best compound is not less than σ^2 or simply, since T_1 cannot be improved upon, $l_2 = 0$, which means $e = \rho\sqrt{e}$.

Example 4.   If T_1, T_2 are two unbiased statistics having the same variance, then their correlation is $\geq 2e - 1$, where e is the ratio of the variance of the best estimate to the common variance of T_1 and T_2.

[Hint: Consider the statistic $T = (T_1 + T_2)/2$ and express the condition $V(T) \geq$ the least variance.]

4a.5   Distributions Admitting Sufficient Statistics

The necessary and sufficient condition that a distribution admits a sufficient statistic is that the probability density can be written in the form

$$\phi = \Phi(T, \theta)\phi_1(x_1, \cdots, x_n) \tag{4a.5.1}$$

where $\Phi(T, \theta)$ is the density of the statistic T and $\phi_1(x_1, \cdots, x_n)$, the density of the sample given T, is independent of θ. It is obviously not enough to state the necessary and sufficient condition as the factorizability of ϕ into $\Phi(T, \theta)$ and $\phi_1(x_1, \cdots, x_n)$, where T is a function of x_1, $\cdots$, x_n, and ϕ_1 is independent of θ unless the range of x is independent of θ. For instance consider

$$\phi = \left(\frac{\theta}{e^{\theta^2} - 1}\right)^n e^{\theta(x_1 + \cdots + x_n)} \tag{4a.5.2}$$

where the range of each x is from 0 to θ. This does not admit a sufficient statistic.

Let us now assume that $x_1, \cdots, x_n$ are independent observations from the same distribution so that

$$\phi = p(x_1, \theta) \cdots p(x_n, \theta)$$

If this is factorizable into $\Phi(T, \theta)$ and $\phi_1(x_1, \cdots, x_n)$ then, assuming that the functions are partially differentiable with respect to θ, we obtain

$$\Sigma \frac{\partial \log p(x_i, \theta)}{\partial \theta} = \frac{\partial \log \Phi(T, \theta)}{\partial \theta} = G(T, \theta) \tag{4a.5.3}$$

Since this holds for all θ, any value of θ can be substituted in (4a.5.3) to obtain the relation

$$u = \Sigma u(x_i) = g(T)$$

connecting T and the statistic $u = \Sigma u(x_i)$. If $g(T)$ and $u(x)$ are differentiable functions, it follows that

$$\frac{\partial u}{\partial x_i} = \frac{du(x_i)}{dx_i} = \frac{dg(T)}{dT} \frac{\partial T}{\partial x_i}$$

Also from (4a.5.3)

$$\frac{\partial G(T, \theta)}{\partial T} \frac{\partial T}{\partial x_i} = \frac{\partial^2 \log p(x_i, \theta)}{\partial \theta \, \partial x_i}$$

Therefore, for all i

$$\frac{\partial^2 \log p(x_i, \theta)}{\partial \theta \, \partial x_i} \div \frac{du(x_i)}{dx_i} = \frac{\partial G(T, \theta)}{\partial T} \div \frac{dg(T)}{dT}$$

$$= \lambda_1(\theta) \qquad \text{a function of } \theta \text{ only}$$

Integrating with respect to T,

$$G(T, \theta) = \lambda_1(\theta) g(T) + \lambda_2(\theta)$$

and then with respect to θ,

$$\log \phi(x_1, \cdots, x_n) = \Theta_1 g(T) + \Theta_2 + h(x_1, \cdots, x_n)$$

$$\phi(x_1, \cdots, x_n) = \phi_2 e^{\Theta_1 g(T) + \Theta_2} \tag{4a.5.4}$$

where $g(T)$, ϕ_2 are functions of $x_1, \cdots, x_n$ only, and Θ_1, Θ_2 are functions of θ only. This is obviously not a necessary and sufficient condition because the only condition used is the factorizability of ϕ. In fact the illustration in (4a.5.2) has the same form as (4a.5.4). But when a sufficient statistic exists, the distribution must necessarily be of the form (4a.5.4).

4a.6   An Optimum Property of Sufficient Statistics

In 4a.5 it was shown that the distribution admitting a sufficient statistic is of the form

$$\phi = \exp\,[t_1\Theta_1 + \Theta_2 + t_2]$$

Let $F(t_1)$ be any function of t_1 with the expectation $\psi(\theta)$. Consider an alternative function unbiased for $\psi(\theta)$ but differing from $F(t_1)$ by $f(t_1)$. Then

$$\int f(t_1)\,\exp\,[t_1\Theta_1 + \Theta_2 + t_2]\,dv = 0$$

Continuous differentiation, when permissible, yields

$$\int t_1{}^k f(t_1)\,\exp\,[t_1\Theta_1 + \Theta_2 + t_2]\,dv = 0 \qquad \text{for all } k$$

or

$$\int e^{it_1\alpha} f(t_1)\,\exp\,[t_1\Theta_1 + \Theta_2 + t_2]\,dv = 0$$

From Fourier's inversion theorem it is known that, if $f(t_1)\,\exp\,(t_1\Theta_1 + \Theta_2 + t_2)$ is continuous, then it must be zero almost everywhere. Since the second expression cannot be zero, it follows that $f(t_1) = 0$, which shows that $F(t_1)$ is unique as an estimate of its expected value, and therefore the best possible. Hence the following theorem is obtained.

Theorem: Any function of the sufficient statistic is the best estimate of its expected value under the regularity conditions assumed above.

This is a general demonstration of the properties discussed in examples 1 and 2 below. The result is true under less stringent conditions than those assumed above.

Example 1.   Consider n independent observations from the normal population

$$\frac{1}{\sigma\sqrt{2\pi}}\,\exp\left[\frac{-(x - \mu)^2}{2\sigma^2}\right]dx$$

$$\phi = \phi_1\exp\left[\frac{-n(\bar{x} - \mu)^2}{2\sigma^2}\right]$$

where ϕ_1 is independent of μ and $n\bar{x} = x_1 + \cdots + x_n$. This shows that $\bar{x}$ is sufficient for μ. In fact, we have seen that $\bar{x}$ has the minimum variance (4a.2.2) as an estimate of μ. Suppose that instead of μ we are seeking the estimate of μ^2. Evidently $\bar{x}$ is sufficient for μ^2 or for any function of μ. The parameter σ^2 being considered known, an unbiased estimate of μ^2 is

$$X = \bar{x}^2 - \frac{\sigma^2}{n}$$

$$V(X) = E(\bar{x}^4) - \left(\mu^2 + \frac{\sigma^2}{n}\right)^2$$

$$= \mu^4 + \frac{6\mu^2\sigma^2}{n} + \frac{3\sigma^4}{n^2} - \mu^4 - \frac{2\sigma^2\mu^2}{n} - \frac{\sigma^4}{n^2}.$$

$$= \frac{4\mu^2\sigma^2}{n} + \frac{2\sigma^4}{n^2}$$

The minimum variance (4a.2.2) is

$$\frac{(d\mu^2/d\mu)^2}{I} = \frac{4\mu^2\sigma^2}{n}$$

since $I = n/\sigma^2$, which is smaller than $V(X)$. But X is the best unbiased estimate since, as shown below, it has the minimum attainable variance. To prove this it will be shown that there exists no function of $\bar{x}$, the sufficient statistic, such that its expectation is μ^2 and its variance less than that of $V(X)$. Let the alternative function differ from X by $f(\bar{x})$. Since both are unbiased, it follows that

$$\exp\left[\frac{-n\mu^2}{2\sigma^2}\right] \int f(\bar{x}) \exp\left[\frac{-n(\bar{x}^2 - 2\mu\bar{x})}{2\sigma^2}\right] d\bar{x} = 0$$

Omitting the term before the integral and differentiating twice with respect to μ, the following relation is obtained.

$$\int \frac{n^2 f(\bar{x})\bar{x}^2}{\sigma^4} \exp\left[\frac{-n(\bar{x}^2 - 2\mu\bar{x})}{2\sigma^2}\right] d\bar{x} = 0$$

This shows that cov $\{f(\bar{x}), \bar{x}^2\} = 0$.

$$V\{X + f(\bar{x})\} = V(X) + V\{f(\bar{x})\} + 2 \operatorname{cov}\left\{f(\bar{x}), \bar{x}^2 - \frac{\sigma^2}{n}\right\}$$

$$= V(X) + V\{f(\bar{x})\}$$

$$\geq V(X)$$

which shows that X is better than any other estimate, or, in other words, it has minimum variance as an estimate of μ^2.

Example 2.   Consider n independent observations from the population

$$\frac{\alpha^p}{\Gamma(p)}\, e^{-\alpha x} x^{p-1}\, dx$$

$$\phi = \frac{\alpha^{pn}}{\{\Gamma(p)\}^n}\, e^{-\alpha n \bar{x}} \Pi(x_i)^{p-1}$$

which shows that $\bar{x}$ is sufficient for α.   Since $E[(np-1)/\bar{x}] = \alpha$, the statistic $(np-1)/\bar{x}$ is unbiased for α.

$$V\left(\frac{np-1}{\bar{x}}\right) = \alpha^2 \left\{\frac{np-1}{np-2} - 1\right\} = \frac{\alpha^2}{np-2}$$

The minimum variance (4a.2.2) is

$$\frac{1}{I} = \frac{\alpha^2}{pn}$$

which is smaller than $V[(np-1)/\bar{x}]$.   Let an alternative estimate differ from $(np-1)/\bar{x}$ by $f(\bar{x})$.   Then

$$\int f(\bar{x}) \exp[-\alpha\bar{x}]\, d\bar{x} = 0 \qquad \text{for all } \alpha > 0$$

which gives the result that

$$\int \bar{x}^r f(\bar{x}) \exp[-\alpha\bar{x}]\, d\bar{x} = 0 \qquad \text{for all } r$$

or

$$\int e^{it\bar{x}} f(\bar{x}) \exp[-\alpha\bar{x})\, d\bar{x} = 0, \qquad \text{where } i = \sqrt{-1}$$

From the Fourier inversion theorem we obtain

$$f(\bar{x}) \exp[-\alpha\bar{x}] = 0$$

or $f(\bar{x}) = 0$ almost everywhere, so that the function $(np-1)/\bar{x}$ is unique as the estimate of α.

Example 3.   Consider n independent observations $x_1, \cdots, x_n$ from a rectangular distribution in the range 0 to β.   The biggest observation x_b has the distribution

$$n\beta^{-n} x_b{}^{n-1}\, dx_b$$

so that

$$E(x_b) = \frac{n}{n+1}\beta$$

or

$$E\left(\frac{n+1}{n}x_b\right) = \beta \qquad V\left(\frac{n+1}{n}x_b\right) = \frac{\beta^2}{n(n+2)}$$

Also, x_b is sufficient for β; hence the unbiased minimum variance estimate must be a function of x_b only. The statistic $(1 + 1/n)x_b$ is unbiased for β. It is also unique for, if another statistic differs from this by $\phi(x_b)$, then

$$\int_0^\beta \phi(x_b)x_b{}^{n-1}\, dx_b = 0$$

for all β. This means that

$$\phi(x)x^n = 0$$

or $\phi(x) = 0$ almost everywhere. The statistic $(1 + 1/n)x_b$ is the best unbiased estimate of β.

Example 4. Consider a rectangular distribution in the range α to β. The biggest and smallest observations x_b and x_s form a sufficient set of statistics for α and β. The joint distribution of x_b and x_s is

$$n(n-1)(\beta - \alpha)^{-n}(x_b - x_s)^{n-2}\, dx_b\, dx_s$$

The statistics

$$T_1 = \frac{n}{n-1}\left(x_b - \frac{x_s}{n}\right)$$

and

$$T_2 = \frac{n}{n-1}\left(x_s - \frac{x_b}{n}\right)$$

are unbiased for α and β, respectively. It can also be shown, as in example 3, that these are the best.

Example 5. The unbiased minimum variance estimates of the central point $(\alpha + \beta)/2$ and the range $(\beta - \alpha)$ are

$$\frac{x_b + x_s}{2} \qquad \text{and} \qquad \frac{n+1}{n-1}(x_b - x_s)$$

Example 6. Show that in example 3 any function $t(x_b)$ of x_b unbiased for β has the terminal value

$$t(\beta) = \left(1 + \frac{1}{n}\right)\beta$$

4a.7 More Stringent Inequalities for the Variance of an Estimate

It was shown in 4a.2 that the minimum variance for an unbiased estimate of $\psi(\theta)$ is not less than

$$\frac{[\psi'(\theta)]^2}{I}$$

Considering the equality

$$\int t\phi \, dv = \psi(\theta)$$

and differentiating k times

$$\int t \frac{d^k\phi}{d\theta^k} \, dv = \frac{d^k\psi}{d\theta^k}$$

which leads to the relationship

$$V(t) \nleq \frac{(d^k\psi/d\theta^k)^2}{J_{kk}}$$

where

$$J_{kk} = V\left(\frac{1}{\phi}\frac{d^k\phi}{d\theta^k}\right) \qquad k = 1, 2, \cdots$$

Thus a chain of relationships can be derived of which the result obtained in 4a.2 is a special case. More generally, if

$$J_{kr} = \text{cov}\left(\frac{1}{\phi}\frac{d^k\phi}{d\theta^k}, \frac{1}{\phi}\frac{d^r\phi}{d\theta^r}\right)$$

then the square of the multiple correlation of t on $\dfrac{1}{\phi}\dfrac{d\phi}{d\theta}, \dfrac{1}{\phi}\dfrac{d^2\phi}{d\theta^2}, \cdots$ is

$$\left[\Sigma\Sigma J^{kr}\frac{d^k\psi(\theta)}{d\theta^k}\frac{d^r\psi(\theta)}{d\theta^r}\right] \div V(t)$$

where (J^{kr}) is the matrix inverse to (J_{kr}). Since this is not greater than unity, we obtain the relationship

$$V(t) \nleq \Sigma\Sigma J^{kr}\frac{d^k\psi(\theta)}{d\theta^k}\frac{d^r\psi(\theta)}{d\theta^r}$$

This result is due to Bhattacharya (1947). Since the multiple correlation obtained by considering all the variables of a group is greater than that for a subset, it follows that the lower bound to the variance of an estimate can be improved by the addition of more variables of the type $(1/\phi)(d^k\phi/d\theta^k)$.

4a.8   The Case of Several Parameters

Minimal Set of Sufficient Statistics.   A set of statistics $T_1, \cdots, T_m$ is said to be a minimal set of sufficient statistics if m is the smallest number for which

$$\phi(x \mid \theta) = P_1(T_1, \cdots, T_m \mid \theta)P_2(x \mid T) \qquad (4a.8.1)$$

where P_1 is the probability density of $T_1, \cdots, T_m$, and P_2 the probability of the observations given the statistics $T_1, \cdots, T_m$, is independent of θ. There is no restriction on m, which may be greater than, equal to, or less than k, the number of parameters involved in ϕ.

Information Matrix: Let

$$\phi_{ij} = - \frac{\partial^2 \log \phi}{\partial \theta_i \, \partial \theta_j} \quad \text{and} \quad E(\phi_{ij}) = I_{ij}$$

The matrix $I = (I_{ij})$, $(i, j, = 1, \cdots, k)$, is called the information matrix. If (S_{ij}) denotes the information matrix obtained from the distribution $P_1(T \mid \theta)$, then it follows from the definition given in (4a.8.1) that $(I_{ij}) \equiv (S_{ij})$. Also, if $\phi(x, \theta)$ is the probability density corresponding to n independent sets of observations from the same population, then $I_{ij} = nJ_{ij}$, where J_{ij} is the element of the information matrix corresponding to a single set of observations. This is the additive property of information.

The following theorem may now be proved.

Theorem.   Let $t_1, \cdots, t_r$ be $r \leq k$ functionally independent statistics such that

(i) $\qquad E(t_i) = \psi_i(\theta_1, \cdots, \theta_k)$

(ii) $\qquad E(t_i - \psi_i)(t_j - \psi_j) = V_{ij}$ $\Bigg\}$ $i, j = 1, \cdots, r$

then:

(A) There exist functions $M_1, \cdots, M_r$ of the minimal set of sufficient statistics such that

(a) $E(M_i) = \psi_i(\theta_1, \cdots, \theta_k)$;
(b) if $U = (U_{ij})$ where $U_{ij} = E(M_i - \psi_i)(M_j - \psi_j)$ and $V = (V_{ij})$, then the matrix $(V - U)$ is positive definite or semi-definite.

(B) If the ranges of integration do not involve the parameters, and I^{-1}, the inverse of I, exists, and $\Delta = (\partial \psi_i / \partial \theta_j)$, $(i = 1, \cdots, r, j = 1, \cdots, k)$, then the matrix $V - \Delta I^{-1} \Delta'$, where Δ' is the transpose of Δ, is positive definite or semi-definite.

Proof. Since

$$\int t_i \phi(x \mid \theta) \, dv = \int P_1(T \mid \theta) \, dT \int t_i P_2(x \mid T) \, dv'$$

$$= \int M_i(T) P_1(T \mid \theta) \, dT \qquad (4a.8.2)$$

it follows that M_i is a function of T only such that

$$E(M_i) = E(t_i) = \psi_i \qquad i = 1, 2, \cdots, r$$

This proves (A)(a) of the theorem.

Consider $\Sigma l_i t_i$ where l_i are arbitrary constants.

$$E(\Sigma l_i t_i) = \Sigma l_i \psi_i = E(\Sigma l_i M_i)$$

$$\int [\Sigma l_i (t_i - \psi_i)]^2 \phi(x \mid \theta) \, dv$$

$$= \int [\Sigma l_i (t_i - M_i) + \Sigma l_i (M_i - \psi_i)]^2 \phi(x \mid \theta) \, dv$$

$$= \int [\Sigma l_i (t_i - M_i)]^2 \phi(x \mid \theta) \, dv + \int [\Sigma l_i (M_i - \psi_i)]^2 \phi(x \mid \theta) \, dv$$

$$+ 2 \int [\Sigma l_i (M_i - \psi_i)] P_1(T \mid \theta) \, dT \int [\Sigma l_i (t_i - M_i)] P_2(x \mid T) \, dv'$$

By virtue of the result (4a.8.2), the last term vanishes identically, leaving only two positive quantities. If we retain only the latter, the following relationship is obtained.

$$V(\Sigma l_i t_i) \nless V(\Sigma l_i M_i)$$

or

$$\Sigma\Sigma l_i l_j V_{ij} \nless \Sigma\Sigma l_i l_j U_{ij} \qquad \text{or} \qquad \Sigma\Sigma l_i l_j [V_{ij} - U_{ij}] \nless 0$$

This means that $(V - U)$ is positive or semi-definite. This proves the result (A)(b) of the theorem.

Since

$$\int t_j \phi(x \mid \theta) \, dv = \psi_j$$

$$\int t_j \frac{d\phi}{d\theta_i} \, dv = \frac{d\psi_j}{d\theta_i}$$

so that by considering the dispersion matrix of $t_1, \cdots, t_r, \dfrac{1}{\phi}\dfrac{d\phi}{d\theta_1}, \cdots,$

$\dfrac{1}{\phi}\dfrac{d\phi}{d\theta_k}$, we find that the partitioned matrix

$$\left(\begin{array}{c|c} V & \Delta \\ \hline \Delta' & I \end{array} \right)$$

is positive or semi-definite.*

Consider the determinant

$$\left| \begin{array}{c|c} \delta_r & -\Delta I^{-1} \\ \hline 0 & I^{-1} \end{array} \right|$$

where δ_r is the unit square matrix of order r, which is always positive. The product

$$\left| \begin{array}{c|c} \delta_r & -\Delta I^{-1} \\ \hline 0 & I^{-1} \end{array} \right| \left| \begin{array}{c|c} V & \Delta \\ \hline \Delta' & I \end{array} \right| = \left| \begin{array}{c|c} V - \Delta I^{-1}\Delta' & 0 \\ \hline I^{-1}\Delta' & \delta_k \end{array} \right| \geq 0$$

or $\left| V - \Delta I^{-1}\Delta' \right| \geq 0$. This result holds true even for a subset of the statistics $t_1, \cdots, t_r$, which means that the matrix $V - \Delta I^{-1}\Delta'$ is positive definite or semi-definite. This proves result (B) of the theorem.

A series of corollaries can be obtained from results (A) and (B) of the above theorem.

Corollary 1. By considering only the diagonal elements in $V - \Delta I^{-1}\Delta'$

$$V_{ii} \nless \Sigma\Sigma I^{mn} \frac{\partial\psi_i}{\partial\theta_m} \frac{\partial\psi_i}{\partial\theta_n} \tag{4a.8.3}$$

where I^{mn} are the elements of the matrix reciprocal to the information matrix (I_{mn}). This shows that the variance of the estimate of ψ_i is not less than a quantity which is defined independently of any method of estimation. This is the generalization to many parameters of the expression derived in (4a.2.2). If $\psi_i = \theta_i$, $(i = 1, \cdots, k)$, the relationship (4a.8.3) reduces to

$$V_{ii} \nless I^{ii}$$

These are not necessarily the minima attainable. Observe that I^{ii} is greater than $1/I_{ii}$ which is the limit obtained in (4a.2.2) for the estimate of θ_i. When the values of $\theta_1, \cdots, \theta_{i-1}, \theta_{i+1}, \cdots, \theta_k$ are known, then

---

* The matrix I is the information matrix, not to be misunderstood for the unit matrix introduced in Chapter 1. To distinguish this the unit matrix is here represented by δ which is also an accepted symbol for a diagonal matrix.

the limit (4a.2.2) is applicable. If not, the estimate of θ_i has to be independent of the above quantities and for this reason the limit is increased.

Corollary 2. Since the matrix $(V - U)$ is positive definite or semi-definite, it follows that $V_{ii} \not< U_{ii}$, $(i = 1, \cdots, r)$, which shows that estimates with the minimum attainable variances are explicit functions of sufficient statistics.

Corollary 3. Since the matrix $(V - \Delta I^{-1}\Delta')$ is positive definite or semi-definite, it follows that (see example 1 in 1c.5)

$$|V| \not< |\Delta I^{-1}\Delta'|$$

The quantity $|V|$ is called the generalized variance of the estimates. The above result shows that this is not less than a quantity which is defined independently of any method of estimation.

Corollary 4. Since $(V - U)$ is positive definite or semi-definite, it follows that $|V| \not< |U|$ (example 1 in 1c.5). This shows that the estimates with the minimum possible generalized variance are functions of the sufficient statistics.

Corollary 5. If

$$V_{ii} = \Sigma\Sigma I^{mn} \frac{\partial \psi_i}{\partial \theta_m} \frac{\partial \psi_i}{\partial \theta_n}$$

in which case the estimate of ψ_i has the minimum variance, then

$$V_{ij} = \Sigma\Sigma I^{mn} \frac{\partial \psi_i}{\partial \theta_m} \frac{\partial \psi_j}{\partial \theta_n}$$

so that the covariance of this best estimate with any estimate of any other parametric function has a fixed value defined independently of any method of estimation. This follows from the fact that the determinant

$$\begin{vmatrix} V_{ii} - \Sigma\Sigma I^{mn} \dfrac{\partial \psi_i}{\partial \theta_m} \dfrac{\partial \psi_i}{\partial \theta_n} & V_{ij} - \Sigma\Sigma I^{mn} \dfrac{\partial \psi_i}{\partial \theta_m} \dfrac{\partial \psi_j}{\partial \theta_n} \\ V_{ij} - \Sigma\Sigma I^{mn} \dfrac{\partial \psi_i}{\partial \theta_m} \dfrac{\partial \psi_j}{\partial \theta_n} & V_{jj} - \Sigma\Sigma I^{mn} \dfrac{\partial \psi_j}{\partial \theta_m} \dfrac{\partial \psi_j}{\partial \theta_n} \end{vmatrix}$$

which is a subdeterminant of $|V - \Delta I^{-1}\Delta'|$, is not less than zero.

Example. Consider n independent observations from the normal population

$$\frac{1}{\sigma\sqrt{2\pi}} \exp\left[\frac{-(x - \mu)^2}{2\sigma^2}\right] dx$$

It is easy to verify that the information matrix for μ and σ^2 is

$$(I_{\mu,\sigma^2}) = \begin{bmatrix} \dfrac{n}{\sigma^2} & 0 \\ 0 & \dfrac{n}{2\sigma^4} \end{bmatrix}$$

with its reciprocal

$$(I^{\mu,\sigma^2}) = \begin{bmatrix} \dfrac{\sigma^2}{n} & 0 \\ 0 & \dfrac{2\sigma^4}{n} \end{bmatrix}$$

Since $\bar{x}$ as an estimate of μ has the minimum possible variance, it follows that *any* estimate of σ^2 has zero correlation with $\bar{x}$, since $I^{m\sigma^2} = 0$. This result can be extended to the case of multivariate normal populations where it can be shown that the means are uncorrelated with all possible estimates of the variances and covariances.

As for the estimate of σ^2, let us consider

$$s^2 = \frac{\Sigma(x_i - \bar{x})^2}{n - 1}$$

$$E(s^2) = \sigma^2$$

$$V(s^2) = \frac{2\sigma^4}{n - 1}$$

which shows that the minimum variance $2\sigma^4/n$ is not attained. But this is the minimum attainable, as shown below. If any estimate of σ^2 differs from s^2 by $f(s, \bar{x})$, then

$$\int f(s, \bar{x}) \exp\left[\frac{-\{n(\bar{x} - \mu)^2 + (n - 1)s^2\}}{2\sigma^2} \right] dv = 0$$

Twice differentiation with respect to μ leads to the result

$$E\{(\bar{x} - \mu)^2 f(s, \bar{x})\} = 0$$

Differentiation with respect to σ^2 gives

$$E\{n(\bar{x} - \mu)^2 f(s, \bar{x}) + (n - 1)s^2 f(s, \bar{x})\} = 0$$

or

$$\operatorname{cov}\,[s^2, f(s, \bar{x})] = 0$$

Consider

$$V[s^2 + f(\bar{x}, s)] = V(s^2) + V[f(s, \bar{x})]$$

which means that $V(s^2)$ is the least possible. Thus $\bar{x}$ and s^2 are the best unbiased estimates of μ and σ^2.

4a.9 Properties of Distributions Admitting Sufficient Statistics: Several Parameters

It has been shown by Koopman (1936) that under some general conditions the distribution function $\phi(x_1, \cdots, x_r \mid \theta_1, \cdots, \theta_q)$ admitting a set of statistics $T_1, \cdots, T_s$ sufficient for $\theta_1, \cdots, \theta_q$ can be expressed in the form

$$\phi = \exp [\Theta_1 X_1 + \Theta_2 X_2 + \cdots + \Theta_q X_q + \Theta + X]$$

where X depends on T only and Θ on θ only. Using the relation

$$\int \phi \, dv = 1$$

we find on suitable differentiations

$$E(X_i) = -\frac{\partial \Theta}{\partial \Theta_i}$$

$$V(X_i) = -\frac{\partial^2 \Theta}{\partial \Theta_i^2}$$

$$\operatorname{cov}(X_i X_j) = -\frac{\partial^2 \Theta}{\partial \Theta_i \partial \Theta_j}$$

The element I_{ij} of the information matrix for the functions $\theta_i' = \Theta_i$, $(i = 1, \cdots, q)$, is

$$E\left(-\frac{\partial^2 \log \phi}{\partial \theta_i' \partial \theta_j'}\right) = -\frac{\partial^2 \Theta}{\partial \theta_i' \partial \theta_j'}$$

If (I^{ij}) is the matrix inverse to (I_{ij}), then the minimum possible variance for an estimate of the parameter $-\partial \Theta / \partial \Theta_i$ is

$$\Sigma\Sigma I^{mn} \frac{\partial^2 \Theta}{\partial \Theta_m \partial \Theta_i} \frac{\partial^2 \Theta}{\partial \Theta_n \partial \Theta_i} = \Sigma\Sigma I^{mn} I_{mi} I_{in} = \sum_m I_{mi} \sum_n I^{mn} I_{in} = I_{ii} = V(X_i)$$

so that the minimum variance (4a.8.3) is attainable for the estimates of $-\partial \Theta / \partial \Theta_i$, $(i = 1, \cdots, q)$. This shows that, when sufficient statistics equal in number to the unknown parameters exist, it is possible to find functions of parameters which admit estimates with the minimum variance (4a.8.3).

Example. For the example considered in 4a.8, ϕ can be expressed

$$\phi = \exp\left[-\frac{n(\bar{x} - \mu)^2}{2\sigma^2} - \frac{(n-1)s^2}{2\sigma^2} - n \log \sigma + X \right]$$

$$= \exp\left[\frac{n\bar{x}\mu}{\sigma^2} - \frac{(n-1)s^2 + n\bar{x}^2}{2\sigma^2} - \frac{n\mu^2}{2\sigma^2} - n \log \sigma + X \right]$$

$$\Theta_1 = \frac{\mu}{\sigma^2} \qquad \Theta_2 = -\frac{1}{2\sigma^2} \qquad \Theta = -\left(n \log \sigma + \frac{n\mu^2}{2\sigma^2} \right)$$

$$\frac{\partial \Theta}{\partial \mu} = -\frac{n\mu}{\sigma^2} = \frac{\partial \Theta}{\partial \Theta_1}\frac{\partial \Theta_1}{\partial \mu} + \frac{\partial \Theta}{\partial \Theta_2}\frac{\partial \Theta_2}{\partial \mu} = \frac{\partial \Theta}{\partial \Theta_1}\frac{1}{\sigma^2}$$

or

$$-\frac{\partial \Theta}{\partial \Theta_1} = n\mu$$

Similarly,

$$-\frac{\partial \Theta}{\partial \Theta_2} = n(\mu^2 + \sigma^2)$$

The parametric functions μ and $(\mu^2 + \sigma^2)$ admit estimation with the minimum possible variance. Their estimates are $\bar{x}$ and $\{(n-1)s^2 + n\bar{x}^2\}/n$. It is seen in the previous example that $\bar{x}$ and s^2 are the best for μ and σ^2. In general, it can be proved that any function of the sufficient set of statistics has the minimum attainable variance as an estimate of its expected value.

This fundamental concept of sufficient statistics is due to R. A. Fisher, who recommended, as a first step in any methodological problem, the replacement of a sample by an exhaustive set of sufficient statistics. It is already known that *efficient* estimates derived by the method of maximum likelihood are functions of sufficient statistics. The author has shown (Rao, 1945) that minimum variance estimates must necessarily be functions of sufficient statistics. The 1945 paper contains the bulk of the matter (on limits to variance) treated in 4a.

4b   Estimation by the Method of Maximum Likelihood

4b.1   The Principle of Maximum Likelihood

If ϕ is the probability density of the observations, then the likelihood * of the parameters' occurring in ϕ is defined to be any function

---

* In statistical literature the term "likelihood of the observations" is often wrongly used to mean the probability density of the observations. The probability density for a given set of observations may be considered as a function of the parameters which is otherwise termed as the likelihood of the parameters.

proportional to ϕ, the constant of proportionality being independent of the parameters. The principle of maximum likelihood consists in accepting as the best estimate of the parameters those values of the parameters which maximize the likelihood for a given set of observations. The estimates thus obtained from a primitive postulate satisfy some optimum properties which are considered below.

If $T_1, \cdots, T_m$ constitute a minimal set of sufficient statistics, then ϕ is of the form

$$\phi = P_1(T_1, \cdots, T_m \mid \theta_1, \cdots, \theta_q) P_2(x_1, x_2, \cdots \mid T_1, \cdots, T_m)$$

so that maximizing ϕ is equivalent to maximizing $P_1(T \mid \theta)$. The estimates of the parameters are necessarily functions of these sufficient statistics. This shows that the maximum likelihood estimates satisfy the necessary condition for possessing the minimum attainable variance. Under some conditions, when the number of sufficient statistics is equal to the number of parameters to be estimated, it was shown in 4a.9 that this is a sufficient condition for minimum variance estimates of suitably chosen parametric functions to exist. The existence of sufficient statistics equal in number to the parameters to be estimated is rare, and it is of importance to study what properties the maximum likelihood estimates obey in general.

4b.2 Consistency and Bias

A statistic t_n, a function of the n observations in the sample, is said to be a consistent estimate of a parameter θ if, for any two positive numbers δ and ϵ, a number n_0 exists such that when n exceeds n_0 the probability that

$$\left| t_n - \theta \right| > \delta$$

is less than ϵ. This implies that with the increase in n, the sample size, the chance that the difference between the statistic t_n and the parameter θ will exceed any given amount decreases. If such statistics are used, the accuracy of the estimate increases with the increase in the observations, and ultimately the true value of the parameter is approached.

The property of consistency can be simply expressed as

$$P\{\left| t_n - \theta \right| < \delta\} > 1 - \epsilon$$

or $t_n \to \theta$ stochastically. This must be differentiated from the mathematical limit where the property $\left| t_n - \theta \right| < \delta$ holds unconditionally when $n > n_0$. In a stochastic limit the statistic t_n can differ from θ by more than δ when $n > n_0$, but it does so with a frequency tending to zero as n becomes large. If n_0, so determined, is independent of θ in an interval (a, b) the consistency is said to be uniform in (a, b).

It may be noted that consistency does not imply unbiasedness of the statistic for any given sample size; it may not be so even in the limit. Since only moderately large sample sizes are met with in practice, it is important to calculate the bias in any estimate and correct for it, if possible. In some cases the bias may be ignored if it is known to be small enough not to invalidate any inference drawn by using the estimate.

Example 1.   Consider the sample of n observations from a normal population. The m.l. (maximum likelihood) estimate of σ^2 is $\Sigma(x_i - \bar{x})^2/n$ which has the expected value $(n - 1)\sigma^2/n$, so that there is some underestimation. In such a case the bias can be corrected by using the estimate $\Sigma(x_i - x)^2/(n - 1)$ whose expectation is exactly σ^2. Such a correction is unimportant when the sample is large.

Example 2.   Consider n observations from the Cauchy distribution. It was shown in 2a.7 that the mean of n observations has the same probability density as that of a single observation. The probability of

$$\left| \bar{x} - \mu \right| > \delta$$

where δ is an assigned quantity remains the same for any n so that $\bar{x}$ is not consistent for μ.

Example 3.   A statistic T_n such that

$$E(T_n) = \theta_n \to \theta \qquad \text{and} \qquad V(T_n) \to 0 \qquad \text{as} \qquad n \to \infty$$

is consistent.

To prove this we shall first prove a lemma due to Tschebyscheff.

Lemma.   If x is a stochastic variable such that $E(x) = \mu$ and $V(x) = \sigma^2$, then

$$P(\left| x - \mu \right| > \delta) < \frac{\sigma^2}{\delta^2}$$

where δ^2 is any assigned quantity.

Proof.   If $f(x)$ denotes the probability density of x, then

$$\sigma^2 = \int_{-\infty}^{+\infty} (x - \mu)^2 f(x) \, dx$$

$$\geq \int_{-\infty}^{\mu-\delta} (x - \mu)^2 f(x) \, dx + \int_{\mu+\delta}^{+\infty} (x - \mu)^2 f(x) \, dx$$

$$\geq \delta^2 \left[\int_{-\infty}^{\mu-\delta} f(x) \, dx + \int_{\mu+\delta}^{+\infty} f(x) \, dx \right]$$

Hence the lemma. Using this lemma in the above problem we have

$$P(|T_n - \theta_n| < \delta) > 1 - \frac{V(T_n)}{\delta^2}$$

If $|T_n - \theta_n| < \delta$, then $|T_n - \theta| < \delta + |\theta - \theta_n|$ and

$$P(|T_n - \theta| < \delta + |\theta - \theta_n|) > P(|T_n - \theta_n| < \delta) > 1 - \frac{V(T_n)}{\delta^2}$$

Since $\theta_n \to \theta$ and $V(T_n) \to 0$, there exists an n_0 such that for all $n > n_0$

$$|\theta - \theta_n| < \delta_1 \quad \text{and} \quad V(T_n) < \delta^2 \epsilon$$

If $|T_n - \theta| < \delta + |\theta - \theta_n|$, then $|T_n - \theta| < \delta + \delta_1$; therefore for $n > n_0$

$$P(|T_n - \theta| < \delta + \delta_1) > P(|T_n - \theta| < \delta + |\theta - \theta_n|) > 1 - \epsilon$$

Since δ and δ_1 are arbitrary, the result is established. It may be inferred that the stochastic convergence is uniform if the mathematical convergence of $E(T_n)$ and $V(T_n)$ is uniform.

Example 4. Consider the bivariate normal distribution

$$\text{const. exp} - \frac{1}{2(1 - \rho^2)}$$

$$\left[\frac{(x - \mu_1)^2}{\sigma_1{}^2} - \frac{2\rho(x - \mu_1)(y - \mu_2)}{\sigma_1 \sigma_2} + \frac{(y - \mu_2)^2}{\sigma_2{}^2} \right] dx \, dy$$

The bivariate moment μ_{rs} is defined by

$$E(x - \mu_1)^r (y - \mu_2)^s = \sigma_1{}^r \sigma_2{}^s E(\xi^r \eta^s)$$

where

$$E(\xi^r \eta^s) = \text{const.} \int \exp\left[-\frac{1}{2(1 - \rho^2)} (\xi^2 - 2\rho\xi\eta + \eta^2) \right] \xi^r \eta^s \, d\xi \, d\eta$$

$$= \text{const.} \int \xi^r e^{-\frac{1}{2}\xi^2} d\xi \int \eta^s \exp\left[-\frac{1}{2(1 - \rho^2)} (\eta - \rho\xi)^2 \right] d\eta$$

$$= \alpha^s \nu_r \nu_s + s\alpha^{s-1} \rho \nu_{s-1} \nu_{r+1} + {}^s c_2 \alpha^{s-2} \rho^2 \nu_{s-2} \nu_{r+2} + \cdots$$

$$= \alpha^r \nu_r \nu_s + r\alpha^{r-1} \rho \nu_{r-1} \nu_{s+1} + \cdots \qquad \text{(by symmetry)}$$

where

$$\alpha = (1 - \rho^2)^{\frac{1}{2}}$$

$$\nu_t = \frac{1}{\sqrt{2\pi}} \int_{-\infty}^{+\infty} x^t e^{-x^2/2}\, dx = 0 \qquad \text{if } t \text{ is odd}$$

$$= \frac{[t!\,2^{-t/2}]}{(t/2)!} \qquad \text{if } t \text{ is even}$$

It is easy to see that the expression for $E(\xi^r \eta^s)$ vanishes whenever $(r + s)$ is odd. We thus obtain

$$\mu_{20} = \sigma_1{}^2 \qquad \mu_{02} = \sigma_2{}^2 \qquad \mu_{11} = \rho\sigma_1\sigma_2$$

$$\mu_{40} = 3\sigma_1{}^4 \qquad \mu_{04} = 3\sigma_2{}^4 \qquad \mu_{13} = 3\rho\sigma_1\sigma_2{}^3$$

$$\mu_{31} = 3\rho\sigma_1{}^3\sigma_2 \qquad \mu_{22} = (1 + 2\rho^2)\sigma_1{}^2\sigma_2{}^2 \qquad \text{and so on}$$

The ratio y/x is called an index. To determine the moments of y/x it can be formally expanded.

$$\frac{y}{x} = \frac{\mu_2}{\mu_1}\left(1 + \frac{\eta}{\mu_2}\right)\left(1 + \frac{\xi}{\mu_1}\right)^{-1}$$

$$= \frac{\mu_2}{\mu_1}\left\{1 - \frac{\xi}{\mu_1} + \frac{\xi^2}{\mu_1{}^2} - \cdots + \frac{\eta}{\mu_2}\left(1 - \frac{\xi}{\mu_1} + \frac{\xi^2}{\mu_1{}^2} - \cdots\right)\right\}$$

Taking expectations of both sides,

$$E\left(\frac{y}{x}\right) = \frac{\mu_2}{\mu_1}\left\{1 + \frac{\mu_{20}}{\mu_1{}^2} + \frac{\mu_{40}}{\mu_1{}^4} + \cdots - \frac{\mu_{11}}{\mu_1\mu_2} - \frac{\mu_{31}}{\mu_1{}^3\mu_2} - \cdots\right\}$$

$$= \frac{\mu_2}{\mu_1}\left\{\sum_0^\infty \frac{(2t)!\,2^{-t}v_1{}^{2t}}{t!} - \rho v_2 \sum_0^\infty \frac{(2t+2)!\,2^{-(t+1)}v_1{}^{2t+1}}{(t+1)!}\right\}$$

$$= \frac{\mu_2}{\mu_1}\left\{1 + (v_1 - \rho v_2)\sum_1^\infty \frac{(2t)!\,2^{-t}v_1{}^{2t-1}}{t!}\right\}$$

where v_1 and v_2 are the coefficients of variation of x and y, respectively. The series on the right-hand side converges only when the coefficient of variation v_1 is small.

If n pairs of observations on x and y are available, we can construct two statistics

$$T_1 = \frac{1}{n}\Sigma\frac{y_i}{x_i} \qquad T_2 = \frac{\bar{y}}{\bar{x}}$$

$$E(T_1) = \frac{\mu_2}{\mu_1}\left\{1 + (v_1 - \rho v_2)\sum_1^\infty \frac{(2t)!\,2^{-t}v_1{}^{2t-1}}{t!}\right\}$$

$$E(T_2) = \frac{\mu_2}{\mu_1}\left\{1 + \frac{1}{\sqrt{n}}(v_1 - \rho v_2)\Sigma\frac{(2t)!\,2^{-t}}{t!}\left(\frac{v_1}{\sqrt{n}}\right)^{2t-1}\right\}$$

since the coefficient of variation of $\bar{x}$ is $v_1/\sqrt{n}$ and of y is $v_2/\sqrt{n}$. It is seen that $E(T_2) \to \mu_2/\mu_1$ while $E(T_1)$ remains the same for all n and since both have variances of $O\left(\dfrac{1}{n}\right)$, T_2 converges stochastically to μ_2/μ_1 and T_1 to some other value.

T_1 is a biased estimate of μ_2/μ_1 and does not admit a simple correction for bias. Since the bias does not tend to zero as $n \to \infty$, it should be considered inconsistent as an estimate of the parametric function μ_2/μ_1. On the other hand, T_2 is a consistent estimate of the ratio.

In biometric work, extensive use is made of the indices, and in many cases the *mean index* is calculated by taking the ratio of the mean values of two characters. The estimate so obtained is not strictly comparable with that obtained by taking the average of all indices. The expected value of the index may be different from the ratio of the expected values of the two characters for which T_2 is a good estimate. The index should be treated as a separate character for evaluation of its constants, mean, standard deviation, etc. A comparison of the indices involves the comparison of a function of both the mean values and second-order moments.

4b.3   The Concept of Efficiency

Of all statistics which converge stochastically to a parameter θ, the practically important ones are those that converge rapidly. Such statistics give large deviations from the true value less frequently, at least in large samples, thus satisfying the requirements of a good estimate considered in 4b.2. We need, then, a criterion for judging which of two statistics converges more rapidly. If only statistics which are asymptotically normally distributed are considered, then the rapidity of convergence is measured by invariance or the reciprocal of variance. This is because in a normal distribution the probability of a departure exceeding λ times the standard deviation is a decreasing function of λ only, so that the probability of a departure's exceeding a given value decreases with decrease in the variance. Therefore that statistic with the smallest asymptotic variance is preferred and is called the efficient estimate. The efficiency of any other estimate can be measured by the ratio of variance of the efficient estimate to that of the other.

Efficiency, though linked with minimum variance, is essentially a large sample concept. Statistics with minimum variances considered in 4a are, no doubt, the most efficient ones in large samples, in which case variance acquires a special significance. But in small samples there is not sufficient justification for using invariance as the criterion for selecting a good estimate.

It may be argued that the comparison is confined only to the class of statistics which are asymptotically normally distributed. This is no serious objection in view of the fact that a large class of statistics obeys this property.

The properties of minimum variance estimates considered in examples of 4a.4 hold good for efficient estimates also.

Example 1.   *Asymptotic distribution of quantiles.*   Let $f(x)\, dx$ be the probability differential of x, and define

$$F(x) = \int_{-\infty}^{x} f(x)\, dx$$

If x is the quantile of order p, $(0 < p < 1)$, in a series of n observations, then $\mu = [np]$ observations are less than x, and $(n - \mu - 1)$ are greater than $x + dx$; the remaining value falls between x and $x + dx$.   Hence the probability differential of x is

$$\frac{n!}{\mu!(n - \mu - 1)!} \{F(x)\}^{\mu}\{1 - F(x)\}^{n-\mu-1} f(x)\, dx$$

Let $y = F(x)$ so that $dy = f(x)\, dx$.   The distribution of y is

$$\frac{n!}{\mu!(n - \mu - 1)!} y^{\mu}(1 - y)^{n-\mu-1}\, dy$$

Let $z = \{\sqrt{n}(y - p)\}/\sqrt{pq}$; then the distribution of z becomes

$$\text{const.} \left(1 + \frac{z\sqrt{q}}{\sqrt{np}}\right)^{[np]} \left(1 - \frac{z\sqrt{p}}{\sqrt{nq}}\right)^{n-[np]-1} dz = \text{const.}\ e^{\psi}\, dz$$

where

$$\psi = [np] \log\left(1 + z\sqrt{\frac{q}{np}}\right) + (n - [np] - 1) \log\left(1 - z\sqrt{\frac{p}{nq}}\right) \sim -\frac{z^2}{2}$$

which shows that y is asymptotically normal with p as mean and pq/n as variance.   Since $y = F(x)$, assuming that the inverse function exists, we can write

$$x = F^{-1}(y) = \phi(y)$$

or, expanding at $y = p$,

$$x = \phi(p) + (y - p)\phi'(p) + \frac{(y - p)^2}{2!} \phi''(p) + \cdots$$

Neglecting terms of the order $(y - p)^2$, we find that x is distributed normally in large samples with mean $\phi(p)$ and variance $[\phi'(p)]^2 V(y)$

(see 5e.1). The value of $\phi(p) = \zeta$ is determined from the relation

$$p = \int_{-\infty}^{\zeta} f(x)\, dx$$

Also, since

$$\phi'(p) = \frac{1}{F'(\zeta)} = \frac{1}{f(\zeta)}$$

$$V(x) = [f(\zeta)]^{-2} V(y) = [f(\zeta)]^{-2} \frac{pq}{n}$$

It must be noted that convergence to normality is rapid only for quantiles of order p near about $\frac{1}{2}$. For lower or higher quantiles normality is realized only in very large samples.

Example 2. Efficiency of the median as an estimate of the mean of a normal population. For a normal population the average of the observations is the most efficient estimate of the mean, and its variance is σ^2/n. The asymptotic variance of the median is

$$\frac{[f(\mu)]^{-2}}{4n}$$

where $f(\mu)$, the ordinate at the mean of the normal distribution, is equal to $1/\sqrt{2\pi}\sigma$. The variance of the median is

$$\frac{\pi\sigma^2}{2n}$$

so that its efficiency is $2/\pi$ or 63.7%.

4b.4 Some Optimum Properties of Maximum Likelihood Estimates

Let $f(x, \theta)\, dx$ be the probability distribution from which a sample of size n, $(x_1, \cdots, x_n)$, is observed. We shall denote $f(x_i, \theta)$ by f_i and the product by L. The following assumptions are made.

(i) The derivatives $\partial \log L/\partial\theta$ and $\partial^2 \log L/\partial\theta^2$ exist and are continuous for every θ in a range R, including the true value, and for almost all x. For every θ in R,

$$\left| \frac{\partial \log L}{\partial \theta} \right| < F_1(x) \qquad \left| \frac{\partial^2 \log L}{\partial \theta^2} \right| < F_2(x)$$

where F_1 and F_2 are integrable functions over $(-\infty, +\infty)$.

(ii) The derivative $\partial^3 \log L / \partial\theta^3$ exists and is such that

$$\left| \frac{\partial^3 \log L}{\partial\theta^3} \right| < M(x) \qquad E\{M(x)\} < K \qquad \text{(a positive quantity)}$$

(iii) For every θ in R,

$$\int_{-\infty}^{+\infty} - \frac{\partial^2 \log L}{\partial\theta^2} L \, dx \equiv I(\theta)$$

is finite and non-zero.

(iv) The range of integration is independent of θ.

Under these conditions the following theorems will be proved.

Theorem 1. With probability approaching unity as $n \to \infty$, the likelihood equation $\partial \log L / \partial\theta = 0$ has a solution which converges in probability to the true value θ_0. (Dugue, 1937.)

Theorem 2. Any consistent solution of the likelihood equation provides a maximum of the likelihood with probability tending to unity as the sample size tends to infinity. (Huzurbazar, 1948.)

Theorem 3. A consistent solution of the likelihood equation is asymptotically normally distributed about the true value θ. (Cramér, 1946.)

Some of the limiting theorems used in this connection are given without proof in an appendix at the end of this chapter. Under the conditions assumed we have, following Cramér (1946),

$$\frac{\partial \log L}{\partial\theta} = \left(\frac{\partial \log L}{\partial\theta} \right)_{\theta=\theta_0} + (\theta - \theta_0) \left(\frac{\partial^2 \log L}{\partial\theta^2} \right)_{\theta_0} + \frac{(\theta - \theta_0)^2}{2} \left(\frac{\partial^3 \log L}{\partial\theta^3} \right)_{\theta'}$$

where θ' lies in (θ, θ_0). Dividing both sides by n, we have

$$\frac{1}{n} \frac{\partial \log L}{\partial\theta} = B_0 + B_1(\theta - \theta_0) + \frac{B_2}{2} (\theta - \theta_0)^2$$

where

$$B_0 = \frac{1}{n} \sum_1^n \left(\frac{\partial \log f_i}{\partial\theta} \right)_{\theta_0} \qquad E(B_0) = 0$$

$$B_1 = \frac{1}{n} \sum_1^n \left(\frac{\partial^2 \log f_i}{\partial\theta^2} \right)_{\theta_0} \qquad E(B_1) = -\frac{I(\theta)}{n} \qquad \text{where } I(\theta) \text{ is the information}$$

$$B_2 = \frac{1}{n} \sum_1^n \left(\frac{\partial^3 \log f_i}{\partial\theta^3} \right)_{\theta'}$$

By Kintchine's theorem the quantities B_0, B_1, and B_2 stochastically converge to their mean values. Given two quantities δ and ϵ, it is possible to find $n > n_0(\delta, \epsilon)$ such that

$$P_1 = P\{|\ B_0\ | \geq \delta^2\} < \frac{\epsilon}{3}$$

$$P_2 = P\left\{B_1 \geq -\frac{1}{2}\frac{I(\theta)}{n}\right\} < \frac{\epsilon}{3}$$

$$P_3 = P\{|\ B_2\ | \geq 2K\} < \frac{\epsilon}{3}$$

The probability that the sample point is such that the inequalities

$$|\ B_0\ | < \delta^2 \qquad B_1 < -\frac{1}{2}\frac{I(\theta)}{n} \qquad |\ B_2\ | < 2K$$

are simultaneously satisfied is evidently greater than $1 - P_1 - P_2 - P_3\ (= 1 - \epsilon)$. Let S denote the set of such points.
For $\theta = \theta_0 \pm \delta$

$$\frac{\partial \log L}{\partial \theta} = B_0 \pm \delta B_1 + \frac{1}{2}B_2\delta^2$$

For every point in S, $B_0 + \frac{1}{2}B_2\delta^2 < (K + 1)\delta^2$, and $B_1\delta < -\frac{1}{2}[I(\theta)]\delta/2n$. If $\delta < [I(\theta)/2n(K + 1)]$, the sign of the whole expression for $\theta = \theta_0 \pm \delta$ will be determined by $B_1\delta$ so that $(\partial \log L/\partial \theta) > 0$ for $\theta = \theta_0 - \delta$ and $(\partial \log L/\partial \theta) < 0$ for $\theta = \theta_0 + \delta$. Since $\partial \log L/\partial \theta$ is a continuous function of θ in R, for almost all x, it follows that the likelihood equation has a root in $\theta_0 \pm \delta$ with probability tending to unity. This establishes theorem 1.

Let $\hat{\theta}$ be a consistent solution of the likelihood equation so that

$$P\{|\ \hat{\theta} - \theta_0\ | < \gamma\} \to 1 \qquad \text{as } n \to \infty$$

By the mean value theorem

$$\frac{1}{n}\frac{\partial^2 \log L}{\partial \hat{\theta}^2} - \frac{1}{n}\frac{\partial^2 \log L}{\partial \theta_0{}^2} = \frac{1}{n}\left(\frac{\partial^3 \log L}{\partial \theta_1{}^3}\right)(\hat{\theta} - \theta_0)$$

Hence the modulus of the left-hand side is less than $K\gamma$ with probability tending to unity, which means that $(1/n)(\partial^2 \log L/\partial \hat{\theta}^2)$ converges in probability to $(1/n)(\partial^2 \log L/\partial \theta_0{}^2)$ which tends to $-i(\theta_0)$, where $i(\theta_0)$ is the information per single observation. Therefore, for any arbitrarily small ϵ' we have

$$P\left(\frac{1}{n}\frac{\partial^2 \log L}{\partial\hat{\theta}^2} < -i(\theta_0) + \epsilon'\right) \to 1 \quad \text{as } n \to \infty$$

The quantity $-i(\theta_0)$ is fixed and negative and for small ϵ', $-i(\theta_0) + \epsilon'$ is also negative. Therefore

$$P\left(\frac{1}{n}\frac{\partial^2 \log L}{\partial\hat{\theta}^2} < 0\right) \to 1$$

i.e.,

$$P\left(\frac{\partial^2 \log L}{\partial\hat{\theta}^2} < 0\right) \to 1 \quad \text{as } n \to \infty$$

This shows that the probability that the likelihood is a maximum at $\hat{\theta}$ approaches certainty as n tends to ∞, thus establishing theorem 2.

If $\hat{\theta}_1$ and $\hat{\theta}_2$ are two consistent solutions of the likelihood equation, it follows from Rolle's theorem that $\partial^2 \log L/\partial\theta^2 = 0$ has at least one solution θ_3 lying between $\hat{\theta}_1$ and $\hat{\theta}_2$. Since $\hat{\theta}_1$ and $\hat{\theta}_2$ converge to θ_0 in probability, θ_3 also does. Therefore

$$P\left\{\frac{\partial^2 \log L}{\partial\theta_3{}^2} < 0\right\} \to 1 \quad \text{as } n \to \infty$$

which is a contradiction because $\partial^2 \log L/\partial\theta_3{}^2 \equiv 0$. We thus obtain the following corollary.

Corollary. A consistent solution of the likelihood equation is unique.

Wald (1949) has recently proved that the solution of the likelihood equation which makes the likelihood function an absolute maximum is necessarily consistent. This is more powerful than theorem 2 which says that the likelihood has a relative maximum at the unique consistent solution of the likelihood equation. This proof is not given here.

Let the consistent solution of the likelihood equation be denoted by $\hat{\theta}$. We have

$$\sqrt{I(\theta_0)}(\hat{\theta} - \theta_0) = \frac{\dfrac{1}{\sqrt{I(\theta_0)}}\Sigma\left(\dfrac{\partial \log f_i}{\partial\theta}\right)_{\theta_0}}{-\dfrac{nB_1}{I(\theta_0)} - \dfrac{nB_2(\hat{\theta} - \theta_0)}{2I(\theta_0)}}$$

The denominator of the right-hand fraction converges to 1 in probability. By the Lindeberg-Levy theorem the sum $\sum_1^n (\partial \log f_i/\partial\theta)_\theta$ is asymptotically normal with zero mean and variance $I(\theta)$. Therefore the numerator is asymptotically normal with zero mean and unit variance. Finally, it follows from the convergence theorem 1 in the appendix that the ratio $\sqrt{I(\theta_0)}(\hat{\theta} - \theta_0)$ is asymptotically normal with zero mean and unit variance. This means that $\hat{\theta}$ is distributed about θ_0 with the variance $1/I(\theta_0)$. Since this is the minimum possible variance, we have the following result, when $E(\hat{\theta})$ and $V(\hat{\theta})$ exist.

Corollary. The consistent solution of the maximum likelihood equation is fully efficient.

4c   Some Examples of Maximum Likelihood Estimates

4c.1   Improved Estimates of Means from Incomplete Data on Several Variables

Suppose that each individual of a population is characterized by two measurements but in a sample only one measurement is recorded in some cases. Thus, out of a total of $N = (n_1 + n_2 + n)$ individuals observed, n_1 of them may provide the first measurement alone, n_2 the second alone, and n both the measurements. The characteristics of, say, the first measurement, such as the mean, scatter, etc., can be estimated from the available set of $(n_1 + n)$ observations on the first measurement alone. If the two measurements are correlated, it is possible that the observations on the second measurement may throw some more information on the characteristics of the first. If this is so, the estimates of the characteristics of any particular measurement obtained by taking all the data into account will be more accurate than those obtained from the available set of observations on that particular measurement alone.

Assuming normal distributions for the measurements, the probability density of the observations can be written

$$\text{const. exp} -\frac{1}{2}\left[\frac{\Sigma_1(x - \mu_1)^2}{\sigma_1{}^2} + \frac{1}{(1 - \rho^2)}\right.$$

$$\left\{\frac{\Sigma(x - \mu_1)^2}{\sigma_1{}^2} - \frac{2\rho\Sigma(x - \mu_1)(y - \mu_2)}{\sigma_1\sigma_2} + \frac{\Sigma(y - \mu_2)^2}{\sigma_2{}^2}\right\} + \frac{\Sigma_2(y - \mu_2)^2}{\sigma_2{}^2}\right]$$

where x and y are the two measurements, μ_1 and μ_2 their mean values, σ_1, σ_2, and ρ the standard deviations and the correlation coefficient between x and y, Σ_1 the summation over the n_1 observations, Σ_2 the summation over the n_2 observations, and Σ the summation over the common set of n observations.

Equating the derivatives of the logarithm of the likelihood with respect to μ_1 and μ_2 to zero,

$$S_1 = \frac{\Sigma_1(x - \mu_1)}{\sigma_1^2} + \frac{1}{1 - \rho^2}\left\{\frac{\Sigma(x - \mu_1)}{\sigma_1^2} - \frac{\rho\Sigma(y - \mu_2)}{\sigma_1\sigma_2}\right\} = 0$$

$$S_2 = \frac{\Sigma_2(y - \mu_2)}{\sigma_2^2} + \frac{1}{1 - \rho^2}\left\{\frac{\Sigma(y - \mu_2)}{\sigma_2^2} - \frac{\rho\Sigma(x - \mu_1)}{\sigma_1\sigma_2}\right\} = 0$$

or

$$\mu_1\left\{\frac{n_1}{\sigma_1} + \frac{n}{\sigma_1(1 - \rho^2)}\right\} - \frac{\rho}{1 - \rho^2}\frac{n\mu_2}{\sigma_2} = \frac{\Sigma_1 x}{\sigma_1} + \frac{1}{1 - \rho^2}\left\{\frac{\Sigma x}{\sigma_1} - \frac{\rho\Sigma y}{\sigma_2}\right\}$$

$$-\frac{\rho}{1 - \rho^2}\frac{n\mu_1}{\sigma_1} + \mu_2\left\{\frac{n_2}{\sigma_2} + \frac{n}{\sigma_2(1 - \rho^2)}\right\} = \frac{\Sigma_2 y}{\sigma_2} + \frac{1}{1 - \rho^2}\left\{\frac{\Sigma y}{\sigma_2} - \frac{\rho\Sigma x}{\sigma_1}\right\}$$

These are simultaneous equations giving the estimates of μ_1 and μ_2 when σ_1, σ_2, and ρ are known. The equations giving the estimates of σ_1, σ_2, and ρ are complicated, but the following estimates may be safely used when the sample sizes are moderately large.

$$\sigma_1^2 = \left\{\Sigma_1 x^2 + \Sigma x^2 - \frac{(\Sigma_1 x + \Sigma x)^2}{n_1 + n}\right\} \div (n_1 + n - 1)$$

$$\sigma_2^2 = \left\{\Sigma_2 y^2 + \Sigma y^2 - \frac{(\Sigma_1 y + \Sigma y)^2}{n_2 + n}\right\} \div (n_2 + n - 1)$$

$$\rho = \left\{\Sigma xy - \frac{(\Sigma x)(\Sigma y)}{n}\right\} \div \sqrt{\left\{\Sigma x^2 - \frac{(\Sigma x)^2}{n}\right\}\left\{\Sigma y^2 - \frac{(\Sigma y)^2}{n}\right\}}$$

To obtain the measures of accuracy of the estimates of μ_1 and μ_2 the information matrix is derived.

$$(I_{ij}) = \begin{bmatrix} E(S_1^2) & E(S_1 S_2) \\ E(S_1 S_2) & E(S_2^2) \end{bmatrix}$$

$$= \begin{bmatrix} \dfrac{n_1}{\sigma_1^2} + \dfrac{n}{\sigma_1^2(1 - \rho^2)} & \dfrac{-n\rho}{\sigma_1\sigma_2(1 - \rho^2)} \\[2ex] \dfrac{-n\rho}{\sigma_1\sigma_2(1 - \rho^2)} & \dfrac{n_2}{\sigma_2^2} + \dfrac{n}{\sigma_2^2(1 - \rho^2)} \end{bmatrix}$$

$$(I^{ij}) = \begin{bmatrix} \dfrac{[n_2(1 - \rho^2) + n]\sigma_1^2}{\Delta} & -\dfrac{n\rho\sigma_1\sigma_2}{\Delta} \\[2ex] -\dfrac{n\rho\sigma_1\sigma_2}{\Delta} & \dfrac{[n_1(1 - \rho^2) + n]\sigma_2^2}{\Delta} \end{bmatrix}$$

where $\Delta = (n + n_1)(n + n_2) - \rho^2 n_1 n_2$. If m_1 and m_2 are the estimates of μ_1 and μ_2, then

$$V(m_1) = \frac{n_2(1 - \rho^2) + n}{(n + n_1)(n + n_2) - \rho^2 n_1 n_2} \sigma_1^2$$

$$V(m_2) = \frac{n_1(1 - \rho^2) + n}{(n + n_1)(n + n_2) - \rho^2 n_1 n_2} \sigma_2^2$$

The estimate of μ_1 obtained from the mean of $(n + n_1)$ observations on the first measurement has the variance $\sigma_1^2/(n + n_1)$ so that the efficiency of this estimate is

$$\frac{n + n_1}{1} \quad \frac{(n + n_2) - \rho^2 n_2}{(n + n_1)(n + n_2) - \rho^2 n_1 n_2}$$

$$= \left\{ 1 - \frac{n_2}{n + n_2} \rho^2 \right\} \div \left\{ 1 - \frac{n_1 n_2}{(n + n_1)(n + n_2)} \rho^2 \right\}$$

Of 188 skeletons of Anglo-Saxons (Münter, 1936) 103 provided maximum lengths of both the right and left femora, 48 of the right femur alone, and 37 of the left. The 151 observations on the right femur gave the estimates

$$\text{Mean} = 463.3 \qquad s_1 = 22.4 \text{ *}$$

and the 140 observations on the left femur gave the estimates

$$\text{Mean} = 465.7 \qquad s_2 = 24.4$$

The 103 pairs of observations gave the estimated correlation $r = 0.9835$. The equations for the combined estimates m_1 and m_2 of μ_1 and μ_2 are

$$m_1 \left\{ \frac{n_1}{s_1} + \frac{n}{s_1(1 - r^2)} \right\} - m_2 \frac{r}{1 - r^2} \frac{1}{s_2} = \frac{\Sigma_1 x}{s_1} + \frac{1}{1 - r^2} \left\{ \frac{\Sigma x}{s_1} - r \frac{\Sigma y}{s_2} \right\}$$

$$- m_1 \frac{r}{1 - r^2} \frac{n}{s_1} + m_2 \left\{ \frac{n_2}{s_2} + \frac{n}{s_2(1 - r^2)} \right\} = \frac{\Sigma_2 y}{s_2} + \frac{1}{1 - r^2} \left\{ \frac{\Sigma y}{s_2} - r \frac{\Sigma x}{s_1} \right\}$$

In this example

$$\frac{n_1}{s_1} = \frac{48}{22.4} = 2.1428 \qquad \frac{n_2}{s_2} = \frac{37}{24.4} = 1.5164$$

$$\frac{n}{s_1(1 - r^2)} = \frac{103}{22.4(1 - 0.9835^2)} = 140.4989$$

$$\frac{n}{s_2(1 - r^2)} = \frac{103}{24.4(1 - 0.9835^2)} = 128.9826$$

* The estimates of σ_1, σ_2, and ρ are represented by s_1, s_2, and r, respectively.

$\Sigma_1 x = 21851.4$ (The sum of observations on 48 maximum lengths of right femora)

$\Sigma_2 y = 16999.3$ (The sum of observations on 37 maximum lengths of left femora)

$\Sigma x \;\; = 48096.9$ (The sum of 103 observations on the right femur from the common set)

$\Sigma y \;\; = 48198.7$ (The sum of 103 observations on the left femur from the common set)

With these values the equations can be written

$$142.6418 m_1 - 126.8544 m_2 = 7221.5778$$

$$-138.1807 m_1 + 130.4990 m_2 = -3470.9599$$

The solutions are

$$m_1 = 462.43 \qquad m_2 = 463.06$$

The variance of m_1 is

$$\frac{n_2(1 - r^2) + n}{(n + n_1)(n + n_2) - \rho^2 n_1 n_2} s_1{}^2 = \frac{104.21093}{19422.1245} s_1{}^2 = 0.0053655 s_1{}^2$$

The standard error is

$$\sqrt{0.0053655} s_1 = 0.07324 \times 22.4 = 1.64$$

The standard error of the average of 151 observations is

$$\frac{22.4}{\sqrt{151}} = 1.79$$

which is greater than the standard error of the maximum likelihood estimate m_1, which is as efficient as the mean of about $1/0.0053655 = 186$ observations. Similarly, the standard error of $m_2 = 1.82$ and is as efficient as a mean based on about 185 observations. There is, however, some loss of efficiency due to errors in the estimates of σ_1, σ_2, and ρ, but this is very small.

This technique can be employed in many situations. For instance, the maximum length including spine cannot be obtained for all femora since the spine is usually broken. If the maximum lengths including and excluding spine are available for some femora, and only excluding spine for others, the best estimates of the means of both the measurements can be obtained by following the above procedure. If there are no observations for the maximum length including spine alone, the quantity n_1 is equated to zero in the above equations. It may happen as in 3f.2 that the skeletons providing measurements on both the right and left femora may be undersized. Using this portion of the material two prediction formulae can be derived, one for predicting the length of the left femur given that of the right, and another for predicting the length of the right femur given that of the left. With the help of the first prediction formula the average length of the left femur can be estimated for those skeletons providing measurement on the right femur only. Let this be $\bar{l}_1$, based on n_1 right femur measurements. The direct averages of the length of the left femur for the n skeletons providing both the measurements and n_2 skeletons only the left femur length are denoted by $\bar{l}$ and $\bar{l}_2$. If all three types of material are random samples from the original skeletal population, then the three estimates $\bar{l}_1$, $\bar{l}$, $\bar{l}_2$ should agree, in which case the estimate obtained by the method of maximum likelihood is the best. If they do not agree, then the estimate of the mean left femur length of the skeletal population may be obtained as

$$\frac{n_1\bar{l}_1 + n\bar{l} + n_2\bar{l}_2}{n_1 + n + n_2}$$

Similarly the mean length of the right femur can be estimated.

4c.2 The Method of Scoring for the Estimation of Parameters

The maximum likelihood equations are usually complicated so that the solutions cannot be obtained directly. A general method in such cases is to assume a trial solution and derive linear equations for small additive corrections. The process can be repeated till the corrections become negligible. A great mechanization is introduced by adopting the method known as the scoring system for obtaining the linear relations connecting the additive corrections.

The quantity $d(\log L)/d\theta$, where L is the likelihood of the parameter θ, is defined as the efficient score for θ. The maximum likelihood estimate of θ is that value of θ for which the efficient score vanishes. If θ_0 is the trial value of the estimate, then expanding $d(\log L)/d\theta$ and retaining only the first power of $\delta\theta = \theta - \theta_0$,

$$\frac{d\log L}{d\theta} \approx \frac{d\log L}{d\theta_0} + \delta\theta \frac{d^2\log L}{d\theta_0{}^2}$$

$$\approx \frac{d\log L}{d\theta_0} - \delta\theta\, I(\theta_0)$$

where $I(\theta_0)$, the information at the value $\theta = \theta_0$, is the expected value of $d^2(\log L)/d\theta^2$. In large samples the difference between $-I(\theta_0)$ and $d^2(\log L)/d\theta_0{}^2$ will be of $O(1/n)$, where n is the number of observations, so that the above approximation holds to the first order of small quantities. The correction $\delta\theta$ is obtained from the equation

$$\delta\theta \, I(\theta_0) = \frac{d \log L}{d\theta_0}$$

$$\delta\theta = \frac{d \log L}{d\theta_0} \div I(\theta_0)$$

The first approximation is $(\theta_0 + \delta\theta)$, and the above process can be repeated with this as the new trial value.

Example 1. Consider a sample of size n from the Cauchy distribution.

$$\frac{1}{\pi} \frac{dx}{1 + (x - \theta)^2}$$

The likelihood equation is

$$\frac{d \log L}{d\theta} = +\Sigma \frac{2(x_i - \theta)}{1 + (x_i - \theta)^2} = 0$$

The efficient score for any θ is

$$S(\theta) = +\Sigma \frac{2(x_i - \theta)}{1 + (x_i - \theta)^2}$$

Information for a single observation is $\frac{1}{2}$ so that the asymptotic variance is $2/n$ and the additive correction to a trial value θ_0 is

$$\frac{2S(\theta_0)}{n}$$

This process can be continued until a stable value is attained. Fortunately in the above example $I(\theta)$ happened to be independent of θ so that $I(\theta)$ need not be calculated at each trial value.

Example 2. Score and information for grouped data.

Let $\pi_1, \pi_2, \cdots, \pi_k$, $(\Sigma\pi_i = 1)$, be the probabilities in k mutually exclusive classes, and suppose that $\pi_i = \phi_i(\theta)$ so that all the proportions π_i are defined as functions of a single parameter θ. If $f_1, f_2, \cdots, f_k$ are the observed frequencies, then

$$\log L = f_1 \log \pi_1 + \cdots + f_k \log \pi_k$$

The score at θ is

$$\frac{\partial \log L}{\partial \theta} = \frac{f_1}{\pi_1} \frac{\partial \pi_1}{\partial \theta} + \cdots + \frac{f_k}{\pi_k} \frac{\partial \pi_k}{\partial \theta}$$

Information is the variance of $\partial \log L / \partial \theta$ which is a linear function of the frequencies. Hence by (2a.9.1)

$$I(\theta) = f \sum_{i=1}^{k} \frac{1}{\pi_i} \left(\frac{\partial \pi_i}{\partial \theta} \right)^2 \qquad f = f_1 + \cdots + f_k$$

The quantities

$$\frac{1}{\pi_i} \frac{\partial \pi_i}{\partial \theta} \qquad \text{and} \qquad \frac{1}{\pi_i} \left(\frac{\partial \pi_i}{\partial \theta} \right)^2$$

which may be called the score and information supplied by the ith class, are to be derived in any particular problem before proceeding with the problem of estimation.

If two factors are linked with a recombination fraction p, then the intercrosses $AB/ab \times AB/ab$ (coupling) and $Ab/aB \times Ab/aB$ (repulsion) give rise to the following expected proportions and information as given by Mather (1938).

Class	Coupling		Repulsion	
	Probability	Score	Probability	Score
	4π	$\dfrac{1}{\pi}\dfrac{d\pi}{d\theta}$	4π	$\dfrac{1}{\pi}\dfrac{d\pi}{d\theta}$
AB	$3 - 2p + p^2$	$\dfrac{-2(1-p)}{3-2p+p^2}$	$2 + p^2$	$\dfrac{2p}{2+p^2}$
Ab	$2p - p^2$	$\dfrac{2(1-p)}{2p-p^2}$	$1 - p^2$	$\dfrac{-2p}{1-p^2}$
aB	$2p - p^2$	$\dfrac{2(1-p)}{2p-p^2}$	$1 - p^2$	$\dfrac{-2p}{1-p^2}$
ab	$1 - 2p + p^2$	$\dfrac{-2(1-p)}{1-2p+p^2}$	p^2	$\dfrac{2}{p}$
Information:	$\dfrac{2(3-4p+2p^2)}{p(2-p)(3-2p+p^2)}$		$\dfrac{2(1+2p^2)}{(2+p^2)(1-p^2)}$	

The amount of information can be used to judge the relative efficiency of one type of cross with respect to the other for the estimation of the recombination fraction. For instance, if $p = \frac{1}{4}$, the amounts of information for coupling and repulsion are 3.7909 and 1.1636, respectively. This means that, using intercrosses with repulsion, the number of offsprings needed will be three times as great as that for coupling to estimate the recombination fraction with the same precision.

Consider coupling data with values for AB, Ab, aB, and ab as shown below. With the trial value $p = 0.21$, the score and information are obtained.

	4π	$4\dfrac{\partial \pi}{\partial p}$	$\dfrac{1}{\pi}\dfrac{\partial \pi}{\partial p}$	Observed Frequency
AB	2.6241	-1.58	-0.60211	125
Ab	0.3759	1.58	4.20325	18
aB	0.3759	1.58	4.20325	20
ab	0.6241	-1.58	-2.53164	34
Absolute sum			11.54025	197

$$\text{Information per observation} = \frac{1.58}{4}(11.54025) = 4.55840$$

$$\text{Efficient score} = -0.60211(125) + 4.20325(18 + 20)$$

$$- 2.53164(34)$$

$$= -1.61601$$

$$\text{Correction term} = -\frac{1.61601}{197(4.55840)} = -0.0018$$

$$\text{Second approximation} = 0.21 - 0.0018 = 0.2082$$

The correction is small so that the process may not be repeated. The variance of the estimate is given by

$$\frac{1}{197(4.55840)} = 0.00111357$$

A better estimate of the variance is the reciprocal of the information at the value $p = 0.2082$

The scores for trial values from 1 to 50% are given in Table XIV_1 of Fisher and Yates (1948). They can be directly used by retaining two decimal places at each stage of approximation, and finally when two places are stabilized a complete calculation with more places may be carried out.

Example 3. Scoring for several parameters.

The method of scoring developed in example 2 can be extended to the case of the simultaneous estimation of several parameters. If θ_1,

$\theta_2, \cdots, \theta_q$ are the parameters, the ith efficient score is defined by

$$S_i = \frac{\partial \log L}{\partial \theta_i} \qquad i = 1, 2, \cdots$$

where L is the likelihood of the parameters, and the information matrix is defined by (I_{ij}) where

$$I_{ij} = E(S_i S_j)$$

If the values of the efficient scores and information at the trial values $\theta_1^0, \cdots, \theta_q^0$ are indicated with index zero, then small additive corrections to the trial values are given by the simultaneous equations

$$I_{11}^0 \, d\theta_1 + I_{12}^0 \, d\theta_2 + \cdots + I_{1q}^0 \, d\theta_q = S_1^0$$

$$\cdot \qquad\qquad \cdot \qquad\qquad \cdots \qquad\qquad \cdot \qquad\qquad \cdot$$

$$I_{q1}^0 \, d\theta_1 + I_{q2}^0 \, d\theta_2 + \cdots + I_{qq}^0 \, d\theta_q = S_q^0$$

This operation is repeated with corrected values each time until stable values of $\theta_1, \cdots, \theta_q$ are obtained. The variance of the final estimate $\hat{\theta}_i$ of θ_i is given by I^{ii}, the co-factor of I_{ii} in the determinant $| I_{ij} |$.

In the case of grouped distributions with π_i and f_i as probability and frequency in the ith class,

$$S_t = \Sigma \frac{f_i}{\pi_i} \frac{\partial \pi_i}{\partial \theta_t}$$

and

$$I_{ut} = \Sigma \frac{1}{\pi_i} \frac{\partial \pi_i}{\partial \theta_u} \frac{\partial \pi_i}{\partial \theta_t}$$

so that the calculations become simple as illustrated below.

Blood Groups, ABO System. Every human being can be classified into one of the four blood groups O, A, B, AB. The inheritance of these blood groups is controlled by three allelomorphic genes—O, A, B—of which O is recessive to A and B. If r, p, and q are gene frequencies of O, A, and B, then the expected probabilities of the six genotypes (four phenotypes) in random mating will be

Phenotype	Genotype	Probabilities
O	OO	r^2
A	AA AO	$\left. \begin{array}{l} p^2 \\ 2pr \end{array} \right\} p^2 + 2pr$
B	BB BO	$\left. \begin{array}{l} q^2 \\ 2qr \end{array} \right\} q^2 + 2qr$
AB	AB	$2pq$

If $\bar{O}$, $\bar{A}$, $\bar{B}$ and $\overline{AB}$ are the observed frequencies adding to N, the problem is to estimate the gene frequencies p, q, and r. A rough estimate is supplied by

$$r' = \sqrt{\frac{\bar{O}}{N}}$$

$$p' = 1 - \sqrt{\frac{\bar{O} + \bar{B}}{N}}$$

$$q' = 1 - \sqrt{\frac{\bar{O} + \bar{A}}{N}}$$

These may not necessarily add to unity, whereas the true values should. Let D denote the deviation

$$- D = p' + q' + r' - 1$$

Better estimates due to Bernstein are obtained as follows.

$$r = (1 + \tfrac{1}{2}D)(r' + \tfrac{1}{2}D)$$

$$p = (1 + \tfrac{1}{2}D)p'$$

$$q = (1 + \tfrac{1}{2}D)q'$$

where p', q', r', and D are as defined above.

There is still some deviation, $(1 - p - q - r) = \tfrac{1}{4}D^2$. If this is small, then Bernstein's method supplies fairly good estimates. We shall now show how these estimates can be improved by the method of maximum likelihood, using the frequencies $\bar{O} = 176$, $\bar{A} = 182$, $\bar{B} = 60$, and $\overline{AB} = 17$. Approximate solutions obtained by Bernstein's method are

$$p = 0.26449 \qquad q = 0.09317 \qquad r = 0.64234$$

The probabilities and derivatives, with respect to the independent parameters p, and q in the general case, are

	Probability π	Derivatives $\dfrac{\partial \pi}{\partial p}$	$\dfrac{\partial \pi}{\partial q}$
O	r^2	$-2r$	$-2r$
A	$p(p + 2r)$	$2r$	$-2p$
B	$q(q + 2r)$	$-2q$	$2r$
AB	$2pq$	$2q$	$2p$

The probabilities and coefficients for the calculation of efficient scores at the approximate values obtained above are set out below.

	Probability π	Coefficients for Scores $\dfrac{1}{\pi}\dfrac{\partial\pi}{\partial p}$	$\dfrac{1}{\pi}\dfrac{\partial\pi}{\partial q}$	Observed Frequency
O	0.41260	−3.11362	− 3.11362	176
A	0.40974	3.13543	− 1.27104	182
B	0.12838	−1.45217	10.00685	60
AB	0.04928	3.75086	10.73307	17

The scores are

$$\phi_p = (-3.11362)176 + (3.13543)182 + (-1.45217)60 + (3.75086)17$$
$$= -0.20444$$
$$\phi_q = (-3.11362)176 + (-1.27104)182 + (10.00685)60 + (10.73307)17$$
$$= -0.09321$$

The information matrix * for a single observation is

$$I_{pp} = 9.00315 \qquad I_{pq} = 2.47676$$

$$I_{pq} = 2.47676 \qquad I_{qq} = 23.21612$$

Small corrections δp and δq to p and q are given by

$$N(9.00315\ \delta p + 2.47676\ \delta q) = -0.20444$$

$$N(2.47676\ \delta p + 23.21612\ \delta q) = -0.09321$$

The inverse of the information matrix per single observation is

$$I^{pp} = 0.114430 \qquad I_{pq} = -0.012208$$

$$I^{pq} = -0.012208 \qquad I^{qq} = 0.044376$$

The solutions are

$$\delta p = \frac{I^{pp}\phi_p + I^{pq}\phi_q}{N} = -0.00005116$$

$$\delta q = \frac{I^{pq}\phi_p + I^{qq}\phi_q}{N} = -0.00000377$$

The corrections are hardly necessary in this particular case. If the corrections are not small, the whole process has to be repeated with the

$$* I_{pp} = \Sigma\frac{1}{\pi}\left(\frac{\partial\pi}{\partial p}\right)^2 = \Sigma\frac{\partial\pi}{\partial p}\left(\frac{1}{\pi}\frac{\partial\pi}{\partial p}\right)$$

$$= -2r(-3.11362) + 2r(3.13543) - 2q(-1.45217) + 2q(3.75086)$$

$$= 9.00315 \quad \text{etc.}$$

second approximations. It is important to note that after some stage the information matrix need not be recalculated for each approximation. Only the new scores have to be calculated at each stage and used in conjunction with the same inverse matrix of information (kept constant from some stage) to obtain closer approximations. When convergence is achieved, the information matrix and scores may be calculated for the last approximate values and the final approximation obtained.

The maximum likelihood estimates and the variances are

$$p = 0.26444 \qquad V(\hat{p}) = \frac{I^{pp}}{N} = 0.00026305$$

$$q = 0.09317 \qquad V(\hat{q}) = \frac{I^{qq}}{N} = 0.00010202$$

$$r = 0.64239 \qquad V(\hat{r}) = \frac{I^{pp} + 2I^{pq} + I^{qq}}{N} = 0.00030893$$

4c.3 Combination of Data

The advantage of the scoring system can be best seen in the mechanization it introduces when various sets of data giving information on some parameters have to be combined for estimation. If L is the joint likelihood based on all the data and L_i for the ith part, then

$$L = L_1 L_2 \cdots$$

$$\frac{\partial \log L}{\partial \theta_r} = \frac{\partial \log L_1}{\partial \theta_r} + \frac{\partial \log L_2}{\partial \theta_r} + \cdots$$

which shows that the efficient scores are additive. Also, if I_{rs} is an element of the information matrix for the whole body of data and $I_{rs}{}^j$ for the jth part, then

$$I_{rs} = I_{rs}{}^1 + I_{rs}{}^2 + \cdots$$

Thus, to obtain the best estimates it is necessary to replace each part of the data by the scores and information matrix at a trial value and obtain the total scores and information matrix by simple addition. The correction to trial values can be obtained by solving simultaneous equations as shown in the previous section.

Appendix: Some Limiting Theorems

A general convergence theorem (Cramér, 1946). Let $\xi_1, \xi_2, \cdots$ be a sequence of random variables with distribution functions $F_1, F_{2}, \cdots$.

Suppose that $F_n(x) \to F(x)$ as $n \to \infty$. Let $\eta_1, \eta_2, \cdots$ be another sequence of random variables, and suppose that η_n converges in probability to a constant c. If

$$X_n = \xi_n + \eta_n \qquad Y_n = \xi_n \eta_n \qquad Z_n = \frac{\xi_n}{\eta_n}$$

then the distribution functions

of $X_n \to F(x - c)$

of $Y_n \to F\left(\frac{x}{c}\right) \qquad$ if $c > 0$

of $Z_n \to F(cx) \qquad$ if $c > 0$

The theorem covers the case of $c < 0$ also, in which case the variables $-\eta_1, -\eta_2, \cdots$ would be considered.

The theorem is proved for Z_n, the proof being similar for the rest. The set S of points satisfying $\xi_n/\eta_n \leq x$ consists of two non-overlapping sets:

$$S_1: \qquad \frac{\xi_n}{\eta_n} \leq x \qquad | \eta_n - c | \leq \epsilon$$

$$S_2: \qquad \frac{\xi_n}{\eta_n} \leq x \qquad | \eta_n - c | > \epsilon$$

Thus

$$P_n(S) = P_n(S_1) + P_n(S_2)$$

For every ϵ

$$P_n(S_2) < P_n(| \eta_n - c | > \epsilon) \to 0$$

by hypothesis, in which case $P_n(S)$ lies within the limits

$$P_n\{\xi_n \leq (c \pm \epsilon)x \qquad | \eta_n - c | \leq \epsilon\}$$

This differs from the corresponding quantity

$$P_n\{\xi_n \leq (c \pm \epsilon)x\} = F_n\{(c \pm \epsilon)x\}$$

by less than $P_n(| \eta_n - c | > \epsilon)$. As $n \to \infty$, $P_n(| \eta_n - c | > \epsilon) \to 0$. $P_n(S)$ is thus enclosed between two limits which can be made to lie as close as possible to $F(cx)$ by choosing ϵ small. The theorem is thus proved. It may be noted that no condition of independence of the variables involved is assumed.

Slutsky's theorem (1925). If $\xi_n, \eta_n, \cdots, \rho_n$ are random variables converging in probability to constants $x, y, \cdots, r$, respectively, any rational function $R(\xi_n, \eta_n, \cdots, \rho_n)$ converges in probability to the constant

$R(x, y, \cdots, r)$, provided that the latter is finite. It follows that any power $R^k(\xi_n, \eta_n, \cdots, \rho_n)$ with $k > 0$ converges in probability to $R^k(x, y, \cdots, r)$.

Kintchine's theorem. Let $\xi_1, \xi_2, \cdots$ be independent random variables, all having the same distribution function $F(x)$, and suppose that $F(x)$ has a finite mean m. Then the variable $\bar{\xi} = \dfrac{1}{n} \sum_1^n \xi_v$ converges in probability to m.

Levy's theorem (1925). A necessary and sufficient condition for the convergence of the sequence $\{F_n(x)\}$ of distribution functions to a distribution function $F(x)$ is that, for every t, the sequence $\{\phi_n(t)\}$ of characteristic functions converges to the limit $\phi(t)$ which is continuous for the special value t and is the characteristic function for $F(x)$.

Central limit theorems. (1) *Lindberg and Levy* (1922, 1925). If $\xi_1, \xi_2, \cdots$ are independent random variables, all having the same probability distribution, and if m and σ denote the mean and standard deviation of every ξ_n, then the sum $\xi = \sum_1^n \xi_v$ is asymptotically normally distributed with mean nm and standard deviation $\sigma\sqrt{n}$.

(2) *Liapounoff* (1901). Let $\xi_1, \xi_2, \cdots$ be independent random variables with means and standard deviations m_v and σ_v, $(v = 1, 2, \cdots)$. Suppose that the third absolute moment of ξ_v about its mean

$$\rho_v{}^3 = E(|\, \xi_v - m_v \,|^3)$$

is finite for every v. If $\rho/\sigma \to 0$ as $n \to \infty$, where

$$\rho^3 = \rho_1{}^3 + \rho_2{}^3 + \cdots$$

then the sum $\sum_1^n \xi_v$ is asymptotically normal with mean $m = m_1 + m_2 + \cdots$ and variance $\sigma^2 = \sigma_1{}^2 + \sigma_2{}^2 + \cdots$.

References

BERNSTEIN, F. (1925). Zusammenfassunde Betrachtungen über die erblichen Blutstrukturen des Menschen. *Z. indukt. Astamm. u. Vererb. Lehre,* **37,** 237.

BHATTACHARYA, A. (1946). On some analogues of the amount of information and their uses in statistical estimation. (In three parts.) *Sankhyā,* **8,** 1, 201, 315.

CRAMÉR, H. (1946). Mathematical methods of statistics. Princeton University Press.

DUGUÉ, D. (1937). Application des propriétés de la limité au sens du calcul des probabilités á l'étude des diverses questions d'estimation. *J. Écol. Poly.* **3,** no. 4, 305.

FISHER, R. A. (1921). On mathematical foundations of theoretical statistics. *Philos. Trans. Roy. Soc.* **A, 222,** 309.

FISHER, R. A. (1938). Statistical theory of estimation. Calcutta University Readership lectures.

FISHER, R. A., and F. YATES (1948). Statistical tables for biological, agricultural and medical research. Oliver & Boyd. Third edition.

HUZURBAZAR, V. S. (1948). The likelihood equation, consistency, and maxima of the likelihood function. *Ann. Eugen. London,* **14,** 185.

KOOPMAN, B. O. (1936). On distributions admitting a sufficient statistic. *Trans. Am. Math. Soc.,* **39,** 399.

LEVY, P. (1925). Calcul des probabilités. Gauthier Villars, Paris.

LEVY, P. (1937). Théorie de l'addition des variables aléatoires. Paris.

LIAPOUNOFF, A. (1901). Nouvelle forme du théorème sur la limite de probabilité. *Mém. acad. sci. St. Petersbourg,* **12,** 5.

LINDENBERG, J. W. (1922). Eine neue Herleitung des Exponentialgesetzes in der Wahrscheinlichkeitesrechnung. *Math. Zeitschr.,* **15,** 211.

MATHER, K. (1938). Measurement of linkage in heredity. Methuen & Co. London.

MERRILL, A. S. (1928). Frequency distribution of an index when both the components follow the normal law. *Biom.,* **20A,** 53.

MÜNTER, A. H. (1936). A study of the lengths of long bones of the arms and legs in man, with special reference to Anglo-Saxon skeletons. *Biom.,* **28,** 258.

NEYMAN, J. (1937). Outline of a theory of statistical estimation based on the classical theory of probability. *Philos. Trans. Roy. Soc.* **A, 236,** 333.

RAO, C. R. (1945). Information and accuracy attainable in the estimation of statistical parameters. *Bull. Calcutta Math. Soc.,* **37,** 81.

RAO, C. R. (1947). Minimum variance and the estimation of several parameters. *Proc. Cam. Phil. Soc.,* **43,** 280.

RAO, C. R. (1948). Sufficient statistics and minimum variance estimates. *Proc. Cam. Phil. Soc.,* **45,** 213.

SLUTSKY, E. (1925). Über stochastiche Asymptoten und Grenzwerte. *Metron.,* **5,** 3, 3.

WALD, A. (1949). A note on the consistency of the maximum likelihood estimate. *Ann. Math. Stats.,* **20,** 595.

CHAPTER 5

Large Sample Tests of Hypotheses with Applications to Problems of Estimation

5a The General Theory of Tests in Large Samples

5a.1 The Nature of Statistical Hypotheses

If the probability differential of a set of stochastic variables contains k unknown parameters, the statistical hypotheses concerning them may be simple or composite. The hypothesis leading to a complete specification of the values of the k parameters is a simple hypothesis, and the one leading to a collection of admissible sets a composite hypothesis. In this chapter are discussed tests of these two types of hypotheses on the basis of a large number of observations from any probability distribution satisfying some mild restrictions and also their use in problems of estimation.

5a.2 The Problem of Distribution

There are two problems of distribution that are useful in deriving tests of significance for simple and composite hypotheses. Let

$$x_1, \cdots, x_p; y_1, \cdots, y_p; \cdots$$

be independent sets of observations from probability laws with densities represented by $f_1(x \mid \theta), f_2(y \mid \theta), \cdots$ such that each function contains at least one of the unknown parameters $\theta_1, \cdots, \theta_k$. The likelihood of the parameters which is the same as the probability density of the observed sets of data is

$$L = f_1(x \mid \theta) f_2(y \mid \theta) \cdots$$

As defined in Chapter 4 the ith efficient score is represented by

$$\phi_i = \frac{\partial \log L}{\partial \theta_i}$$

176

The mean values of these scores are zero. Their covariance matrix is represented by (α_{ij}), and its reciprocal by (α^{ij}). Let there exist a positive quantity η such that

$$E \left(\frac{1}{f_i} \frac{\partial f_i}{\partial \theta_j} \right)^{2+\eta} \qquad i = 1, \cdots, k \qquad (5a.2.1)$$

are finite. Under these conditions, if the non-vanishing terms in the sequence $\partial \log f_i / \partial \theta_j$, $(i = 1, 2, \cdots)$, for any j form a sufficiently large set, it follows from an extension of the central limit theorem to many variables that the limiting distribution of $\phi_1, \cdots, \phi_k$ at the true values $\theta_1, \cdots, \theta_k$ tends to the multivariate normal form with zero mean and covariance matrix (α_{ij}).

$$\text{const. } e^{-\frac{1}{2}Q} \, d\phi_1 \cdots d\phi_k$$

where

$$Q = \Sigma\Sigma \alpha^{ij} \phi_i \phi_j$$

Hence Q is distributed, in large samples, as χ^2 with k degrees of freedom when the true values of the parameters are $\theta_1, \cdots, \theta_k$.

If the probability densities $f_1, f_2, \cdots$ are the same, it is enough for the limiting properties to hold that

$$E \left(\frac{1}{f} \frac{\partial f}{\partial \theta_j} \right)^2$$

is finite for every j which is less restrictive than the condition (5a.2.1).

Suppose that the θ parameters are subject to s restrictions defined by s independent relations.

$$\psi_i(\theta_1, \cdots, \theta_k) = 0 \qquad i = 1, 2, \cdots s \qquad (5a.2.2)$$

The maximum likelihood estimates are given by

$$\phi_i + \sum_j \lambda_j \frac{\partial \psi_j}{\partial \theta_i} = 0 \qquad i = 1, 2, \cdots, k$$

$$\psi_i = 0 \qquad i = 1, 2, \cdots, s \qquad (5a.2.3)$$

where λ_i are Lagrangian multipliers. Let $\hat{\theta}_1, \cdots, \hat{\theta}_k$ be the maximum likelihood estimates. Since the set of equations (5a.2.3) involve $(k - s)$ linear restrictions on $\phi_i(\hat{\theta})$, it is expected that the statistic

$$\chi^2 = \Sigma\Sigma \alpha^{ij}(\hat{\theta}) \phi_i(\hat{\theta}) \phi_j(\hat{\theta})$$

is distributed as χ^2 with s degrees of freedom which is $(k - s)$ less than the degrees of freedom for true values.

This can be demonstrated if we assume that the restrictions (5a.2.2) specify s of the parameters $\theta_{k-s+1}, \cdots, \theta_k$ (say) as functions of $(k - s)$

free parameters $\theta_1, \cdots, \theta_{k-s}$, so that the likelihood is an explicit function of these parameters only, and further that the joint distribution of $\hat{\theta}_1, \cdots, \hat{\theta}_{k-s}$ tends to the multivariate normal form in large samples with variances and covariances of $O(n^{-1})$. It is known that the latter assumption is true provided that the probability laws satisfy the condition (5a.2.1), and further that the maximum likelihood estimates are uniformly consistent (Wald, 1949). This does not seem to be a necessary condition, and the approach to normality is probably true under less stringent conditions.

Let us take the case of two parameters and one restrictive condition which may be taken as $\theta_2 = w(\theta_1)$. The differential coefficient $d\theta_2/d\theta_1$ is denoted by $\lambda(\theta_1)$. The maximum likelihood estimates satisfy the equations

$$\phi_1(\hat{\theta}) + \lambda(\hat{\theta}_1)\phi_2(\hat{\theta}) = 0 \qquad \hat{\theta}_2 = w(\hat{\theta}_1) \qquad (5a.2.4)$$

If the given relation is true, then the statistic

$$\chi_0^2 = \Sigma\Sigma \alpha^{ij}(\theta)\phi_i(\theta)\phi_j(\theta) \qquad (5a.2.5)$$

depends only on θ_1 and is distributed as χ^2 with 2 degrees of freedom at the true value of θ_1. The expression (5a.2.5) treated as a function of θ_1 may be expanded in the neighborhood of $\hat{\theta}_1$. The first term is

$$\chi_1^2 = \Sigma\Sigma \alpha^{ij}(\hat{\theta})\phi_i(\hat{\theta})\phi_j(\hat{\theta})$$

The second term is

$$-2(\theta_1 - \hat{\theta}_1)[\phi_1(\hat{\theta})\{\alpha^{11}(\alpha_{11} + \lambda\alpha_{12}) + \alpha^{12}(\alpha_{12} + \lambda\alpha_{22})\}$$
$$+ \phi_2(\hat{\theta})\{\alpha^{22}(\alpha_{12} + \lambda\alpha_{22}) + \alpha^{12}(\alpha_{11} + \lambda\alpha_{12})\}]$$
$$= -2(\theta_1 - \hat{\theta}_1)[\phi_1(\hat{\theta}) + \lambda\phi_2(\hat{\theta})] = 0 \quad (5a.2.6)$$

by virtue of (5a.2.4). In the expression (5a.2.6) terms $O(n^0)$ only have been retained, $\partial\phi_i/\partial\theta_j$ being replaced by α_{ij}, and terms of the type

$$(\theta_1 - \hat{\theta}_1)\frac{\partial\alpha_{ij}}{\partial\theta_i}\phi_i\phi_j$$

being omitted as they are of $O(n^{-1/2})$.

The third term can be easily shown to be

$$\chi_2^2 = (\theta_1 - \hat{\theta}_1)^2[\alpha_{11}(\hat{\theta}) + 2\lambda\alpha_{12}(\hat{\theta}) + \lambda^2\alpha_{22}(\hat{\theta})]$$

Neglecting terms of higher order of smallness, we obtain

$$\chi_0^2 = \chi_1^2 + \chi_2^2$$

Since

$$\frac{1}{V(\theta_1 - \hat{\theta}_1)} \simeq \alpha_{11}(\hat{\theta}) + 2\lambda\alpha_{12}(\hat{\theta}) + \lambda^2\alpha_{22}(\hat{\theta})$$

it follows that $\chi_2{}^2$ is distributed in large samples as χ^2 with 1 degree of freedom.

It can be demonstrated by expanding $\phi_i(\theta)$ in powers of $(\theta_1 - \hat{\theta}_1)$ that $(\theta_1 - \hat{\theta}_1)$ and $\phi_i(\hat{\theta})$ tend to be uncorrelated in large samples, so that $\chi_1{}^2$ and $\chi_2{}^2$ are independently distributed in the limiting case.

Since $\chi_0{}^2$ is distributed as χ^2 with 2 degrees of freedom and $\chi_2{}^2$ with 1 degree of freedom, it follows that the residual part $\chi_1{}^2$ is distributed as χ^2 with 1 degree of freedom.

For s relations and $k(\geq s)$ parameters, $\chi_0{}^2$ can be expressed as a function of $(k - s)$ parameters and split into two portions, one of which is $\chi_2{}^2$ with $(k - s)$ degrees of freedom measuring the discrepancy of the $(k - s)$ estimated parameters from their true values, and another $\chi_1{}^2$ with s degrees of freedom measuring the departures from the assigned relationships.

5b Applications of the General Theory

5b.1 The χ^2 Test of Departure from a Simple Hypothesis

The problem is to test whether $n_1, \cdots, n_k$, $(\Sigma n_i = n)$, the frequencies in k classes, are in accordance with some hypothetical proportions π_1, $\cdots$, π_k, $(\Sigma \pi_i = 1)$. The probability of the sample on the given hypothesis is

$$L = \frac{n!}{n_1! \cdots n_k!} \pi_1{}^{n_1} \cdots \pi_k{}^{n_k}$$

There are only $(k - 1)$ independent parameters which may be taken as $\pi_1, \cdots, \pi_{k-1}$. The efficient scores are

$$\phi_i = \frac{\partial \log L}{\partial \pi_i} = \frac{n_i}{\pi_i} - \frac{n_k}{\pi_k}$$

Their variances and covariances are

$$\alpha_{ii} = n\left(\frac{1}{\pi_i} + \frac{1}{\pi_k}\right) \quad \text{using the formula (2a.9.1)}$$

$$\alpha_{ij} = \frac{n}{\pi_k} \quad \text{using the formula (2a.9.1)}$$

$$\left| \alpha_{ij} \right| = \frac{n^{k-1}}{\pi_1 \cdots \pi_k}$$

$$\alpha^{ii} = \frac{\pi_i(1 - \pi_i)}{n} \qquad \alpha^{ij} = \frac{-\pi_i\pi_j}{n}$$

The χ^2 statistic is

$$\Sigma\Sigma\alpha^{ij}\phi_i\phi_j$$

$$= \Sigma \frac{\pi_i(1-\pi_i)}{n}\left(\frac{n_i}{\pi_i}-\frac{n_k}{\pi_k}\right)^2 - \Sigma\Sigma\frac{\pi_i\pi_j}{n}\left(\frac{n_i}{\pi_i}-\frac{n_k}{\pi_k}\right)\left(\frac{n_j}{\pi_j}-\frac{n_k}{\pi_k}\right)$$

$$= \Sigma \frac{\pi_i(1-\pi_i)}{n}\left(\frac{d_i}{\pi_i}-\frac{d_k}{\pi_k}\right)^2 - \Sigma\Sigma\frac{\pi_i\pi_j}{n}\left(\frac{d_i}{\pi_i}-\frac{d_k}{\pi_k}\right)\left(\frac{d_j}{\pi_j}-\frac{d_k}{\pi_k}\right)$$

where $d_i = n_i - n\pi_i$, $(i = 1, \cdots, k)$. The above expression reduces to

$$\frac{d_1{}^2}{n\pi_1}+\cdots+\frac{d_k{}^2}{n\pi_k} = \Sigma\frac{(\text{Observed}-\text{Expected})^2}{\text{Expected}} = \Sigma\frac{(O-E)^2}{E}$$

As shown in 5a.2 the large sample distribution of the above statistic is that of χ^2 with $(k-1)$ degrees of freedom because the test is based on $(k-1)$ independent parameters. We shall, however, present an alternative way of deriving its distribiition.

In 2a.3 it was shown that the multinomial distribution is equivalent to a product of Poisson distributions subject to the condition that the sum of the variates is n. If each of the individual cell frequencies is large, then the Poisson probabilities could be replaced by the normal approximation. If $x_i = (n_i - n\pi_i)/\sqrt{n\pi_i}$, then the approximate distribution of $x_1, \cdots, x_k$ is

$$\text{const. } e^{-\frac{1}{2}(x_1{}^2+\cdots+x_k{}^2)}\,dx_1 \cdots dx_k$$

subject to the condition

$$\sqrt{n\pi_1}x_1 + \sqrt{n\pi_2}x_2 + \cdots + \sqrt{n\pi_k}x_k$$

$$= (n_1 - n\pi_1) - \cdots - (n_k - n\pi_k) = \Sigma n_i - n = 0$$

Therefore by using the result in 2c.3 the distribution of χ^2 is that of the sum of squares of k variates $N(0, 1)$ subject to one homogeneous linear restraint, i.e., χ^2 with $(k-1)$ degrees of freedom.

If the deviations of the observed from the expected frequencies are subject to t linear homogeneous restrictions on the total, then Σx^2 is a χ^2 with $(k-t)$ degrees of freedom.

Example 1.   Bateson gives the following data concerning the segregation of two genes for purple-red flower color and long-round pollen shape in sweet pea.

The results are from an intercross so that the expected frequencies on the hypothesis of independent segregation are in the ratio 9:3:3:1. Are the data in agreement with the expected frequencies?

	Purple-Long	Red-Long	Purple-Round	Red-Round	Total
Observed	296	27	19	85	427
Expected	3843 ÷ 16	1281 ÷ 16	1281 ÷ 16	427 ÷ 16	427
$\dfrac{(\text{Observed})^2}{\text{Expected}}$	364.7817	9.1054	4.5090	270.7260	649.1221

$$\chi^2 = \Sigma \frac{O^2}{E} - \Sigma O = 649.1221 - 427 = 222.1221$$

This is significant on 3 degrees of freedom, showing that there is a departure from the expected. For the large sample test to hold, it is necessary that each cell frequency should be at least greater than 5. If any such frequency is small, two suitable cells can be combined to form one cell with a higher frequency.

Example 2. The number of deaths due to cholera is 350 out of a total of 976 due to all causes in a certain week. Is cholera on the increase if it accounted for ⅓ of the deaths in the last week?

The expected number of deaths due to cholera on the basis of ⅓ proportion is $976/3 = 325.\dot{3}$. The value of χ^2 with 1 degree of freedom is

$$\frac{(350)^2}{325.\dot{3}} + \frac{(626)^2}{650.\dot{6}} - 976 \quad \text{or} \quad \frac{[2(350) - 626]^2}{(1)(2)(976)} = 2.80$$

the probability of exceeding which is just less than 10%. This probability is not appropriate in answering the problem whether cholera is on the increase. χ^2 gives the probability for deviations both in excess or defect of the expected, whereas only the probability of deviations in excess of the expected is relevant to this problem. To determine this we observe that

$$\sqrt{\chi^2} = 1.6733$$

can be used as a normal deviate with zero mean and unit standard deviation. The probability of a normal deviate's exceeding this value is less than 5%, which shows that cholera is on the increase.

Example 3. Test whether the frequencies 8, 3, 1 could have arisen from a trinomial with equal probabilities.

The expected values 4, 4, 4 are all small so that the χ^2 approximation cannot be used. If we ignore this condition, the χ^2 with 2 degrees of freedom is

$$\frac{8^2}{4} + \frac{3^2}{4} + \frac{1^2}{4} - 12 = 6.50$$

which has a probability between 2 and 5%. In problems where the expected frequencies are small in some cells, they can be combined with other cells so as to have frequencies at least greater than 5 in each class. Such a procedure is not possible in the present example because all the expectations are small. This necessitates the evaluation of the probability of the observed distribution 8, 3, 1 and those less probable than this on the hypothesis of equal probabilities of the three classes of events. The probability for any observed distribution x, y, z is

$$\frac{12!}{x!\,y!\,z!}\left(\frac{1}{3}\right)^{12}$$

There are 91 partitions of 12 for which the probabilities are calculated below.

Partitional Type			Number	Probability
12	0	0	3	0.0^51882
11	1	0	6	0.0^42258
10	2	0	6	0.0^31242
10	1	1	3	0.0^32484
9	3	0	6	0.0^34140
9	2	1	6	0.0^21242
8	4	0	6	0.0^39314
8	3	1	6	0.0^23726
8	2	2	3	0.0^25589
7	5	0	6	0.0^21490
7	4	1	6	0.0^27452
7	3	2	6	0.01490
6	6	0	3	0.0^21737
6	5	1	6	0.01043
6	4	2	6	0.02608
6	3	3	3	0.03477
5	5	2	3	0.03130
5	4	3	6	0.05216
4	4	4	1	0.06520

The sum of probabilities less than or equal to 0.0^23726 corresponding to (8, 3, 1) is 0.0537, which exceeds the probability obtained by the χ^2 approximation. The approximation overestimated significance. Even according to the exact test, the probability being near 5%, the hypothesis may be rejected.

Example 4. Out of 8 fossils discovered, 2 and 6 were identified as belonging to male and female. Is this compatible with the sex ratio 1:1?

The expected values are small, as in example 3, so that an exact treatment is needed. The problem is the same as that of finding the probability of 6 or more *heads or tails* in 8 tosses with an unbiased coin. The total chance for 6, 7, and 8 heads is

$$(^8c_6 + {}^8c_7 + {}^8c_8)2^{-8} = \frac{37}{2^8}$$

The total for heads as well as tails is twice the above probability equal to $37/2^7 = 0.289$, which is quite high, so that there is no definite evidence against the 1:1 sex proportion. In a general case the term-by-term evaluation may be a difficult job. It is shown in 2a.1 that the sum of the probabilities for $0, 1, \cdots, r$ successes is given by the incomplete β-integral,

$$\frac{n!}{r!(n-r-1)!} \int_0^q x^{n-r-1}(1-x)^r \, dx$$

where $q(= 1 - p)$ is the chance of a failure. This function is tabulated in the incomplete beta tables edited by K. Pearson. In the above problem

$$p = q = \tfrac{1}{2} \qquad n = 8 \qquad r = 2$$

In the notation of incomplete beta tables *

$$\text{index } p = (n - r - 1) + 1 = \quad 6$$

$$\text{index } q = r + 1 \qquad\qquad = \quad 3$$

$$x = \text{probability } q \qquad = 0.5$$

The tabular entry for $x = 0.5$, index $p = 6$, and index $q = 3$ is 0.1445312, which is the probability for 0, 1, and 2 heads. By symmetry the probability for tails is also the same, so that the required total is 0.2890624, which agrees with the value obtained above.

5b.2   The χ^2 Test of Goodness of Fit

The general problem in judging goodness of fit is to test whether the cell proportions can be expressed as functions of a fewer number of parameters. Thus, if O, A, B, and AB represent the four blood group classes, it may be desired to test whether the cell frequencies can be expressed in terms of gene frequencies of O, A, and B, or two independent parameters p and q (example 3 in 4c.2). Here the values of p and q are not known, but what is needed is a test of the consistency relations among the probability expressions for the four classes.

If the observed frequency distribution has arisen from a normal distribution, the probability π_i in the ith class bounded by a_i and

---

* There are three quantities to be entered into this table. Index p is equal to 1 plus the power of x in the above integral, and index q is 1 plus the power of $(1 - x)$. The entry x of the table is the upper limit of the integral. The probabilities p and q are not to be confused with indices p, q of the table.

a_{i+1} is

$$\int_{a_i}^{a_{i+1}} \frac{1}{\sigma\sqrt{2\pi}} e^{-(x-\mu)^2/2\sigma^2}\, dx$$

so that the cell probabilities could be expressed in terms of two parameters μ and σ.

There are in general $(k-1)$ independent proportions $\pi_1, \cdots, \pi_{k-1}$ specifying the distribution in k classes. If these proportions can be expressed as functions of s independent parameters, then all the $(k-1)$ proportions can be expressed as functions of s suitably chosen proportions. Thus there are $(k-1-s)$ restrictions on $\pi_1, \cdots, \pi_{k-1}$. If we construct

$$\chi^2 = \Sigma\Sigma\alpha^{ij}\phi_i\phi_j = \Sigma \frac{(O-E)^2}{E}$$

over all classes and substitute for $\pi_1, \cdots, \pi_{k-1}$ their best estimates subject to the $(k-1-s)$ restrictions, then the χ^2 has $(k-1-s)$ degrees of freedom. This can be used to test whether the specification is correct or not.

To estimate $\pi_1, \cdots, \pi_{k-1}$ subject to $(k-1-s)$ restrictions, it is enough to estimate s parameters in terms of which $\pi_1, \cdots, \pi_{k-1}$ are completely defined. The degrees of freedom for χ^2 is $(k-1)$ *minus* s, the number of parameters estimated. It is necessary for the formula of the degrees of freedom to hold that the parameters should be estimated by the most efficient method (e.g., maximum likelihood).

In example 3 of 4c.2 the estimates of the blood-group gene frequencies are found by the method of maximum likelihood. To test whether the proportions in the four blood-group classes can be expressed as functions of gene frequencies, the χ^2 is calculated as below. Using the estimates $p = 0.2644$, $q = 0.0932$, and $r = 0.6424$, the expected values are derived.

	Observed	Expected		(Observed)²/Expected
O	176	$n(r^2)$	$= 179.51$	172.56
A	182	$n(p^2 + 2pr)$	$= 178.18$	185.90
B	60	$n(q^2 + 2qr)$	$= 55.87$	64.43
AB	17	$n(2pq)$	$= 21.44$	13.48
Total	435	n	435.00	436.37
				-435
			$\chi^2 =$	1.37 (1 D.F.)

The χ^2 with $(3-2) = 1$ degree of freedom is not significant, thus indicating that the cell expectations could be expressed in terms of the gene frequencies.

5b.3   Tests of Homogeneity of Parallel Samples

Let the frequencies in k classes for two samples be

	Classes			Total
Sample	1	2	$\cdots$ k	
First	n_1	n_2	$\cdots$ n_k	n
Second	n_1'	n_2'	n_k'	n'
Total	$n_1 + n_1'$	$n_2 + n_2'$ $\cdots$	$n_k + n_k'$	$n + n'$

These classes may refer to a discrete classification or to intervals of a continuous variable. Nothing being known about the actual distributions, how can it be tested that the two samples have arisen from the same population?

If $\pi_1, \cdots, \pi_k$ and $\pi_1', \cdots, \pi_k'$ are the cell proportions in populations from which the samples are drawn, then the hypothesis to be tested is $\pi_i = \pi_i'$, $(i = 1, \cdots, k - 1)$. If π_i and π_i' are known, then the χ^2 test of departure from the expected is

$$\Sigma \frac{(n_i - n\pi_i)^2}{n\pi_i} + \Sigma \frac{(n_i' - n'\pi_i')^2}{n'\pi_i}$$

which has $(k - 1) + (k - 1)$ degrees of freedom. If $\pi_i = \pi_i'$, there are $(k - 1)$ restrictions, and the best estimate of the common value is

$$\pi_i = \pi_i' \sim \frac{(n_i + n_i')}{(n + n')}$$

If this value is substituted in the above expression, χ^2 reduces to

$$\frac{1}{nn'} \Sigma \frac{(n_i n' - n_i' n)^2}{n_i + n_i'}$$

which has now $(k - 1)$ degrees of freedom. This tests the departure from the equality of proportions. If

$$p_1 = \frac{n_1}{n_1 + n_1'}, \; p_2 = \frac{n_2}{n_2 + n_2'}, \; \cdots$$

and

$$p = \frac{n}{n + n'}$$

then the above χ^2 could also be written

$$\chi^2 = \frac{1}{p} \Sigma (n_i + n_i') p_i^2 - n = \frac{1}{p} \Sigma n_i p_i - n$$

which is convenient to calculate if the problem needs the evaluation of the p_i also.

Example 1.   The distributions in four blood-group classes O, A, B, and AB of 140 Christians who are army cadets and 295 other Christians are given below.

TABLE 5b.3α.   Blood-Group Frequencies in Two Samples of Christians

	O	A	B	AB	Total
Army cadets	56	60	18	6	140
Others	120	122	42	11	295
Total	176	182	60	17	435
p	0.3182	0.3297	0.3000	0.3529	0.3218

$$\Sigma n_i p_i = 56(0.3182) + 60(0.3297) + 18(0.3000) + 6(0.3529) = 45.1186$$

$$\frac{1}{p}\Sigma n_i p_i = \frac{45.1186}{0.3218} = 140.2069$$

$$\chi^2 = 140.2069 - 140 = 0.2069$$

The probability that χ^2 exceeds 0.2069 with 3 degrees of freedom is greater than 95%, showing thereby that the two samples may be considered to have arisen from the same population.

Example 2.   The test given above is not necessarily the best and is recommended only when nothing is known about the frequency distributions.   In the above example of blood groups it is known that the frequencies can be expressed in terms of two independent gene frequencies (example 3, in 4c.2).   If p, q and p', q' are the parameters appropriate for the two samples, then the test of agreement between the two samples reduces to that of testing the hypothesis $p = p'$ and $q = q'$.   The χ^2 test for hypothetical values of p, q and p', q' has 4 degrees of freedom, whereas if they are estimated subject to the conditions $p = p'$, $q = q'$ the resulting χ^2 has only 2 degrees of freedom.   There are only two essential comparisons needed, and the χ^2 with 2 degrees of freedom is sufficient for this purpose.   But in the example worked out above, the χ^2 test of discrepancy has 3 degrees of freedom, one more than that of the hypothesis specifying two relationships.   The χ^2 test with 2 degrees of freedom is to be preferred, and this is possible because the nature of distributions is known.

In general, if the distributions are specified by r parameters, then the χ^2 test for equality of parameters given in 5a.2 has r degrees of freedom.

If the discrepancies in the k classes arise owing to the parameters' being different, then the test based on a direct comparison of the estimated parameters appears to be reasonable.

For carrying out the proposed test it is necessary to estimate the gene frequencies from the totals. This is worked out in example 3 of 4c.2. The estimates of p, q are

$$\hat{p} = 0.26444 \qquad \hat{q} = 0.09317$$

and the inverse to the information matrix (example 3 in 4c.2) per single observation is

$$I^{pp} = \quad 0.114430 \qquad I^{pq} = -0.012208$$

$$I^{pq} = -0.012208 \qquad I^{qq} = \quad 0.044376$$

The scores ϕ_p and ϕ_q for the two samples and χ^2 are calculated below.

Sample	n	ϕ_p	ϕ_q	$\chi^2 = \dfrac{1}{n}\Sigma\Sigma I^{ij}\phi_i\phi_j$
1	140	10.37497	−7.27341	0.11704
2	295	−10.37497	7.27341	0.05554
Total	435	0	0	0.17258

In the last column the values of χ^2 differ only in the multiplier $1/n$ so that the total χ^2 can be simply obtained from the formula

$$\left(\frac{1}{n_1} + \frac{1}{n_2}\right)\Sigma\Sigma I^{ij}\phi_i\phi_j$$

$$= \left(\frac{1}{n_1} + \frac{1}{n_2}\right)[0.114430(10.37497)^2$$

$$+ 2(-0.012208)(10.37497)(-7.27341) + 0.044376(7.27341)^2]$$

$$= 0.17258$$

The χ^2 with 2 degrees of freedom is small so that the data do not provide any evidence for differences in gene frequencies. In fact, the probability of exceeding the observed value with 2 degrees of freedom is just over 90%, which is smaller than the corresponding probability of example 1 above. In general, the test given in example 2 is more sensitive than the overall test of example 1. The common estimates of p and q are as found above.

Example 3. The tests proposed above can be extended to the general case of testing whether a number of samples come from the same population. When nothing is known about the distributions except that they are identical the χ^2 is based on $(k-1)(s-1)$ degrees of freedom where k is the number of cells and s is the number of samples. If n_{ij} denotes the frequency in the ith cell for the jth sample and $n_i. = \Sigma n_{ij}$, $n._j = \Sigma n_{ij}$, then the expected value of n_{ij} is $n_i. \times n._j/n$, when the hypothesis is true. The χ^2 on $(k-1)(s-1)$ degrees of freedom is

$$\Sigma\Sigma \frac{\left(n_{ij} - \dfrac{n_i.n._j}{n}\right)^2}{\dfrac{n_i.n._j}{n}}$$

The test should, however, be modified if the nature of the distribution is known. The following example illustrates the method.

TABLE 5b.3β. Distribution of Animals Bred for Linkage between Two Factors A and B

Sex of Heterozygotes	Phase	Sex of Animals Bred	Phenotype				Total
			AB	Ab	aB	ab	
♂ ♂	Coupling	♀	12	13	11	8	44
		♂	13	15	16	16	60
	Repulsion	♀	11	13	13	19	56
		♂	15	10	10	16	51
♀ ♀	Coupling	♀	30	17	20	13	80
		♂	18	18	20	24	80
	Repulsion	♀	17	12	13	17	59
		♂	15	12	11	14	52
Total			131	110	114	127	482

First it is necessary to test whether there is sex difference within a mating type. The results are from backcrosses so that the probabilities in the four classes are $(1-p)/2$, $p/2$, $p/2$, $(1-p)/2$ for coupling and $p/2$, $(1-p)/2$, $(1-p)/2$, $p/2$ for repulsion. The score and information for the recombination fraction p are

$$S = -\frac{(AB)}{1-p} + \frac{(Ab)+(aB)}{p} - \frac{(ab)}{1-p} \quad \text{and} \quad I = \frac{n}{p(1-p)}$$

for coupling and

$$S = \frac{(AB) + (ab)}{p} - \frac{(Ab) + (aB)}{1 - p} \quad \text{and} \quad I = \frac{n}{p(1 - p)}$$

for repulsion. The χ^2 is S^2/I.

To test for homogeneity of the first two samples

♀	12	13	11	8	44
♂	13	15	16	16	60

25	28	27	24	104

we obtain the estimate of p from the totals.

$$p = \frac{28 + 27}{104} = \frac{55}{104}$$

$$S_1 = -\frac{20}{1 - p} + \frac{24}{p} = \frac{(49 \times 24 - 55 \times 20)104}{55 \times 49}$$

$$I_1 = \frac{44}{p(1 - p)} = \frac{104^2 \times 44}{55 \times 49}$$

$$\frac{S_1^2}{I_1} = \frac{(49 \times 24 - 55 \times 20)^2}{44 \times 55 \times 49} = \frac{5776}{2695}\frac{1}{44}$$

$$\frac{S_2^2}{I_2} = \frac{(49 \times 31 - 55 \times 29)^2}{60 \times 55 \times 49} = \frac{5776}{2695}\frac{1}{60}$$

$$\chi_1^2 = \frac{S_1^2}{I_1} + \frac{S_2^2}{I_2} = \frac{5776 \times 104}{2695 \times 60 \times 44} = 0.0844$$

Similarly, we obtain the following four values of χ^2 to test for sex homogeneity within mating types.

Mating Type		χ^2	D.F.	Probability $\chi^2 \geq \chi_0^2$
♂♂	(C)	0.0844	1	>0.75
♂♂	(R)	0.5575	1	>0.45
♀♀	(C)	0.0251	1	>0.87
♀♀	(R)	0.0389	1	>0.84
Total		0.7059	4	>0.95

The total χ^2, 0.7059 with 4 degrees of freedom, and the individual χ^2's with 1 degree of freedom have very high probabilities, thus showing re-

markable agreement within mating types. The probability of observing a χ^2 less than 0.7059 with 4 degrees of freedom is less than 5%,
which shows that such good agreement can be expected very rarely.
This might lead the experimenter to suspect his material. In such a
case nothing can be said for or against the offered hypothesis. For
instance, an unconscious bias as to the nature of things to be expected
on the part of the experimenter may result in wrong recording.

Accepting, however, the fact that there is no sex difference within
mating types, we may proceed to test whether any difference is caused
by the mating types. The total frequencies are

							χ^2
♂♂	(C)	25	28	27	24	104	0.0015
♂♂	(R)	26	23	23	35	107	0.7982
♀♀	(C)	48	35	40	37	160	2.1757
♀♀	(R)	32	24	24	31	111	0.7339
Total						482	3.7093

The common value of p is obtained by equating the total score to zero.

$$S_1 + S_2 + S_3 + S_4 = -\frac{25 + 24}{1 - p} + \frac{28 + 27}{p}$$

$$-\frac{23 + 23}{1 - p} + \frac{26 + 35}{p}$$

$$-\frac{48 + 37}{1 - p} + \frac{35 + 40}{p}$$

$$-\frac{24 + 24}{1 - p} + \frac{32 + 31}{p} = 0$$

or

$$\frac{228}{1 - p} = \frac{254}{p} \qquad p = \frac{254}{482}$$

The values of χ^2 in the last column above are calculated for the value
of $p = 254/482$. For instance, the first value is

$$\frac{(49 \times 254 - 55 \times 228)^2}{254 \times 228 \times 104} = 0.0015$$

The total χ^2 is 3.7093, which is not significant on 3 degrees of freedom,
thus indicating close agreement of the four samples. The best estimate

of the recombination fraction is

$$\frac{254}{482} \quad \text{or} \quad 52.7\%$$

thus indicating the possibility of the recombinants' exceeding 50%.

5c   Contingency Tables

5c.1   The Probability of an Observed Configuration and Tests in Large Samples

If the individuals of a population can be described as belonging to one of r categories, $A_1, \cdots, A_r$ with respect to an attribute A, and to one of s categories, $B_1, \cdots, B_s$ with respect to an attribute B, and so on, then we have a frequency distribution of individuals in $r \times s \times \cdots$ classes, a typical class being represented by $A_i B_j \cdots$. If there are k attributes on the total, the arrangement described above is called a k-fold contingency table.

In this section various problems connected with two attributes are discussed, the treatment being similar in the general case. Let the observed frequency in the class $A_i B_j$ be denoted by n_{ij} and the probability by π_{ij}. Also let

$$n_{i1} + n_{i2} + \cdots + n_{is} = n_i. \qquad \pi_{i1} + \pi_{i2} + \cdots + \pi_{is} = \pi_i.$$

$$n_{1j} + n_{2j} + \cdots + n_{rj} = n_{\cdot j} \qquad \pi_{1j} + \pi_{2j} + \cdots + \pi_{rj} = \pi_{\cdot j}$$

$$n_1. + n_2. + \cdots = n_{\cdot 1} + n_{\cdot 2} + \cdots = n_{\cdot\cdot}$$

$$\pi_1. + \pi_2. + \cdots = \pi_{\cdot 1} + \pi_{\cdot 2} + \cdots = 1$$

The probability of the observed frequencies is

$$n_{\cdot\cdot}! \Pi\Pi \frac{(\pi_{ij})^{n_{ij}}}{n_{ij}!} = n_{\cdot\cdot}! \Pi \frac{(\pi_i.)^{n_i.}}{n_i.!} \times n_{\cdot\cdot}! \Pi \frac{(\pi_{\cdot j})^{n_{\cdot j}}}{n_{\cdot j}!}$$

$$\times \frac{\Pi n_i.! \Pi n_{\cdot j}!}{n_{\cdot\cdot}!} \Pi\Pi \frac{1}{n_{ij}!} \left(\frac{\pi_{ij}}{\pi_i.\pi_{\cdot j}} \right)^{n_{ij}}$$

If $\pi_{ij} = \pi_i.\pi_{\cdot j}$, then the above expression becomes

$$n_{\cdot\cdot}! \Pi \frac{(\pi_i.)^{n_i.}}{n_i.!} \times n_{\cdot\cdot}! \Pi \frac{(\pi_{\cdot j})^{n_{\cdot j}}}{n_{\cdot j}!} \times \frac{\Pi n_i.! \Pi n_{\cdot j}!}{n_{\cdot\cdot}!} \Pi\Pi \frac{1}{n_{ij}!}$$

The first two expressions give the probability of the marginal totals, and the third gives the probability of the class frequencies for fixed values of the marginal totals.

$$P(n_{ij} \mid n_i., n._j) = \frac{\Pi n_i.! \Pi n._j!}{n..!} \Pi\Pi \frac{1}{n_{ij}!} \qquad (5c.1.1)$$

It is interesting to observe that the above expression is independent of the hypothetical values of the proportions, provided, of course, that the attributes are independent, i.e., that the probability π_{ij} is the product of the probabilities for the ith category of the first attribute and the jth category of the second attribute.

In some situations, especially in designed experiments, one set of marginals is determined in advance. Thus, for instance, we might choose a number of individuals and inoculate them against an infection. Another chosen number of individuals could be kept as controls. Both groups supply the number of individuals infected and not infected from which a 2×2 contingency table can be set up. In general, if the row totals are fixed in advance, then, assuming the same set of probabilities $p_1, \cdots, p_s$ for different categories in each row, the joint probability of the observations is

$$P(n_{ij} \mid n_i.) = \prod_{i=1}^{r} \frac{n_i.!}{n_{i1}! \cdots n_{is}!} p_1^{n_{i1}} \cdots p_s^{n_{is}}$$

The probability of the marginal totals $n._j$ in this case is

$$P(n._j \mid n_i.) = \frac{n..!}{n._1! \cdots n._s!} p_1^{n._1} \cdots p_s^{n._s}$$

which is obtained by summing the previous expression over $n._j = \sum_i n_{ij}$ for $j = 1, \cdots, s$. Hence

$$P(n_{ij} \mid n_i., n._j) = \frac{P(n_{ij} \mid n_i.)}{P(n._j \mid n_i.)}$$

$$= \frac{\Pi n_i.! \Pi n._j!}{n..!} \Pi\Pi \frac{1}{n_{ij}!}$$

which is the same as the expression (5c.1.1) obtained in the general case.

5c.2 Tests of Independence in a Contingency Table

If the probabilities π_{ij} of the cells in a contingency table are assigned, then to test the hypothesis that the data are in agreement with these hypothetical values the statistic

$$\chi^2 = \sum_i \sum_j \frac{(n_{ij} - n..\pi_{ij})^2}{n..\pi_{ij}} = \Sigma \frac{(O - E)^2}{E} \qquad \text{(over all classes)}$$

can be used as χ^2 with $(rs - 1)$ degrees of freedom, the only restriction being $\Sigma\Sigma n_{ij} = n...$. If the attributes are independent, then the cell probabilities satisfy the relations

$$\pi_{ij} = \pi_i.\pi._j \qquad \text{for all } i \text{ and } j$$

How can this hypothesis be tested on the basis of the observed data? Two situations may arise.

(i) The hypothetical probabilities $\pi_i.$ and $\pi._j$ specifying the marginal distributions may be known, in which case we are required to examine whether the cell probabilities could be constructed by the above law.

(ii) The hypothetical proportions of the marginal frequencies not being known, we are required to test whether the attributes are independent.

In the first problem we have the total

$$\chi^2 = \Sigma\Sigma \frac{(n_{ij} - n..\pi_i.\pi._j)^2}{n..\pi_i.\pi._j} \qquad \text{D.F.} = rs - 1$$

which measures the overall discrepancy of the observed from the expected. From this we can single out two components

$$\chi_1^2 = \sum_i \frac{(n_i. - n..\pi_i.)^2}{n..\pi_i.} \qquad \text{D.F.} = r - 1$$

$$\chi_2^2 = \sum_j \frac{(n._j - n..\pi._j)^2}{n..\pi._j} \qquad \text{D.F.} = s - 1$$

which measure the discrepancy of the observed marginal frequencies from the expected. With these statistics we can test whether the observed marginal totals are as expected. On subtracting χ_1^2 and χ_2^2 from the total, we obtain

$$\chi_3^2 = \chi^2 - \chi_1^2 - \chi_2^2$$

$$= \Sigma\Sigma \frac{\{n_{ij} - n..\pi_i.\pi._j - \pi._j(n_i. - n..\pi_i.) - \pi_i.(n._j - n..\pi._j)\}^2}{n..\pi_i.\pi._j}$$

It may be noted that χ_3^2 is equal to χ^2, χ_1^2 and χ_2^2 being zero, when the frequencies are subject to the restrictions

$$n_i. - n..\pi_i. = 0 \qquad i = 1, \cdots, r$$

out of which $(r - 1)$ are independent, and

$$n_{.j} - n_{..}\pi_{.j} = 0 \qquad j = 1, \cdots, s$$

out of which $(s - 1)$ are independent. The degrees of freedom for χ^2 when the frequencies are subjected to $(r - 1) + (s - 1) + 1$ (for the restriction $\Sigma\Sigma n_{ij} = n_{..}$) restrictions are $(rs - r - s + 1) = (r - 1)(s - 1)$. Therefore χ_3^2 is distributed as χ^2 with $(r - 1)(s - 1)$ degrees of freedom. This component is used to test the departure from independence.

As an example, consider the fourfold contingency table

	B_1	B_2	
A_1	a	b	$a + b$
A_2	c	d	$c + d$
	$a + c$	$b + d$	n

with the marginal hypothetical proportions (p_1, q_1) for A and (p_2, q_2) for B. The total χ^2 with 3 degrees of freedom is

$$\chi^2 = \frac{(a - np_1p_2)^2}{np_1p_2} + \frac{(b - np_1q_2)^2}{np_1q_2} + \frac{(c - nq_1p_2)^2}{nq_1p_2} + \frac{(d - nq_1q_2)^2}{nq_1q_2}$$

The components are

$$\chi_1^2 = \frac{(a + b - np_1)^2}{np_1} + \frac{(c + d - nq_1)^2}{nq_1} = \frac{(a + b - np_1)^2}{np_1q_1}$$

$$\chi_2^2 = \frac{(a + c - np_2)^2}{np_2} + \frac{(b + d - nq_2)^2}{nq_2} = \frac{(a + c - np_2)^2}{np_2q_2}$$

$$\chi_3^2 = \Sigma\Sigma \frac{\{a - np_1p_2 - p_2(a + b - np_1) - p_1(a + c - np_2)\}^2}{np_1p_2}$$

$$= \frac{(aq_1q_2 - bp_2q_1 - cp_1q_2 + dp_1p_2)^2}{np_1p_2q_1q_2}$$

with 1 degree of freedom each.

Example 1.   Bateson found the following distribution of sweet pea plants obtained from an intercross so that the marginal frequencies are expected to be in the ratio $3:1$. If the two characters, flower color and pollen shape, are independently inherited, then the cell frequencies are expected to be in the ratio 9:3:3:1.

Pollen Shape	Flower Color		
	Purple	Red	
Long	296	27	323
Round	19	85	104
	315	112	427

It was seen (example 1, 5b.1) that the total χ^2 of discrepancy with 3 degrees of freedom is 222.1221, which is very high. The first component is

$$\chi_1{}^2 = \frac{(a + b - np_1)^2}{np_1q_1} = \frac{(323 - \frac{3}{4} \times 427)^2}{427 \times \frac{1}{4} \times \frac{3}{4}} = 0.0945$$

which is quite small for 1 degree of freedom, showing that the single factor segregation for pollen shape is as expected. The second component is

$$\chi_2{}^2 = \frac{(a + c - np_2)^2}{np_2q_2} = \frac{(315 - \frac{3}{4} \times 427)^2}{427 \times \frac{1}{4} \times \frac{3}{4}} = 0.3443$$

which again is quite small. The third component is

$$\chi_3{}^2 = \frac{(aq_1q_2 - bp_2q_1 - cp_1q_2 + dp_1p_2)^2}{np_1p_2q_1q_2}$$

$$= \frac{(296 - 27 \times 3 - 19 \times 3 + 85 \times 9)^2}{427 \times 3 \times 3 \times 1 \times 1} = 221.6833$$

which is very high for 1 degree of freedom. The total χ^2 is

$$0.0945 + 0.3443 + 221.6833 = 222.1221$$

thus agreeing with the total calculated earlier. It is seen that the whole discrepancy is concentrated in one component with a single degree of freedom. This shows that the departure of the observed from the expected cell frequencies is due to the dependence of the characters inherited but not to single factor segregations. The success of all statistical tests lies in isolating such components which are most efficient for judging the points at issue.

Suppose the hypothetical values of the marginal probabilities are not known. Then we estimate their values on the hypothesis

$$\pi_{ij} = \pi_i \cdot \pi_{\cdot j}$$

The best estimates are

$$\pi_i \cdot \sim \frac{n_i \cdot}{n \cdot \cdot} \quad \text{and} \quad \pi_{\cdot j} \sim \frac{n_{\cdot j}}{n \cdot \cdot}$$

These values may be substituted in the total χ^2.

$$\chi^2 = \Sigma\Sigma \frac{\left(n_{ij} - \dfrac{n_i \cdot n_{\cdot j}}{n}\right)^2}{\dfrac{n_i \cdot n_{\cdot j}}{n}}$$

Since $(r - 1) + (s - 1)$ parameters have been estimated, the above χ^2 has $(rs - 1) - (r - 1) - (s - 1) = (r - 1)(s - 1)$ degrees of freedom. At the estimated values the components χ_1^2 and χ_2^2 have zero values so that $\chi_3^2 = \chi^2$. Thus χ_3^2 measures the departure from independence.

This test is useful in two situations:

(i) Suppose that in example 1 above it is found that the marginal frequencies deviate significantly from the expected. This indicates that the assigned marginal probabilities may not be correct. In fact, if the single factor segregations are disturbed owing to unequal viability of the two types of plants, then the marginal frequencies will not be in the ratio 3:1. In such a case the third component χ_3^2 loses its importance, or, in other words, the significance of χ_3^2 may be due to the use of wrong proportions. The best course is then to substitute the estimated proportions and use the test obtained above.

(ii) The second situation is when nothing is specified about the marginal proportions. In this case only a test for independence is possible.

It may be observed that the test of independence in a contingency table is the same as the test of homogeneity in parallel samples described in 5b.3.

If the hypothetical proportions are not known in the above example, then the χ^2 for testing independence is

$$\frac{\{a - (a + b)(a + c)/n\}^2}{(a + b)(a + c)/n} + \frac{\{b - (a + b)(b + d)/n\}^2}{(a + b)(b + d)/n} + \cdots + \cdots$$

which reduces to

$$\frac{n(ad - bc)^2}{abcd} = \frac{427(296 \times 85 - 27 \times 19)^2}{315 \times 112 \times 323 \times 104} = 269.3095$$

This gives a χ^2 higher than that obtained by using the hypothetical values of the marginal proportions. Such discrepancies will not in general lead to contradictory conclusions. The earlier test makes use of the information supplied by a total of 427 plants in testing for independence, whereas the latter makes use of the information supplied by the set of configurations having the same marginal totals. Some marginal totals, as in the present case, are more informative than the average, whereas others are less.

Example 2. The following data give the number of skulls excavated in three different seasons and the sex distribution as sexed by investigator A working in the first two seasons and by B working in the third season.

	Seasons			Total
	First	Second	Third	
♂	162	180	210	552
♀	110	125	200	435
Total	272	305	410	987

Let us assume that in each season the excess of males is due to a random deviation from the expected equal numbers for the two sexes. The expected values are

♂	136	152.5	205
♀	136	152.5	205

giving a total of $\chi^2 = 9.9412 + 9.9180 + 0.2440 = 20.1032$, a high value for 3 degrees of freedom. Individually the deviations in the first two seasons ($\chi^2 = 9.9412$ and 9.9180) are significant. If the sex ratio is $1:1$ on the total, the χ^2 resulting from the marginal is

$$\frac{(552)^2}{493.5} + \frac{(435)^2}{493.5} - 987 = 13.8692$$

which leaves $\chi^2 = 20.1032 - 13.8692 = 6.2340$ with 2 degrees of freedom for testing the differences in the sex ratio in the three seasons. This is no doubt significant, showing differences in sex ratio, but the test is not strictly valid owing to the fact that the marginal totals are not compatible with the sex ratio 1:1, the $\chi^2 = 13.8692$ being significant for 1 degree of freedom. Having observed that there is an overall discrepancy from the sex ratio 1:1 in all three seasons put together, we might ask whether the sex ratio is the same for the three seasons although it may not be 1:1. A straight test of independence for fixed marginals or homogeneity of parallel samples (5b.3) can now be calculated. This gives χ^2 equal to 6.3222 with 2 degrees of freedom, showing significant differences in sex ratios in the three seasons. The agreement of this χ^2 with the earlier value of 6.2340 obtained by using the hypothetical ratios is, perhaps, accidental.

One must be careful in drawing conclusions from data of this nature. It must be observed that the skulls are sexed by a subjective method of anatomical appreciation. Different investigators have different methods of sexing, leading to different ratios. The observed discrepancy in the sex ratios for different seasons may be due to the investigator in the third season being different. The observed proportions are

Season	First	Second	Third	Overall
Proportion	0.5956	0.5902	0.5122	0.5593

The same investigator working in the first two seasons shows a smaller proportion in the second though not significantly different from the first, the χ^2 with 1 degree of freedom being 0.0175. But it is just as well that he thought that his method gave an excess of males in the first season and tried to alter his method consciously or unconsciously in the second season. The discrepancy between the investigators is then tested by the χ^2 test of independence from the table:

	First and Second Seasons	Third Season
♂	342	210
♀	235	200

The χ^2 with 1 degree of freedom is 6.3055, which is significant. Thus, out of a total χ^2 of 6.3222 with 2 degrees of freedom, measuring the differences in sex ratios, 1 degree alone accounts for 6.3055, which shows that the whole discrepancy between seasons is due only to the discrepancy between investigators. This might indicate a difference in the method of sexing or that the investigators' proportions referred to different strata from which the skulls are excavated and there might be stratum differences.

It should also be observed that the deviation of the overall sex ratio from 1:1 may be due to a wrong technique of sexing.

Example 3.   Consider the following data, collected from a number of schools, regarding speech defects (S_1, S_2, S_3) and physical defects (P_1, P_2, P_3) of school children.

	S_1	S_2	S_3	
P_1	45	26	12	83
P_2	32	50	21	103
P_3	4	10	17	31
	81	86	50	217

The expected values on the hypothesis of independence are:

30.982	32.894	19.124
38.447	40.820	23.733
11.571	12.286	7.143

The χ^2 with $2 \times 2 = 4$ degrees of freedom is 34.8828, which is significant. It is seen that, although the frequency in one cell is as small as 4, the expected is large enough for the χ^2 approximation to hold. But the frequency also should be large enough for the approximation to be good. In such cases it is reasonable to combine two cells by adding their frequencies and treat them as one cell for purposes of tests of significance. In the above example 4 and 10 may be added to yield an observed frequency of 14 with the corresponding expected $11.571 + 12.286 = 23.857$. The new χ^2 is 33.5763. Although the summation is now taken over one cell less, theoretically 1 degree of freedom is not lost. So to use the new χ^2 with $(4 - 1) = 3$ degrees of freedom is to overestimate significance, whereas to consider it as with 4 degrees of freedom is to underestimate significance. Although definite conclusions can be drawn either when the new χ^2 is not significant for 3 degrees of freedom or when it is significant for 4 degrees of freedom as in the present case, it is not possible to say anything when the new χ^2 is significant for 3 degrees and not for 4 degrees of freedom. In such a situation, for the purpose of the χ^2 test a new set of expected values may be obtained by considering the cells S_1P_3 and S_2P_3 as constituting a single cell. If p_1, q_1, r_1 and p_2, q_2, r_2 are the marginal proportions for physical defects and speech defects, then the probability of the observed frequencies on the hypothesis of independence is

$$\text{const. } (p_1p_2)^{45}(p_1q_2)^{26}(p_1r_2)^{12} \cdots \{(p_2 + q_2)r_1\}^{14}(r_1r_2)^{17}$$

The maximum likelihood estimates are

$$217p_1 = 83 \qquad 217q_1 = 103 \qquad 217r_1 = 31$$

$$217r_2 = 50 \qquad 76p_2 = 77q_2$$

which give

$$p_2 = 0.387308 \qquad q_2 = 0.382278 \qquad r_2 = 0.230414$$

The estimates of p_1, q_1, r_1 are the same as before. The new expectations are

32.147	31.729	19.124
39.893	39.375	23.733
(12.006 + 11.851)		7.143

and the χ^2 with $(7 - 4)$ degrees of freedom is 31.2472. This test is valid in the sense that when significance is noted the hypothesis of independence is rejected.

Fisher recommended a test based on likelihood, which is more appropriate when the cell frequencies are small. This is defined by

$$L \doteq 2\Sigma O \log \frac{O}{E}$$

which in tests of independence in a contingency table can be written

$$L = 2\{\Sigma\Sigma n_{ij} \log_e n_{ij} - \Sigma n_i. \log_e n_i. - \Sigma n_{.j} \log_e n_{.j} + n.. \log_e n..\}$$

In this case L is approximately distributed as χ^2 with $(r - 1)(s - 1)$ degrees of freedom. The value of L in the above problem is 30.4448, which is significant on 4 degrees of freedom. Even the use of L requires a large sample, in which case χ^2 and L tend to equivalence and there is no theoretical justification of one in preference to the other. In small samples the statistic L may be more appropriate, but it cannot be used unless its distribution is known. Therefore some such technique as that followed above may be used. It must be emphasized that the object of the test is first to establish departure from independence in a general way. For this it is enough to use a valid test which is simple to compute. Afterwards more refined tests may be used to examine some portions of the contingency table. For instance, we may inquire whether the two physical defects P_2 and P_3 and the speech defects S_1 and S_2 are associated. This needs a refined technique discussed in the next section.

5c.3 Tests of Independence in Small Samples

In testing for any hypothesis specifying some relations satisfied by the parameters it is seen that the exact values of the parameters estimated do not enter into the large sample distribution of the χ^2 statistic. But in small samples it might happen that the χ^2 approximation breaks down and/or the unknown parameters appear in the exact distribution of χ^2. In the latter case no exact test of significance is possible, owing to the presence of the unknown parameters in the probability distribution. Such unknown parameters are called nuisance parameters.

One way of getting rid of the nuisance parameters is to compare the particular observed sample, not with the whole population of samples with which a comparison might be made if the exact values of the nuisance parameters were known, but with a subpopulation selected with reference to the sample in such a way that the distribution of a statistic in this subpopulation does not involve any unknown parameter (Bartlett, 1937; Hotelling, 1940). For instance, it is shown that on the hypothesis of independence of two attributes the probability of cell frequencies, given the marginal totals, is

$$P(n_{ij} \mid n_i\cdot, n\cdot_j) = \frac{\Pi n_i\cdot !\Pi n\cdot_j!}{n\cdot\cdot!} \Pi\Pi \frac{1}{n_{ij}!}$$

which does not contain the hypothetical values $\pi_i\cdot$ and $\pi\cdot_j$. The distribution of χ^2 may then be found, using the conditional distribution of the cell frequencies. This admits the possibility of determining the exact probabilities in tests of independence.

Consider the fourfold table with frequencies a, b, c, d. The probability of the observed configuration, given the marginal totals, is

$$\frac{(a + b)!(a + c)!(b + d)!(c + d)!}{a!b!c!d!n!} \tag{5c.3.1}$$

If a, b, c, d are considered as four independent Poisson variates having the joint probability

$$e^{-m_1}\frac{m_1{}^a}{a!} e^{-m_2}\frac{m_2{}^b}{b!} e^{-m_3}\frac{m_3{}^c}{c!} e^{-m_4}\frac{m_4{}^d}{d!} \tag{5c.3.2}$$

where

$$m_1 = \frac{(a + b)(a + c)}{n}$$

$$m_2 = \frac{(b + d)(a + b)}{n}$$

$$m_3 = \frac{(a + c)(c + d)}{n}$$

$$m_4 = \frac{(b + d)(c + d)}{n}$$

then the probability of the totals $(a + b)$, $(a + c)$, $(b + d)$, $(c + d)$ is

$$e^{-(m_1+m_2+m_3+m_4)} \left(\frac{a+b}{n}\right)^{a+b} \left(\frac{a+c}{n}\right)^{a+c} \left(\frac{b+d}{n}\right)^{b+d} \left(\frac{c+d}{n}\right)^{c+d}$$

$$\times \Sigma \frac{1}{a!} \frac{1}{b!} \frac{1}{c!} \frac{1}{d!} \qquad (5c.3.3)$$

where the summation is taken over constant values of $(a + b)$, $(a + c)$, $(b + d)$, $(c + d)$. Since

$$\Sigma \frac{1}{a!}\frac{1}{b!}\frac{1}{c!}\frac{1}{d!} = \frac{n!}{(a + b)!(a + c)!(b + d)!(c + d)!}$$

the probability of a, b, c, d for given values of $(a + b)$, $(a + c)$, $(b + d)$, $(c + d)$ is the ratio of the expression (5c.3.2) to (5c.3.3),

$$\frac{(a + b)!(a + c)!(b + d)!(c + d)!}{n!\,a!\,b!\,c!\,d!}$$

which is the same as the expression (5c.3.1). Thus the probability of a given configuration in a contingency table for given marginal totals may be considered as a relative probability of four Poisson variates subject to three independent restrictions. If the values of m_1, m_2, m_3, m_4 or the expected cell frequencies are large, the Poisson distributions tend to normality, in which case the χ^2 statistic is distributed as χ^2 with 1 degree of freedom. On the other hand, if the expectations are small the continuous distribution of χ^2 cannot be used. In such a case a direct approach is to calculate the sum of the probabilities of the observed and the less probable configurations and to reject the hypothesis if this sum is small (either below 5 or 1%). The following illustrations explain the method.

Example 1. Do the following data on sociability (S) and nonsociability (NS) of soldiers recruited in cities (C) and villages (V) suggest that city soldiers are more sociable than village soldiers?

	S	NS	
C	13	4	17
V	6	14	20
	19	18	37

The smaller frequencies in one diagonal suggest that city soldiers are more sociable. But it must be ascertained whether such a configuration as the observed and those indicating a higher degree of sociability of the city recruits can occur by chance if in fact there was no difference in the sociabilities of the city and the village recruits. Since for fixed marginals the probability of a given configuration a, b, c, d in the four cells is

$$\frac{17!20!19!18!}{37!} \quad \frac{1}{a!b!c!d!}$$

we find that the probabilities for configurations with 4, 3, 2, 1, and 0 in the north-east corner cell (these being less favorable to the hypothesis of independence and more to the alternative suggested) are, respectively, 0.0^25218, 0.0^35966, 0.0^43607, 0.0^51097, and 0.0^71075, adding up to 0.0059. The chances are very small, thus indicating that city soldiers are more sociable than village soldiers.

If the cell frequencies are not small, this result could be established by calculating χ^2 for testing independence and determining the probability of a normal deviate with zero mean and unit variance exceeding χ (example 2 in 5b.1). In the above case

$$\chi^2 = \frac{37(13 \times 14 - 6 \times 4)^2}{13 \times 14 \times 6 \times 14} = 7.9435$$

$$\chi = \sqrt{7.9435} = 2.8181$$

so that the normal probability is 0.0025, which is smaller than the actual value 0.0059, the discrepancy being due to smallness of the sample.

Yates suggested that by calculating χ^2 from a table obtained by increasing the smaller frequency * by $\frac{1}{2}$ without altering the marginal totals a closer approximation to the actual probability is realized. In the present example, the new χ^2, said to be corrected for continuity, is 6.1922. The value of $\chi = 2.4884$, so that the normal probability is 0.0064, which is closer to the actual value than in the case of the uncorrected χ^2.

A slightly different method suggested by V. M. Dandekar involves the calculation of χ_0^2, χ_{-1}^2, and χ_1^2 for the observed configuration and those obtained by increasing and decreasing the smallest frequency by unity. From these a corrected χ^2 can be obtained from the formula

$$\chi_c^2 = \chi_0^2 - \frac{\chi_0^2 - \chi_{-1}^2}{\chi_1^2 - \chi_{-1}^2} (\chi_1^2 - \chi_0^2)$$

---

* The reference is to the smaller frequency in the diagonal (6,4) under consideration indicating nonsociability of the village recruits. In the general test of independence $\frac{1}{2}$ is to be added to a frequency so as to obtain a smaller χ^2.

In the present example $\chi_0^2 = 7.9435$, $\chi_1^2 = 12.0995$, $\chi_{-1}^2 = 4.6587$, and

$$\chi_c^2 = 7.9435 - \frac{7.9435 - 4.6587}{12.0995 - 4.6587}(12.0995 - 7.9435) = 6.1086$$

$$\sqrt{\chi_c} = 2.4715$$

The normal probability is 0.0068, which is also close to the actual value. The likelihood test

$$L = 2\Sigma O \log_e \frac{O}{E}$$

in this case gives the value 8.2811. The value of χ is $\sqrt{8.2811} = 2.8778$ so that the probability is much smaller than the actual value. Thus the likelihood test does not improve the situation.

Example 2. In example 1, the object of investigation was to study whether city soldiers are more sociable than village soldiers. This necessitated consideration of the deviations from the expected in one way only. But, in general, if the object is to discover association between two attributes without specifying the nature of the association, it is necessary to consider all possible deviations from the expected. Thus, if a plant can be classified with respect to one of two flower colors and one of two pollen shapes, we pose the question whether the pollen shape and flower color are independent. In such a case we have to determine the total probability of the observed configuration and those less probable than this. Let us consider the same data as in example 1. The configurations less probable than the observed and indicating association in one way have the values 3, 2, 1, and 0 in the north-east cell of the table. The probabilities of these configurations and the observed have been calculated in that example, and they add up to 0.0059. The configurations less probable than the observed but indicating association the other way are those which have 4, 3, 2, 1, and 0 in the north-west corner and their probabilities are, respectively, $0.0^2 2088$, $0.0^3 1864$, $0.0^5 8733$, $0.0^6 1828$, and $0.0^8 1132$, adding up to 0.0023. The total probability is then $0.0059 + 0.0023 = 0.0082$, which is small, thus indicating departure from independence.

If the sample is large, we can find the probability by directly entering the uncorrected χ^2 in a χ^2 table with 1 degree of freedom. In the present example $\chi^2 = 7.9435$ with the associated probability about 0.005, which is smaller than the actual value 0.0082.

Using Yates' correction for continuity, the $\chi^2 = 6.1922$, with the corresponding probability 0.0128, which is higher than the actual value.

To extend Dandekar's correction to this case we first note that the

χ^2 values below and above the observed $\chi^2 = 7.9435$ are 6.0598 and 9.7448, corresponding to the partitions

<table>
<tr><td>5</td><td>12</td><td></td><td>4</td><td>13</td></tr>
<tr><td></td><td></td><td>and</td><td></td><td></td></tr>
<tr><td>14</td><td>6</td><td></td><td>15</td><td>5</td></tr>
</table>

The corrected χ^2 is

$$\chi^2 = 7.9435 - \frac{7.9435 - 6.0598}{9.7448 - 6.0598}(9.7448 - 7.9435)$$

$$= 7.0228$$

which gives a probability 0.0082, almost exactly equal to the actual value. In general, Dandekar's correction is slightly better than that of Yates, although the correction is simpler in Yates' method. In testing for linkage on the basis of data classified according to two factors, it is enough to test for association one way if it is known that the recombination fraction is less than $\frac{1}{2}$. It is now known that the recombination fraction can exceed $\frac{1}{2}$, as demonstrated by Fisher. So it is better first to disprove the hypothesis of independence without inquiring as to the nature of association. Further it must be noted that departure from independence may occur owing to various causes in experimental data, and it is better to use a test which gives a direct appraisal of the data as to its compatibility with the hypothesis of independence.

5d Tests in Poisson Populations

It was shown in 2a.3 that the probability of k independent Poisson variates can be written as the product of

$$P(X_1 + \cdots + X_k) = e^{-\mu_1 - \cdots - \mu_k}\frac{(\Sigma\mu)^{\Sigma X}}{(\Sigma X)!}$$

and

$$P(X_1, \cdots, X_k \mid \Sigma X) = \frac{(\Sigma X)!}{X_1! \cdots X_k!}\left(\frac{\mu_1}{\Sigma\mu}\right)^{X_1} \cdots \left(\frac{\mu_k}{\Sigma\mu}\right)^{X_k}$$

the latter being the multinomial probability. Testing whether the observations have come from the same Poisson population is equivalent to testing whether in a series of $(X_1 + \cdots + X_k)$ trials the frequencies $X_1, \cdots, X_k$ could arise from a multinomial distribution with equal probabilities in the k classes, since $(\mu_i/\Sigma\mu) = 1/k$, if μ_i are all equal. For instance, to test whether the observations 8, 3, 1 could have arisen from the same Poisson population, the test explained in example 3 of 5b.1 could be carried out. If the individual values are not small, then the

χ^2 test of departure from expected values could be used. The expected value is $\overline{X} = \Sigma X/k$, corresponding to each X_i, so that

$$\chi^2 = \frac{\Sigma(X_i - \overline{X})^2}{\overline{X}} = \frac{\Sigma X_i^2}{\overline{X}} - k\overline{X}$$

This has $(k - 1)$ degrees of freedom. We can also test any hypothesis specifying the proportions $\lambda_i = \mu_i/\Sigma\mu$. This is equivalent to testing whether the frequencies could have arisen from a multinomial population with proportions $\lambda_1, \cdots, \lambda_k$ so that the χ^2 with $(k - 1)$ degrees of freedom is

$$\chi^2 = \Sigma \frac{(X_i - \lambda_i\Sigma X)^2}{\lambda_i\Sigma X}$$

Example 1. Four samples of sizes 120, 100, 100, 125 from Poisson populations gave the following mean values: 251/120, 323/100, 180/100, 426/125. Do the populations have the same mean values?

It is seen in 2a.3 that the sum of n independent Poisson variates is also a Poisson variate with mean value equal to n times the mean of the original population. Considering the sums observed and assuming equal mean μ for all the four populations, we have the following.

					Total
Sum	251	323	180	426	1180
Expected	120 μ	100 μ	100 μ	125 μ	445 μ

The test for equality of mean values is equivalent to testing whether the sums are in the ratio $120:100:100:125$. The expected distribution of 1180 is

$$318.20 \qquad 265.17 \qquad 265.17 \qquad 331.46$$

so that $\chi^2 = 81.12$, which is significant for 3 degrees of freedom. The mean values cannot be considered to be the same for all populations.

Example 2. Obtain the distribution of entries in a two-way table for fixed marginals if the observation in the (i,j)th cell is regarded as a Poisson variate with mean value $\tau_i\beta_j$. Assume that $\Sigma\tau_i = \tau$ and $\Sigma\beta_j = \beta$. The joint distribution of n_{ij}, $(i = 1, \cdots, r; j = 1, \cdots, s)$, is

$$e^{-\Sigma\Sigma\tau_i\beta_j}\Pi\Pi\frac{(\tau_i\beta_j)^{n_{ij}}}{n_{ij}!} = e^{-\Sigma\tau_i\beta}\Pi\frac{(\tau_i\beta)^{n_i.}}{n_i.!} \times e^{-\Sigma\tau\beta_j}\Pi\frac{(\tau\beta_j)^{n_{.j}}}{n_{.j}!}$$

$$\times \frac{1}{e^{-\tau\beta}\dfrac{(\tau\beta)^{n..}}{n..!}} \times \frac{\Pi n_i.!\Pi n_{.j}!}{n..!\Pi\Pi n_{ij}!}$$

The last expression is the desired probability, the first three representing the joint probability of the observed marginals. The relative probability is the same as in a contingency table with two independent attributes and fixed marginals. In any problem a test of independence can be carried out to test the hypothesis that the mean of the Poisson population for the (i, j)th cell can be written as the product of two parameters specific for the ith row and the jth column. If this is true, then the marginal totals can be used to test whether τ_i are identical or β_j are identical.

In an analysis of randomized blocks, when the plot yields can be considered to be Poisson variates it seems reasonable to set up the product hypothesis $\tau_i\beta_j$, τ_i representing the treatment effect, and β_j the block effect. The adequacy of the product hypothesis can be tested before testing for treatment differences.

5e   Transformation of Statistics

5e.1   A General Lemma

Let the joint distribution of the statistics $T_1, \cdots, T_k$ tend to the k-variate normal form with mean values $\theta_1, \cdots, \theta_k$ and dispersion matrix $n^{-1}(\sigma_{ij})$, where σ_{ij} are finite and n is the sample size. This means that the variables $\sqrt{n}(T_1 - \theta_1), \cdots, \sqrt{n}(T_k - \theta_k)$ are in the limit distributed as a k-variate normal distribution with zero mean values and dispersion matrix (σ_{ij}).

Lemma: If $f(T_1, \cdots, T_k)$ is a continuous function with continuous first partial derivatives then the variable

$$u = \sqrt{n}[f(T_1, \cdots, T_k) - f(\theta_1, \cdots, \theta_k)]$$

is distributed normally in the limit with zero mean and variance

$$\Sigma\Sigma\sigma_{ij}\frac{\partial f}{\partial \theta_i}\frac{df}{\partial \theta_j}$$

Since $f(T_1, \cdots, T_k)$ has continuous partial derivatives in the neighborhood of $\theta_1, \cdots, \theta_k$, expanding by the mean value theorem we get

$$f(T_1, \cdots, T_k) = f(\theta_1, \cdots, \theta_k) + \Sigma(T_i - \theta_i)\left(\frac{\partial f}{\partial \theta_i} + \eta_i\right)$$

where $\eta_i \to 0$ as $T_i \to \theta_i$. Now

$$u - \sqrt{n}\Sigma(T_i - \theta_i)\frac{\partial f}{\partial \theta_i} = \sqrt{n}\Sigma(T_i - \theta_i)\eta_i$$

so that u and $\sqrt{n}\Sigma(T_i - \theta_i)(\partial_f/\partial\theta_i)$ have the same limiting distribution if $\sqrt{n}\Sigma(T_i - \theta_i)\eta_i \to 0$ stochastically. To prove this it is enough to show that $\sqrt{n}(T_i - \theta_i)\eta_i \to 0$ stochastically for all i.

$$P\{|\sqrt{n}(T_i - \theta_i)\eta_i| < \epsilon\}$$
$$> P\{|\sqrt{n}(T_i - \theta_i)\eta_i| < \epsilon \quad \text{and} \quad |\eta_i| \le \epsilon'\}$$
$$> P\{|\sqrt{n}(T_i - \theta_i)| < \epsilon/\epsilon' \quad \text{and} \quad |\eta_i| \le \epsilon'\}$$
$$> P\{|\sqrt{n}(T_i - \theta_i)| < \epsilon/\epsilon'\} - P\{|\eta_i| > \epsilon'\}$$

Since $\sqrt{n}(T_i - \theta_i)$ is normally distributed in the limit, $P\{|\sqrt{n}(T_i - \theta_i)| < A\}$ can be made greater than $(1 - \delta')$ for any δ' by choosing A and n sufficiently large. Also since $T_i \to \theta_i$ stochastically and $\eta_i \to 0$ as $T_i \to \theta_i$ mathematically, it follows that $P\{|\eta_i| > \epsilon'\} < \delta''$ for large n, however small ϵ' may be. If now ϵ' is chosen such that $\epsilon/\epsilon' = A$, then

$$P\{|\sqrt{n}(T_i - \theta_i)| < \epsilon/\epsilon'\} - P\{|\eta_i| > \epsilon'\} > 1 - \delta' - \delta'' > 1 - \delta$$

since δ' and δ'' are arbitrary. This proves the required result. The statistic $\Sigma(T_i - \theta_i)(\partial f/\partial\theta_i)$, being a linear function of statistics which tend to be normally distributed, is itself normally distributed in the limit with

$$E\left\{\Sigma(T_i - \theta_i)\frac{\partial f}{\partial\theta_i}\right\} = \Sigma E(T_i - \theta_i)\frac{\partial f}{\partial\theta_i} \to 0$$

and

$$V\left\{\Sigma(T_i - \theta_i)\frac{\partial f}{\partial\theta_i}\right\} = \frac{1}{n}\Sigma\Sigma\frac{\partial f}{\partial\theta_i}\frac{\partial f}{\partial\theta_j}\sigma_{ij}$$

Therefore $f(T_1, \cdots, T_k)$ has the asymptotic mean and variance

$$f(\theta_1, \cdots, \theta_k) \quad \text{and} \quad \frac{1}{n}\Sigma\Sigma\frac{\partial f}{\partial\theta_i}\frac{\partial f}{\partial\theta_j}\sigma_{ij} \qquad (5e.1.1)$$

As a particular case of this lemma it follows that, if T is asymptotically distributed normally about θ, then any function $F(T)$ of T is asymptotically normally distributed about $F(\theta)$ with variance $(dF/d\theta)^2 \psi(\theta)$ where $\psi(\theta)$ is the variance of T, provided that dF/dT is continuous in the neighborhood of θ.

If T is an efficient statistic, then $1/\psi(\theta) \simeq I(\theta)$, where I is the information, in which case $F(T)$ as an estimate of $F(\theta)$ has the asymptotic variance $\{F'(\theta)\}^2/I$, which is the minimum attainable. Therefore $F(T)$ is efficient as an estimate of $F(\theta)$.

In some cases $\psi(\theta)$, the variance of T, may be independent of θ. Otherwise it may be necessary to transform the statistic T such that the new statistic has an asymptotic variance independent of θ. Let $F(T)$ be the transformation needed; then

$$V\{F(T)\} = \{F'(\theta)\}^2\psi(\theta)$$

On equating this to a constant, the following differential equation is obtained.

$$\frac{dF}{d\theta} = \frac{c}{\sqrt{\psi(\theta)}}$$

or

$$F = \int \frac{c\, d\theta}{\sqrt{\psi(\theta)}}$$

This result is applied in deriving the following transformations.

5e.2   The Square Root Transformation of the Poisson Variate

If x is a Poisson variate, then

$$E(x) = \mu \qquad V(x) = \mu$$

The functional form of the transformation is supplied by

$$F(\mu) = \int \frac{c\, d\mu}{\sqrt{\mu}}$$

$$= \sqrt{\mu}$$

by choosing c suitably. The transformed variable $\sqrt{x}$ has the asymptotic mean and variance

$$\sqrt{\mu} \qquad \text{and} \qquad \tfrac{1}{4}$$

when μ is large. It was found by Anscombe (1948) that the transformation $\sqrt{x + b}$ where b is a suitably determined constant has some theoretical advantages. Let $(x - \mu) = t$ and $(\mu + b) = \mu'$; then by using Taylor's expansion we find

$$\sqrt{x + b} = \sqrt{\mu'} \left\{ 1 + a_1\frac{t}{\mu'} - a_2\left(\frac{t}{\mu'}\right)^2 + \cdots \right\}$$

where

$$a_s = (-1)^{s+1}(-1)(-3) \cdots \frac{(-2s + 3)}{s!2^s}$$

Observing that the Poisson moments are

$$E(t) = 0 \qquad E(t^2) = \mu \qquad E(t^3) = \mu \qquad E(t^4) = 3\mu^2 + \mu$$

we find, by taking expectations of both sides of the expansion

$$E\sqrt{x+b} = \sqrt{\mu+b} - \frac{1}{8\sqrt{\mu}} + \frac{24b-7}{128\mu\sqrt{\mu}} + \cdots$$

$$V\sqrt{x+b} = \frac{1}{4}\left\{1 + \frac{3-8b}{8\mu} + \frac{32b^2 - 52b + 17}{32\mu^2} + \cdots\right\}$$

which, on choosing the value $b = \frac{3}{8}$, reduce to

$$E\sqrt{x+\tfrac{3}{8}} = \sqrt{\mu+\tfrac{3}{8}} - \frac{1}{8\sqrt{\mu}} + \frac{1}{64\mu\sqrt{\mu}} + \cdots$$

$$V(\sqrt{x+\tfrac{3}{8}}) = \frac{1}{4}\left(1 + \frac{1}{16\mu^2} + \cdots\right)$$

The variance of $\sqrt{x+\frac{3}{8}}$ is more stable than that of $\sqrt{x}$ because the second term in the expansion of the variance of $\sqrt{x+\frac{3}{8}}$ is $O(1/\mu^2)$.

5e.3   The Sin^{-1} Transformation of the Binomial Proportion

The binomial proportion r/n has the mean value π and variance $\pi(1-\pi)/n$. The transformation is obtained by solving the equation

$$F(\pi) = \int \frac{c\sqrt{n}}{\sqrt{\pi(1-\pi)}} \, d\pi$$

$$= \sin^{-1}\sqrt{\pi} \qquad \text{choosing } c \text{ suitably}$$

$$V\left(\sin^{-1}\sqrt{\frac{r}{n}}\right) = \frac{1}{4n} \qquad \text{approximately}$$

It is shown by Anscombe (1948) that a slightly better transformation is

$$\sin^{-1}\sqrt{\frac{r+\frac{3}{8}}{n+\frac{3}{4}}}$$

which has the asymptotic variance $1/(4n+2)$. If n is large, the simpler transformation $\sin^{-1}\sqrt{r/n}$ can be used; for moderately large sample sizes the refined transformation $\sin^{-1}\sqrt{(r+\frac{3}{8})/(n+\frac{3}{4})}$ may be used.

Example. R. A. Fisher (1949) found the following recombination fractions between *undulated* and *agouti* loci in house mice. The data relate to backcrosses so that the estimate of the fraction is the ratio of recombinants to the total offsprings.

TABLE 5e.3α.   Recombination Fractions Observed for Twenty
Classes of Heterozygous Parents *

	$A^Y A^L$	$A^Y A$	$A^Y a^t$	$A^Y a$	$A^L A$
♀	$\frac{12}{194}$	$\frac{5}{118}$	$\frac{12}{235}$	$\frac{10}{146}$	$\frac{2}{78}$
♂	$\frac{9}{128}$	$\frac{9}{126}$	$\frac{6}{160}$	$\frac{16}{243}$	$\frac{7}{214}$

	$A^L a^t$	$A^L a$	$A a^t$	$A a$	$a^t a$	Total
♀	$\frac{9}{182}$	$\frac{4}{210}$	$\frac{10}{231}$	$\frac{8}{178}$	$\frac{11}{159}$	$\frac{83}{1731}$
♂	$\frac{7}{213}$	$\frac{4}{144}$	$\frac{13}{218}$	$\frac{3}{159}$	$\frac{13}{238}$	$\frac{87}{1843}$

* The number in the denominator gives the number of animals contributing to the ratio.

Heterozygote $A^Y A^L$

	Recombinations	Old Combinations	Total
♀	12	182	194
♂	9	119	128

The data for any heterozygote supply a test with 1 degree of freedom for sex difference in the recombination fraction. The (independence) χ^2 for sex difference is 0.0905. Similarly, we obtain the individual χ^2 for each of the ten types of heterozygotes and obtain the sum 4.827 which has nearly 90% probability for 10 degrees of freedom, indicating no sex difference. If we ignore sex differences, then on pooling the data over sex we obtain a contingency table for heterozygotes and the nature of combinations (old or new). This supplies a $\chi^2 = 16.315$ with 9 degrees of freedom showing significant differences in the recombination fractions for the various heterozygotes.

This example is not suitable for further analysis on sex differences. Suppose that it is found that sex differences exist in all the ten types of mating. Then the further problem arises as to whether the sex difference is the same in all the cases. That is, we need to test whether there is interaction between sex and the nature of the heterozygote. This can be done by using the angular transformation and then applying analysis of variance. Corresponding to each observed proportion p, an angle ϕ is determined such that $p = \sin^2\phi$. If ϕ is given in degrees, as in Table 12 of the Fisher and Yates tables, then ϕ has the variance

$8100/n\pi^2$ or approximately $820.7/n$. The 20 angles and the necessary computational steps are as given below.

	$A^Y A^L$	$A^Y A$	$A^Y a^t$	$A^Y a$	$A^L a$
♀	14.4	11.8	13.0	15.1	9.2
♂	15.3	15.4	11.2	14.9	10.4
d = difference	−0.9	−3.6	1.8	0.2	−1.2
$w = n_1 n_2/(n_1 + n_2)$	77.12	60.93	95.19	91.20	57.16
dw	−69.41	−219.35	171.34	18.24	−68.59
$d^2 w = d(dw)$	62.47	789.65	308.41	3.65	82.31

	$A^L a^t$	$A^L a$	$A a^t$	$A a$	$a^t a$	
♀	12.7	7.9	11.9	12.2	15.2	
♂	10.4	9.6	14.2	7.9	13.5	
d	2.3	−1.7	−2.3	4.3	1.7	Total
w	98.14	85.42	112.16	83.98	95.32	856.62
dw	225.72	−145.21	−257.97	361.11	162.04	177.92
$d^2 w$	519.16	246.86	593.33	1552.79	275.47	4434.10

The χ^2 with 10 degrees of freedom for testing sex differences in all the ten types is

$$4434.10 \div 820.7 = 5.40$$

This is slightly above the value 4.827 obtained earlier by a direct χ^2 analysis. From the 10 degrees of freedom χ^2 we subtract the χ^2 with 1 degree

$$\frac{(\Sigma dw)^2}{\Sigma w} \div 820.7 = (177.92)^2 \div (856.62)(820.7) = 0.05$$

due to overall sex difference. The residual

$$5.40 - 0.05 = 5.35$$

is the χ^2 with 9 degrees of freedom for testing whether sex difference depends on the type of the heterozygote. This interaction χ^2 is not significant, nor is that due to sex difference. In such a case, the differences in the various types of heterozygotes can be studied by summing over sex. To complete the analysis, however, we determine the χ^2 due to differences in heterozygotes, eliminating sex difference. The total χ^2 with $(20 - 1) = 19$ degrees of freedom is

$$\left\{ \Sigma n\phi^2 - \frac{(\Sigma n\phi)^2}{\Sigma n} \right\} \div 820.7$$

the summation extending over the 20 angles. The following computations are made.

$$\Sigma n\phi^2 - \frac{(\Sigma n\phi)^2}{\Sigma n}$$

	Σn	$\Sigma n\phi$	$\Sigma n\phi^2$	$= 820.7\chi^2$	χ^2
♀	1731	21,470.9	274,666.21	8,346.43	10.17
♂	1843	22,699.4	290,576.08	10,997.81	13.40
Overall	3574	44,170.3	565,242.29	19,351.02	23.58

The total of χ^2 for ♀ and ♂

$$10.17 + 13.40 = 23.57$$

has 18 degrees of freedom. Subtracting the interaction component of 5.35 on 9 degrees of freedom, the residual χ^2 with 9 degrees of freedom for testing differences in heterozygotes eliminating sex is

$$23.57 - 5.35 = 18.22$$

which is significant. This can also be calculated in a slightly different way. The sex χ^2, ignoring differences in heterozygotes, is obtained as follows.

$$820.7\chi^2 = \frac{21,470.9^2}{1731} + \frac{22,699.4^2}{1843} - \frac{44,170.3^2}{3574}$$

$$\chi^2 = 0.01$$

the values being obtained from $\Sigma n\phi$ and Σn over all heterozygotes. The valid χ^2 for heterozygotes is obtained by subtracting from the total the above value and the interaction sum of squares. This leads to the value, $23.58 - 0.01 - 5.35 = 18.22$, the same as before.

TABLE 5e.3β.   Analysis of χ^2

	Degrees of Freedom	
Sex	1	0.05
Heterozygotes	9	18.22
Interaction	9	5.35
Total	19	23.58

The total χ^2 with 19 degrees of freedom is significant, showing overall differences. The various components of χ^2 do not add up to the total because the proportions are based on different numbers. If the interaction component is high, then a precise test will be to calculate the mean χ^2 for heterozygotes and interaction

$$\frac{18.22}{9} = 2.024 \qquad \frac{5.35}{9} = 0.594$$

and determine the variance ratio

$$\frac{2.024}{0.594} = 3.407$$

with 9 and 9 degrees of freedom. This is significant on the 5% level.

5e.4   Other Useful Transformations

The estimated variance

$$s^2 = \frac{\Sigma(x_i - \bar{x})^2}{n - 1}$$

where $x_1, \cdots, x_n$ are n random observations from a normal population, has the expected value σ^2 and variance $2\sigma^4/(n - 1)$. The transformation needed to make the variance independent of σ is

$$F(\sigma) = \int \frac{c\sqrt{n - 1}\, d\sigma^2}{\sqrt{2\sigma^4}}$$

$$= \log \sigma^2 \qquad \text{choosing } c \text{ suitably}$$

$$V(\log s^2) = \frac{2}{n - 1} \qquad \text{approximately}$$

The estimated correlation from n pairs of observations from a bivariate normal distribution has the asymptotic variance

$$\frac{(1 - \rho^2)^2}{n - 1}$$

The necessary transformation is

$$F(\rho) = \int \frac{c\sqrt{n - 1}}{1 - \rho^2}\, d\rho$$

$$= \tanh^{-1} \rho \qquad \text{choosing } c \text{ suitably}$$

$$V(\tanh^{-1} r) \sim \frac{1}{n - 1}$$

The uses of these transformed statistics with slight refinements will be discussed in Chapter 6.

5f   Large Sample Standard Errors of Moments

5f.1   Variances and Covariances of Raw Moment Statistics

Any population may be defined with respect to a number of frequency classes with probabilities $\pi_1, \cdots, \pi_k$ and the corresponding values of a variate $x_1, \cdots, x_k$. A continuous distribution can be considered to contain an infinite number of class intervals, each of length dx, the differential element. In such a case the raw moments in the population are

$$\nu_r = \pi_1 x_1{}^r + \cdots + \pi_k x_k{}^r \qquad r = 1, 2, \cdots$$

If $n_1, n_2, \cdots, n_k$, $(\Sigma n_i = n)$, are the observed frequencies in the k classes, then the rth sample moment about the origin is

$$O_r = \frac{(n_1 x_1{}^r + \cdots + n_k x_k{}^r)}{n}$$

which is a linear function of the frequencies. If O_s is the sth sample moment, then using the results (2a.9.1) we find

$$E(O_r) = \Sigma x_i{}^r \pi_i = \nu_r$$

$$V(O_r) = \frac{1}{n} \{\Sigma x_i{}^{2r} \pi_i - (\Sigma x_i{}^r \pi_i)^2\}$$

$$= \frac{\nu_{2r} - \nu_r{}^2}{n}$$

$$\text{cov } (O_r, O_s) = \frac{1}{n} \{\Sigma x_i{}^r x_i{}^s \pi_i - (\Sigma x_i{}^r \pi_i)(\Sigma x_i{}^s \pi_i)\}$$

$$= \frac{\nu_{r+s} - \nu_r \nu_s}{n}$$

If the origin is the population mean, then in the above expressions the moments ν_r about an arbitrary origin will be replaced by μ_r, the population rth moment about the mean.

The rth moment about the sample mean is

$$m_r = O_r - \binom{r}{1} O_{r-1} O_1 + \binom{r}{2} O_{r-2} O_1{}^2 - \cdots (-1)^r O_1{}^r$$

Since this is invariant for origin, we can consider O_r to be the sample raw moments about the population mean as the origin. We now use formula (5e.1.1) for determining the asymptotic variance of m_r.

$$\frac{\partial m_r}{\partial O_r} = 1 \qquad \frac{\partial m_r}{\partial O_{r-s}} = (-1)^s \binom{r}{s} O_1{}^s$$

$$\frac{\partial m_r}{\partial O_1} = -rO_{r-1} + \binom{r}{2} O_{r-2}(2O_1) - \cdots$$

Using the approximation

$$m_r - \mu_r \sim (O_r - \mu_r) - r\mu_{r-1}(O_1 - \mu_1)$$

since all the other derivatives vanish at the expected values, we find

$$V(m_r) = E(m_r - \mu_r)^2 \sim V(O_r) - 2r\mu_{r-1} \operatorname{cov}(O_r - \mu_r)(O_1 - \mu_1)$$
$$+ r^2\mu^2{}_{r-1}V(O_1)$$

$$= \frac{1}{n}\{\mu_{2r} - \mu_r{}^2 - 2r\mu_{r-1}\mu_{r+1} + r^2\mu^2{}_{r-1}\mu_2\}$$

Similarly

$$\operatorname{cov}(m_r, m_s) = \frac{1}{n}\{\mu_{r+s} - \mu_r\mu_s + rs\mu_2\mu_{r-1}\mu_{s-1} - r\mu_{r-1}\mu_{s+1} - s\mu_{r+1}\mu_{s-1}\}$$

As special cases we obtain the large sample variances:

$$V(m_2) = \frac{1}{n}(\mu_4 - \mu_2{}^2)$$

$$V(m_3) = \frac{1}{n}(\mu_6 - \mu_3{}^2 - 6\mu_2\mu_4 + 9\mu_2{}^3)$$

$$V(m_4) = \frac{1}{n}(\mu_8 - \mu_4{}^2 - 8\mu_5\mu_3 + 16\mu_2\mu_3{}^2)$$

$$V(O_1, \text{ about the origin}) = \frac{\mu_2}{n}$$

the last formula being exact.

Example. The variance of the coefficient of variation $100\sqrt{m_2}/O_1$, where O_1 is the average about the origin, is

$$\frac{\eta^2}{n}\left(\frac{\mu_4 - \mu_2{}^2}{4\mu_2{}^2} + \frac{\mu_2}{\mu_1{}'^2} - \frac{\mu_3}{\mu_2\mu_1{}'}\right)$$

where η is the population value $100\sqrt{\mu_2}/\mu_1{}'$.

5f.2 Large Sample Tests of Difference between Means and an Illustration of the P_λ Test

Let $\bar{x}_1$, $\bar{x}_2$ be the mean values and $s_1{}^2$, $s_2{}^2$ the estimated variances in two samples of sizes n_1 and n_2, respectively. The standard errors of $\bar{x}_1$ and $\bar{x}_2$ are $\sqrt{s_1{}^2/n_1}$ and $\sqrt{s_2{}^2/n_2}$, and hence that of $\bar{x}_1 - \bar{x}_2$ is $\sqrt{s_1{}^2/n_1 + s_2{}^2/n_2}$. If n_1 and n_2 are large, the statistic

$$w = \frac{\bar{x}_1 - \bar{x}_2}{\sqrt{\dfrac{s_1{}^2}{n_1} + \dfrac{s_2{}^2}{n_2}}}$$

can be used as a normal deviate with zero mean and unit standard deviation to test the hypothesis that the samples are drawn from populations having the same mean, nothing being specified about the variations.

It is not necessary that the original populations be normal, provided that the samples are large enough. How large the sample should be depends on the nature of the populations. Populations with highly skew or multimodal distributions require very large samples.

In a feeding experiment with pasteurized and unpasteurized milk, Elderton (1933) found the following values of w and the associated normal probabilities. The samples were large so that the difference in mean statures divided by the standard error of difference could be used as a normal deviate.

TABLE 5f.2α. Values of w and Probabilities for Each Age Group

Age Group of Boys	Observed $w = w_o$	Probability $P(w \geq w_o)$	$\log_{10} P$
6¾	2.69	0.0035726	$\bar{3}.5529844$
7¾	−0.71	0.7611479	$\bar{1}.8814690$
8¾	1.24	0.1074877	$\bar{1}.0313588$
9¾	1.84	0.0328841	$\bar{2}.5169849$
10¾	1.06	0.1445723	$\bar{1}.1600851$
		Total	$\bar{6}.1428822$
			$= -5.8571178$

It is found that the probabilities are less than 5% only in two cases. Should we then say that pasteurized milk is beneficial only for the age groups 6¾ and 9¾ and not for the other age groups? The positive deviations (of w) in 4 out of 5 cases indicate a taller stature for boys fed on pasteurized milk, and the nonsignificance, in some cases, may be due to the inadequacy of the numbers or to the presence of high variance in the stature of boys chosen for the experiment. On the other hand, it may be argued that 2 significant cases out of 5 could arise by chance, even when pasteurized milk does not affect the stature of boys. In such cases the evidences supplied by the various groups have to be combined to answer the problem of differences caused by feed. This can be done by calculating the statistic

$$P_\lambda = -2\Sigma \log_e P_i$$

$$= -2 \log_e 10 \sum_{i=1}^{5} \log_{10} P_i$$

$$= -2(2.3026)(-5.85712) = 26.9732$$

which is distributed as χ^2 with 5×2 degrees of freedom, as shown in 2a.8. In the above problem $\chi^2 = 26.9732$, which as χ^2 with 10 degrees of freedom is significant on the 1% level. This shows that pasteurized milk causes some difference in stature in general. It is difficult to say from these data alone that in any particular age group pasteurized milk has no effect.

5f.3   Tests of Normality

Biometric measurements relating to homogeneous groups usually have unimodal distributions in which the asymmetry is small and the kurtosis is approximately the same as that of normal distribution. Asymmetry is measured by $\sqrt{\beta_1}$, where

$$\beta_1 = \frac{m_3^2}{m_2^3}$$

m_2 and m_3 being the second and third sample moments. Deviations from normal kurtosis are measured by $(\beta_2 - 3)$, where

$$\beta_2 = \frac{m_4}{m_2^2}$$

m_4 being the fourth moment. Deviations from these normal values, when significant, are important features of distributions of biometric measurements.

If the observed frequency distribution is given, we can fit a normal curve to it and test for the goodness of fit. This is useful in testing for all departures of the observed frequency distribution from the expected on the normal basis, but it is quite insensitive in testing for some specific aspects of the distribution, such as symmetry and kurtosis. If deviations other than those in symmetry and normal kurtosis are not important, then in any problem the observed β_1 and β_2 can be tested for the expected values 0 and 3. If n is the sample size, the asymmetry can be tested by using the statistic

$$w_1 = \pm \sqrt{\frac{\beta_1(n + 1)(n + 3)}{6(n - 2)}} \qquad (5\text{f}.3.1)$$

as a normal deviate with zero mean and unit variance when n is large. The sign in the above statistic is the same as that of m_3, the third moment. In the same way, the probability of departure from normality in kurtosis can be tested by using the normal deviate

$$w_2 = \left(\beta_2 - 3 + \frac{6}{n + 1}\right) \sqrt{\frac{(n + 1)^2(n + 3)(n + 5)}{24n(n - 2)(n - 3)}} \qquad (5\text{f}.3.2)$$

The following table gives for 23 samples the values of n, $\sqrt{\beta_1}$, and $P(\sqrt{\beta_1})$, the probability of $\sqrt{\beta_1}$'s being smaller than the observed on the normal hypothesis.

TABLE 5f.3α. The Values of $\sqrt{\beta_1}$ and $P(\sqrt{\beta_1})$ for Nasal Height Distributions of 23 Castes and Tribes of the United Provinces

Sample	n	$\sqrt{\beta_1}$	$P(\sqrt{\beta_1})$	Sample	n	$\sqrt{\beta_1}$	$P(\sqrt{\beta_1})$
1	86	0.1552	0.73	13	57	−0.5229	0.05 *
2	91	0.1025	0.66	14	191	0.0600	0.63
3	107	−0.5442	0.01 *	15	159	−0.3382	0.04 *
4	139	−0.1910	0.18	16	99	−0.0995	0.34
5	168	−0.3820	0.02 *	17	156	0.1741	0.81
6	150	−0.0100	0.48	18	157	0.1646	0.80
7	124	−0.3950	0.04	19	197	−0.1192	0.25
8	187	0.1000	0.71	20	100	−0.4992	0.02 *
9	113	0.0000	0.50	21	105	0.0693	0.61
10	68	0.4118	0.92	22	101	0.0877	0.36
11	94	−0.0970	0.35	23	182	−0.2002	0.13
12	173	0.0173	0.54				

There are about 5 values (marked with an asterisk in the table above) significant on the 5% level against the expected $^{23}\!/_{20}$ (= 1.15). To test for overall significance the P_λ test explained in 5f.2 may be carried out. The value of P_λ is 69.4880, which as a χ^2 with $2 \times 23 = 46$ degrees of freedom is significant, thus indicating skewness of the nasal height distributions. On the whole the distribution of nasal height is negatively skew.

The values of β_2 can be treated in an exactly similar way, using the formula (5f.3.2).

References

ANSCOMBE, F. J. (1948).   The transformation of Poisson, binonial and negative-binomial data.   *Biom.*, **35**, 246.

BARTLETT, M. S. (1937).   Properties of sufficiency and statistical tests.   *Proc. Roy. Soc.* **A**, **160**, 268.

ELDERTON, E. M. (1933).   The Lanarkshire milk experiment.   *Ann. Eugen. London,* **5**, 326.

FISHER, R. A. (1949).   A preliminary linkage test with *agouti* and *undulated* mice.   *Heredity,* **3**, 229.

HOTELLING, H. (1940).   The selection of variates for use in prediction with some comments on the problem of nuisance parameters.   *Ann. Math. Stats.*, **11**, 271.

RAO, C. R. (1948).   Large sample tests of statistical hypotheses concerning several parameters with application to problems of estimation.   *Proc. Camb. Phil. Soc.*, **44**, 50.

WALD, A. (1949).   Note on the consistency of the maximum likelihood estimate.   *Ann. Math. Stats.*, **20**, 595.

YATES, F. (1934).   Contingency tables involving small numbers and the χ^2 test.   *J. R. S. S. Suppl.*, **1**, 217.

CHAPTER 6

Tests of Homogeneity of Variances and Correlations

6a Homogeneity of Variances

6a.1 Test for a Specified Variance

It is sometimes necessary to test whether an estimated variance is in agreement with a specified hypothetical variance. If s^2 is the estimate based on n degrees of freedom,* of the hypothetical variance σ^2, then the statistic

$$\chi^2 = \frac{ns^2}{\sigma^2}$$

can be used as χ^2 with n degrees of freedom to test the above hypothesis.

The variance for head breadth calculated from measurements on 29 crania from Jebel Moya (Sudan) is 48.5632. Could this sample have arisen from a homogeneous cranial population with a head breadth variance of 18.2313? The degrees of freedom in this case are 28, one less than the number of observations, and

$$\chi^2 = \frac{ns^2}{\sigma^2} = 77.2485$$

The object of inquiry is whether the Jebel Moya population belongs to a homogeneous group. Heterogeneity would increase the internal variance so that high values of χ^2 would indicate significance. The observed value exceeds the 5% value of χ^2 with 28 degrees of freedom so that the hypothesis is rejected. The hypothetical value considered in this case

---

* The estimate s^2 is obtained by dividing the corrected sum of squares by the degrees of freedom equal to one less than the sample size if only a single sample is available.

221

is the variance for head breadth derived from a large series of crania from Egypt and Sudan. The higher variance in the present case suggests that the cranial population of Jebel Moya is heterogeneous.

We could also test by considering the lower tail of the χ^2 distribution whether an observed variance is significantly less than the hypothetical variance. Thus, for a hypothetical variance of 90, the χ^2 in the above problem would be 15.6481, the probability of exceeding which is more than 95%. The probability of obtaining a χ^2 less than the observed is therefore less than 5% so that the observed variance is significantly less than the assigned one.

Suppose that it is not known that the specified value 18.2313 of the variance is for a homogeneous population, and it is desired to know whether the observed variance could have reasonably arisen from a population with a hypothetical variance of 18.2313. In a problem of this nature we are interested in both small and high values of χ^2 that might arise, both disproving the null hypothesis. The test procedure in this case is slightly complicated, and we may consider two situations, depending on the sample size.

(i) When the sample size is large (greater than 30): When the sample size is large, χ^2 tends to be normally distributed with degrees of freedom n as mean and variance $2n$ so that the test reduces to

$$A_1 \qquad \left| \frac{\chi^2 - n}{\sqrt{2n}} \right| \geq \lambda$$

where λ is the 5% or 1% value of the normal deviate, considering both tails. The approach to normality of χ^2 is slow so that the above approximation may not hold good in moderately large samples. A better approximation is to use $\sqrt{2\chi^2}$ as a normal variate with mean $\sqrt{2n-1}$ and unit variance, in which case the test is

$$A_2 \qquad \left| \sqrt{2\chi^2} - \sqrt{2n-1} \right| \geq \lambda$$

A third and a fairly accurate approximation is to use $(\chi^2/n)^{1/3}$ as a normal variate with mean $(1 - 2/9n)$ and variance $2/9n$ so that the test is

$$A_3 \qquad \sqrt{\frac{9n}{2}} \left| \left(\frac{\chi^2}{n} \right)^{1/3} + \frac{2}{9n} - 1 \right| \geq \lambda$$

TABLE 6a.1α.   The Admissible Range of the χ^2 Distribution

D.F.	5% Level χ_1^2	5% Level χ_2^2	1% Level χ_1^2	1% Level χ_2^2
1	0.0^33163	7.8155	0.0^31341	11.3458
2	0.08480	9.5282	0.01746	13.2866
3	0.2961	11.1930	0.1011	15.1251
4	0.6072	12.8008	0.2640	16.9004
5	0.9890	14.3700	0.4965	18.6180
6	1.4250	15.8964	0.7854	20.2980
7	1.9026	17.3922	1.1214	21.9366
8	2.4136	18.8616	1.4984	23.5304
9	2.9529	20.3058	1.9017	25.1352
10	3.5160	21.7290	2.3450	26.6500
11	4.0997	23.1341	2.8061	28.1820
12	4.7004	24.5244	3.2916	29.6808
13	5.3170	25.9012	3.7960	31.1662
14	5.9472	27.2650	4.3162	32.6410
15	6.5910	28.6140	4.8525	34.0995
16	7.2448	29.9552	5.4048	35.5376
17	7.9101	31.2851	5.9670	36.9750
18	8.5842	32.6070	6.5448	38.3886
19	9.2682	33.9188	7.1307	39.8012
20	9.9580	35.2260	7.7300	41.1940
21	10.6554	36.5274	8.3349	42.5880
22	11.3608	37.8180	8.9518	43.9670
23	12.0727	39.1046	9.5772	45.3353
24	12.7896	40.3872	10.2072	46.7064
25	13.5150	41.6575	10.8475	48.0600
26	14.2428	42.9286	11.4946	49.4104
27	14.9769	44.1909	12.1446	50.7600
28	15.7136	45.4552	12.8044	52.0968
29	16.4575	46.7103	13.4676	53.4354
30	17.2050	47.9610	14.1360	54.7680

Consider an example where $\chi^2 = 43.773$ and $n = 30$. The normal deviates corresponding to A_1, A_2, and A_3 are

A_1
$$\frac{43.773 - 30}{\sqrt{60}} = 1.7781 \quad \text{Probability} = 0.075$$

A_2
$$\sqrt{87.546} - \sqrt{59} = 1.6755 \quad \text{Probability} = 0.095$$

A_3
$$\sqrt{\frac{9 \times 30}{2}} \left\{ \left(\frac{43.773}{30}\right)^{\frac{1}{3}} + \frac{2}{9 \times 30} - 1 \right\} = 1.6452 \quad \text{Probability} = 0.100$$

The most accurate of the three approximations is the last one; in fact it gives almost an exact value to the probability of χ^2's exceeding 43.773, which is 0.05 as seen from χ^2 tables. The probability 0.100 corresponding to A_3 is very high so that the value of $\chi^2 = 43.773$ does not give sufficient indication as to whether the observed variance differs from the assigned value.

(ii) When the sample size is small (less than 30): If the observed χ^2 is above the lower 5% value or below the upper 5% value, no further analysis is needed; the hypothesis cannot be rejected. The doubt arises only when χ^2 is beyond these limits, in which case the limits to non-significant values of χ^2 have to be determined.

Table 6a.1α gives the admissible range of χ^2 as determined by the locally most powerful unbiased test (see 8a.4) of Neyman and Pearson (1939). The value of $\chi^2 = 77.2485$ in the case of the Jebel Moya population lies outside the 5% admissible range (15.7136, 45.4552) for 28 degrees of freedom so that the null hypothesis is rejected.

6a.2 Test for a Specified Inequality of Two Estimated Variances

The statistical analysis of data often leads to a number of estimated variances of which it is desirable to test the homogeneity. This problem is considerably simple when there are only two estimated variances and it is desired to test whether a particular estimate significantly exceeds the other. Thus one might have the estimates of the head length variances $s_1{}^2 = 42.302$ and $s_2{}^2 = 34.658$ based on $n_1 = 24$ and $n_2 = 30$ degrees of freedom for males and females. The important question to be asked, in this connection, is whether the male head length is, as commonly believed, more variable than the female head length. The statistic to be constructed for this purpose is

$$F = \frac{s_1{}^2}{s_2{}^2} = 1.2205$$

which can be entered in the variance ratio table with $n_1 = 24$ and $n_2 = 30$ degrees of freedom. The 5% value of F is 1.89, which is greater than the observed F, so that there is no evidence against the equality of variances in the two sexes.

It may be noted that this does not prove that the male and female head lengths are equally variable. The evidence supplied by the above data may not be sufficient to detect the difference, if any. The ratio such as the observed could be expected not infrequently in samples of the above sizes when, in fact, the variances are equal. To detect the difference as indicated by the above ratio a very large number of degrees of freedom, i.e., a large sample, would be necessary.

If sample sizes are large, the test for equality of standard deviations can be carried out in a simple way. If any estimated variance s^2 based on n degrees of freedom is transformed by the relation (see 5e.4)

$$y = \log_e s$$

then y tends to be normally distributed with

$$\text{Mean} = \log \sigma \quad \text{and} \quad \text{Variance} = \frac{1}{2n}$$

so that the variance is independent of σ. Kemsley (1950) found the following standard deviations for heights of males and females.

	Sample Number (n)	s	$\log_e s$	Variance $\frac{1}{2}n$
♂	27515	2.85	1.0473	0.00001817
♀	33562	2.58	0.9478	0.00001490
Difference			0.0995	0.00003307

The standard error of the difference is $\sqrt{0.0^43307} = 0.005751$, and the ratio of the difference to standard error is $w = 17.30$, which as a normal deviate has a very small probability, thus showing that the variabilities are different for ♂ and ♀, females being less variable than males. This is in accordance with an observed fact in biological material that the standard deviation depends on the mean size of organisms: the higher the mean, the greater is the scatter. The female dimensions are smaller than the male, and this is reflected in the standard deviation. We can make a closer examination by considering the data for various ages since the overall standard deviation may be affected by the age composition of the samples for males and females.

TABLE 6a.2α. Standard Deviation of Stature * (Kemsley, 1950)

	Standard Deviation		Sample Size		Statistic
Age	♂	♀	♂	♀	w
14	3.66	2.68	305	244	5.13
14.5	3.71	2.40	892	732	12.35
15.5	3.57	2.50	1404	1378	13.29
16.5	3.07	2.35	1644	1699	10.92
17.5	2.95	2.50	1280	1724	6.34
18.5	2.86	2.23	786	1535	8.02
19.5	2.87	2.34	591	1376	5.87
20.5	2.70	2.31	467	1284	4.08
21.5	2.65	2.34	460	1224	3.21
22.5	2.62	2.37	477	1250	2.63

* The ages in the original table extend up to 74.5, and only the first 10 have been chosen to illustrate the test.

It is found that at each age the statistic w exceeds the upper 5% value of the normal deviate, showing that female variability is less at each age. If samples were not so numerous as those above, it would be difficult to detect the difference in variabilities at each age. In such a situation the normal probabilities for exceeding w could be calculated at each age and the P_λ test (5f.2) carried out to combine the evidences supplied by all age groups.

6a.3   The Likelihood Criterion and Its Use

With two estimated variances a situation different from the one considered in 6a.2 may arise. The estimated variances of nasal indices may be available for two series of male skulls. The question to be asked is whether the variances in the cranial populations from which the two series are samples can be considered equal. In the absence of any knowledge as to the possible inequality relationship between the two population variances, the following statistic

$$L = \frac{(n_1 + n_2)\{(s_1^2)^{n_1}(s_2^2)^{n_2}\}^{1/(n_1 + n_2)}}{n_1 s_1^2 + n_2 s_2^2}$$

which is the ratio of the weighted geometric mean to the arithmetic mean of the estimates, may be constructed. This lies between 0 and 1, the value 0 being reached when the ratio of one estimate to the other is large, and 1 when the two are equal. A small value of L would thus indicate a difference in the population variances.

Instead of L it is convenient, from the point of view of computations, to consider the statistic (due to Bartlett, 1934)

$$M = -n \log_e L = n \log_e \left\{ \frac{n_1 s_1^2 + n_2 s_2^2}{n} \right\} - n_1 \log_e s_1^2 - n_2 \log_e s_2^2$$

where $n = n_1 + n_2$. M varies from 0 to ∞, with small values of L corresponding to high values of M.

This can be extended to the case where k estimated variances have to be tested for homogeneity. If $s_1^2, \cdots, s_k^2$ are the estimated variances with $n_1, \cdots, n_k$ degrees of freedom, then the statistic to be constructed is

$$M = n \log_e \left\{ \frac{n_1 s_1^2 + \cdots + n_k s_k^2}{n} \right\} - n_1 \log_e s_1^2 - \cdots - n_k \log_e s_k^2$$

where $n = n_1 + \cdots + n_k$.

The probability of M's exceeding the observed value M_o can be expanded in an asymptotic series, the first six terms of which are given here.

$$\frac{1}{\sum_0^6 \beta_i} \sum_{i=0}^6 \beta_i P_{k-1+2i}(M_o)$$

where $P_{k-1+2i}(M_o)$ stands for the probability * of the χ^2 with $(k - 1 + 2i)$ degrees of freedom exceeding M_o. The values of β are

$\beta_0 = 1$

$\beta_1 = \frac{1}{6}c_1$ $\qquad\qquad\qquad c_1 = \Sigma \frac{1}{n_t} - \frac{1}{n}$

$\beta_2 = \frac{1}{2}\beta_1{}^2$

$\beta_3 = -\frac{1}{45}c_3 + \frac{1}{6}\beta_1{}^3$ $\qquad c_3 = \Sigma \frac{1}{n_t{}^3} - \frac{1}{n^3}$

$\beta_4 = \beta_1\beta_3 - \frac{1}{4}\beta_2\beta_1{}^2$

$\beta_5 = \frac{8}{315}c_5 - \frac{1}{75}c_3\beta_2 - \frac{1}{5}\beta_1\beta_4$ $\quad c_5 = \Sigma \frac{1}{n_t{}^5} - \frac{1}{n^5}$

$\beta_6 = \frac{4}{189}\beta_1 c_5 - \frac{1}{90}\beta_3 c_3 - \frac{1}{6}\beta_1\beta_5$

6a.4 Practical Applications

The exact formula derived above for evaluating the probability of exceeding the observed value M_o need not always be used in practice. The approximations which can be profitably used in many situations are given below with suitable illustrations.

First Approximation. If the observed value M_o is less than the 5% (or 1%) value of χ^2 with $(k - 1)$ degrees of freedom, then the hypothesis of equality of variances cannot be rejected on the 5% (or 1%) level. This is due to the fact that the exact 5% and 1% limits of M are beyond the corresponding values of the χ^2 limits.

Table 6a.4α gives a set of 10 estimates of variance, calculated from 10 samples of weight records of schoolboys of similar age but from different forms. It is desired to test whether there are any real "form differences" in the weight dispersion of the boys.

* These values can be obtained from *Tables of the Incomplete Γ-Function*, edited by K. Pearson.

TABLE 6a.4α.   The Estimated Variances and Evaluation of the M-Statistic
(Hartley and Pearson, 1946)

Form No. t	No. of Boys	Weight Variance	D.F. $= n_t$	$\log_e s_t^2$	$n_t \log_e s_t^2$	$n_t s_t^2$
1	10	51	9	3.93	35.4	459
2	15	78	14	4.36	61.0	1092
3	21	91	20	4.51	90.2	1820
4	23	52	22	3.95	86.9	1144
5	15	101	14	4.62	64.7	1414
6	11	36	10	3.58	35.8	360
7	31	41	30	3.71	111.3	1230
8	15	76	14	4.33	60.6	1064
9	3	64	2	4.16	8.3	128
10	6	93	5	4.53	22.6	465
Total			140 $= n$		576.8	9176

$$M = n \log \left\{ \frac{(\Sigma n_t s_t^2)}{n} \right\} - \Sigma n_t \log s_t^2$$

$$= 140 \log \left(\tfrac{9176}{140}\right) - 576.8$$

$$= 140 \times 4.183 - 576.8 = 8.8$$

The 5% value of χ^2 with $(10 - 1) = 9$ degrees of freedom is 15.51 so that the observed value 8.8, being less than this, cannot be considered significant.   No further calculations are needed in this case.   The best estimate of the common variance is $(\Sigma n_t s_t^2)/n = 9176/140 = 65.54$.

Second Approximation.   Bartlett (1934) suggested the use of

$$M' = \frac{M}{1 + c_1/3(k - 1)}$$

as χ^2 with $(k - 1)$ degrees of freedom, where $c_1 = \Sigma(1/n_t) - (1/n)$. This approximation tends to increase the probability for an observed M' so that if M' is significant on any desired level then M is certainly so.

The following data give a number of variances estimated on different degrees of freedom.   These have been calculated from the yields of rice observed in successive blocks (columns) when a rectangular lattice is superimposed on a big field.   It is desired to test whether the block variance is independent of its size, i.e., the number of cells it contains.

TABLE 6a.4β.   Variances for Different Block Sizes

No. of Cells in a Block	Mean Variance for Blocks of the Same Size	D.F. n_t	$\log_e s_t^2$	$n_t \log_e s_t^2$	$n_t s_t^2$	$\dfrac{1}{n_t}$
14	48.76	26	3.8870	101.0620	1,267.76	0.038461
23	101.97	44	4.6250	203.5000	4,486.68	0.022727
35	122.67	170	4.8096	817.6320	20,853.90	0.005882
45	94.39	264	4.5474	1200.5136	24,918.96	0.003788
51	78.40	200	4.3618	872.3600	15,680.00	0.005000
Total		704		3195.0676	67,207.30	0.075858

$$M = 704 \log_e \left(\frac{67,207.30}{704} \right) - 3195.0676$$

$$= 704(4.5589) - 3195.0676 = 14.3276$$

This value is greater than the 1% value of χ^2 with 4 degrees of freedom. In this case the alternative statistic is

$$M' = \frac{M}{1 + c_1/3(k - 1)}$$

where $c_1 = 0.075858 - 0.001420 = 0.074438$.

$$M' = \frac{14.3276}{1 - 0.074438/12} = \frac{14.3276}{1.006203} = 14.2393$$

This also exceeds the 1% value of χ^2 with 4 degrees of freedom so that the variances cannot be considered equal.

This shows that the variance is a function of the block size. Contrary to expectation, this is not an increasing function of the block size. The decrease in variance after a certain size of the block may be due to some periodicity in the fertility gradient.

6a.5   Problems Requiring an Exact Treatment

It is seen in 6a.4 that in any practical situation a decision can be reached if $M \leq 5\%$ value of χ^2 with $(k - 1)$ degrees of freedom (not significant) and $M' = M/[1 + c_1/3(k - 1)] \geq 5\%$ value of χ^2 with $(k - 1)$ degrees of freedom (significant). There may arise cases where $M' < 5\%$ value of $\chi^2 < M$. The formula given·in 6a.3 then has to be used. In practice the situation presented above will occur only when the M statistic is just near its significance limit. The decision as to the acceptance or rejection of the hypothesis depends on the further use of these estimated variances in statistical analysis. This being so, the evaluation of the probability to a high degree of accuracy rarely will be necessary in practical problems.

It may be noted that all the tests based on the F and L statistics given in 6a.2 and 6a.3 can be extended to test for an assigned ratio $\rho_1:\rho_2: \cdots :\rho_k$ of the hypothetical variances. The only modification needed is to replace s_i^2 by s_i^2/ρ_i.

6b   Homogeneity of Correlations

6b.1   Exact Test for Zero Correlation

It has been shown (example 2, in 2d.2) that, when the correlation in a bivariate population is zero, the statistic

$$t = \frac{r}{\sqrt{1 - r^2}} \sqrt{n - 2}$$

where r is the correlation coefficient calculated on a sample of size n, is distributed as

$$\frac{1}{\sqrt{n - 2}B\left(\dfrac{n - 2}{2}, \dfrac{1}{2}\right)} \frac{dt}{\left(1 + \dfrac{t^2}{n - 2}\right)^{(n-1)/2}}$$

This is the same as the t distribution with $(n - 2)$ degrees of freedom. To test whether the population correlation coefficient is zero, the statistic t defined above is calculated and tested for significance by the use of the t table.

The correlation between frontal breadth and head breadth calculated from 18 crania of a series is 0.6521. Are the two dimensions, frontal breadth and head breadth, uncorrelated? The value of t is

$$t = \frac{0.6521}{\sqrt{1 - (0.6521)^2}} \sqrt{16} = 4(0.8602)$$

$$= 3.4408$$

with $18 - 2 = 16$ degrees of freedom. This exceeds 2.120, the 5% value of t, so that the observed correlation can be interpreted as establishing an association between frontal breadth and head breadth.

6b.2 Fisher's tanh^{-1} Transformation

It was shown in 5e.4 that the tanh^{-1} transformation of the correlation coefficient r gets rid of the unknown parameter ρ in the expression for variance. Accordingly we consider the transformed values ζ and z instead of ρ and r.

$$\zeta = F(\rho) = \frac{1}{2} \log \frac{(1 + \rho)}{(1 - \rho)} = \tanh^{-1} \rho$$

$$z = F(r) = \frac{1}{2} \log \frac{(1 + r)}{(1 - r)} = \tanh^{-1} r$$

Putting $z - \zeta = x$, the distribution of x may be derived from the distribution of r. The first four moments of z were found by R. A. Fisher and later revised by A. K. Gayen.

$$\mu_1' = \frac{\rho}{2(n - 1)} \left\{ 1 + \frac{5 + \rho^2}{4(n - 1)} + \cdots \right\}$$

$$\mu_2 = \frac{1}{n - 1} \left\{ 1 + \frac{4 - \rho^2}{2(n - 1)} + \frac{22 - 6\rho^2 - 3\rho^4}{6(n - 1)^2} + \cdots \right\}$$

$$\mu_3 = \frac{\rho^3}{(n - 1)^3} + \cdots$$

$$\mu_4 = \frac{1}{(n - 1)^2} \left\{ 3 + \frac{14 - 3\rho^2}{n - 1} + \frac{184 - 48\rho^2 - 21\rho^4}{4(n - 1)^2} + \cdots \right\}$$

$$\beta_1 = \frac{\rho^6}{(n - 1)^3} + \cdots$$

$$\beta_2 = 3 + \frac{2}{n - 1} + \frac{4 + 2\rho^2 - 3\rho^4}{(n - 1)^2} + \cdots$$

Since β_1 and $(\beta_2 - 3)$ are small, even for moderate n, it follows that $(z - \zeta)$ can be considered to be approximately a normal variate with

$$\text{Mean} = \frac{\rho}{2(n - 1)}$$

$$\text{Variance} = \frac{1}{n - 1} + \frac{4 - \rho^2}{2(n - 1)^2} \simeq \frac{1}{n - 3}$$

6b.3   Test for a Given ρ

In a sample of 28 the correlation coefficient is found to be 0.6521. Can such a value have arisen from a population in which the coefficient has the value 0.7211?

$$z = \frac{1}{2} \log_e \frac{1+r}{1-r} = 0.7790 *$$

$$\text{Mean } z = \frac{1}{2} \log_e \frac{1+\rho}{1-\rho} + \frac{\rho}{2(n-1)}$$

$$= 0.9100 + \frac{0.7211}{54} = 0.9233$$

The normal deviate is

$$\sqrt{n-3} \; (z - \text{mean } z) = \sqrt{28-3} \; (0.7790 - 0.9233)$$

$$= 5(-0.1443) = -0.7215$$

The chance of exceeding the value 0.7215 in either direction is about 35% so that the hypothesis cannot be rejected.

The correction term $\rho/2(n-1)$ for the mean z is unimportant if n is large. The probability will be more precisely obtained in any case by its inclusion.

6b.4   Test for the Equality of Two Correlation Coefficients

Two samples consisting of n_1 and n_2 observations give the correlation coefficients r_1 and r_2. Are these values compatible with the hypothesis that the samples arose from two populations having the same correlation coefficient? Let

$$z_1 = \frac{1}{2} \log \frac{1+r_1}{1-r_1}$$

and

$$z_2 = \frac{1}{2} \log \frac{1+r_2}{1-r_2} .$$

The statistic $z_1 - z_2$ is distributed about the mean

$$\frac{\rho}{2(n_1-1)} - \frac{\rho}{2(n_2-1)} \qquad\qquad (6b.4.1)$$

* These values can be directly obtained from the Fisher-Yates tables (transformation of r to z).

where ρ is the common correlation coefficient, with variance

$$\frac{1}{n_1 - 3} + \frac{1}{n_2 - 3}$$

If the samples are not small or if n_1 and n_2 are not very different, the statistic

$$\frac{z_1 - z_2}{\sqrt{1/(n_1 - 3) + 1/(n_2 - 3)}}$$

can be used as a normal deviate. The more exact method given in 6b.6 may be necessary when the value of (6b.4.1) is not small.

6b.5 Test for the Homogeneity of a Set of Correlation Coefficients

Let $r_1, \cdots, r_k$ be k correlation coefficients based on samples of sizes $n_1, \cdots, n_k$. By means of the $\tanh^{-1}$ transformation, the quantities $z_1, \cdots, z_k$ corresponding to $r_1, \cdots, r_k$ can be obtained. If the bias in mean z can be neglected, the test for homogeneity of the correlation coefficients is equivalent to the test of equality of the mean values of z. The scheme of computation is as follows.

TABLE 6b.5α. Test of Homogeneity of a Set of Correlation Coefficients

Sample No. t	Sample Size n	Correlation Coefficient r	$\tanh^{-1}$ $r = z$	Reciprocal of Variance $n - 3$	$(n - 3)z$	$(n - 3)z^2$
1	n_1	r_1	z_1	$n_1 - 3$	$(n_1 - 3)z_1$	$(n_1 - 3)z_1^2$
.	.	.	.	.	.	.
.	.	.	.	.	.	.
.	.	.	.	.	.	.
k	n_k	r_k	z_k	$n_k - 3$	$(n_k - 3)z_k$	$(n_k - 3)z_k^2$
Total				N	T_1	T_2

The best estimate of $\tanh^{-1} \rho$ when the various coefficients are homogeneous is T_1/N. The statistic for testing homogeneity is

$$\chi^2 = T_2 - \frac{T_1^2}{N}$$

which can be used as χ^2 with $(k - 1)$ degrees of freedom.

As an example, let the correlations obtained from 6 samples of sizes 10, 14, 16, 20, 25, 28 be 0.318, 0.106, 0.253, 0.340, 0.116, 0.112. Can these be considered homogeneous?

Correlation Coefficient r	Sample Size Minus 3 $n - 3$	z	$(n - 3)z$	$(n - 3)z^2$
0.318	7	0.3294	2.3058	0.7595
0.106	11	0.1064	1.1704	0.1245
0.253	13	0.2586	3.3618	0.8694
0.340	17	0.3541	6.0197	2.1316
0.116	22	0.1164	2.5608	0.2981
0.112	25	0.1125	2.8125	0.7031
Total	95		18.2310	4.8862

$$\frac{T_1}{95} = \frac{18.2310}{95} = 0.191905$$

$$T_2 - T_1 \frac{T_1}{95} = 4.8862 - 3.4986 = 1.3876$$

The value 1.3876 as χ^2 with 5 degrees of freedom is not significant, so the correlations may be considered homogeneous.

6b.6   Correction for Bias in the Test for Homogeneity and the Best Estimate of ρ

When the sample sizes are not large and not nearly equal, there is a certain amount of bias (extraneous to the hypothesis tested) introduced in the χ^2 statistic used in 6b.5. This is due to neglecting the term $\rho/2(n - 1)$ in the mean value of z. Even if the bias introduced in the χ^2 statistic is small, the bias introduced in the best estimate of ρ when χ^2 is not significant will not be small when compared to the standard error of the estimate. This can be corrected by following a slightly different procedure.

Since z can be considered as a normal deviate with mean $\frac{1}{2} \log_e (1 + \rho)/(1 - \rho) + \rho/2(n - 1)$ and the variance $1/(n - 3)$, the score for ρ obtained from k samples is

$$S = \Sigma(n_i - 3) \left[\frac{1}{1 - \rho^2} + \frac{1}{2(n_i - 1)} \right] \left[z_i - \frac{1}{2} \log \frac{1 + \rho}{1 - \rho} - \frac{\rho}{2(n_i - 1)} \right]$$

$$(6b.6.1)$$

and the information

$$I = E(S^2) = \Sigma(n_i - 3)\left[\frac{1}{1 - \rho^2} + \frac{1}{2(n_i - 1)}\right]^2 \qquad (6b.6.2)$$

If the value of ρ obtained in the last section is taken as a first approximation, then the additive correction $\delta\rho$ to this value is given by

$$\delta\rho = \frac{S_0}{I_0}$$

where S_0 and I_0 are the values of (6b.6.1) and (6b.6.2) calculated at the approximate value chosen. This process may be repeated till the correction becomes negligible. Having obtained the best estimate $\hat{\rho}$ of ρ, the χ^2 statistic with $(k - 1)$ degrees of freedom for testing homogeneity is

$$\chi^2 = \Sigma(n_i - 3)\left\{z_i - \frac{1}{2}\log_e\frac{1 + \hat{\rho}}{1 - \hat{\rho}} - \frac{\hat{\rho}}{2(n_i - 1)}\right\}^2$$

References

BARTLETT, M. S. (1934). The problem in statistics of testing several variances. *Proc. Camb. Phil. Soc.*, **30**, 164.

HARTLEY, H. O., and E. S. PEARSON (1946). Tables for testing the homogeneity of a set of estimated variances. Prefatory note. *Biom.*, **33**, 296.

KEMSLEY, W. F. F. (1950). Weight and height of a population in 1943. *Ann. Eugen. London*, **15**, 161.

NEYMAN, J., and E. S. PEARSON (1936). Contributions to the theory of testing statistical hypotheses 1. Unbiased critical regions of type A and type A_1. *Stat. Res. Mem.*, 1.1.

CHAPTER 7

Tests of Significance
in Multivariate Analysis

7a Review of Work on Multivariate Analysis

Attempts have been made in recent years to generalize the univariate analysis of variance technique to the case of multiple variates. The extension of the theory has been slow, and only a few methods have been made available for practical use. The starting point of these researches, given by Wishart in 1928, is the simultaneous sampling distribution of the variances and covariances in samples from a multivariate normal population. A few years later Hotelling (1931) found the distribution of a quantity T which is a natural extension of Student's distribution to a sample from a multivariate normal population.

Wilks (1932), following the likelihood ratio method (Neyman and Pearson, 1928, 1931; Pearson and Neyman, 1930), obtained suitable generalizations in the analysis of variance applicable to several variables. The statistic Λ proposed by him has been found useful in a variety of problems. Bartlett (1934) applied it for testing the significance of treatments with respect to two variables in a varietal trial and indicated its general use in multivariate tests of significance. Wilks (1935) and Hotelling (1935) found it useful in testing the independence of several groups of variates. Wilks's statistic supplied some of the basic tests in multivariate analysis, but the problem of tabulation has not been tackled except in some limited cases (Wald and Brookner, 1941). A very useful approximation has been suggested by Bartlett (1938), who further demonstrated its use in another paper (1947).

A new line of research was initiated by Fisher (1936) with his introduction of the discriminant function analysis. It has been shown that a set of multiple measurements may be used to provide a discriminant function linear in the observations having the property that, better than any other linear function, it will discriminate between any two chosen classes such as taxonomic species, the two sexes, and so on.

236

The introduction of the discriminant function led to a new method of deriving test criteria suitable for multiple variates. The problem is reduced to the case of a single variate by using a linear compound of the several variables, where the compounding coefficients are chosen to maximize the value of a statistic suitable for a single variate. The application of this method to test the differences in mean values for several groups gave rise to the theory of canonical roots of determinantal equations (Roy, 1939; Fisher, 1939; Hsu, 1939). The distribution of the individual roots and the exact nature of tests require further study. Wilks's statistic, which is a symmetric function of the canonical roots, may be considered as providing an overall test of the hypothesis concerned.

In this chapter a unified approach to the problem of tests of significance in multivariate analysis is developed. The concept of *analysis of dispersion*, which is a natural extension of the univariate analysis of variance, has been found useful in discussing multivariate problems.

In presenting the various tests of significance it has been found convenient to consider the problems arising out of a single sample and two samples in the first stage. They depend on simple tests of significance requiring the use of variance ratio tables alone and are of very great importance in practice. The use of Wilks's statistic in multivariate analysis involving more than two samples is considered in the second stage. Two powerful approximations have been found for the exact distribution of the Λ statistic. A number of examples have been worked out to explain the computational procedure.

7b Tests with Discriminant Functions

7b.1 Two Fundamental Distributions

The method of discriminant functions in deriving test criteria has been found extremely useful in multivariate analysis. The problem is reduced to that of a single variable by choosing a linear compound of the original variables and constructing a statistic suitable for the univariate case. The maximized value of this statistic obtained by a suitable choice of the compounding coefficients is taken as the appropriate test criterion. The distribution of the statistics thus derived in problems involving a single sample and two samples depends on the two fundamental distributions considered below.

Let (w_{ij}), $(i, j = 1, 2, \cdots, p)$, be the matrix giving the estimates, on n degrees of freedom, of the elements in the dispersion matrix (α_{ij}) of p normally correlated variables. The definition of w_{ij} implies that it has been calculated from a certain sum of products by dividing by the appropriate degrees of freedom. Let $d_1, d_2, \cdots, d_p$ be p normal variates with the same dispersion matrix (α_{ij}) but distributed independently of w_{ij}. Considering only the first r variables, $d_1, \cdots, d_r$, the statistic T_r is defined by

$$nT_r = \sum_1^r \sum_1^r w_r^{ij} d_i d_j \qquad (7\text{b}.1.1)$$

where (w_r^{ij}) is the matrix reciprocal to (w_{ij}), $(i, j = 1, 2, \cdots, r)$. It was shown in 2d.2 that, when $E(d_1) = \cdots = E(d_r) = 0$, the statistic

$$\frac{|\, nw_{ij}\, |}{|\, nw_{ij} + d_i d_j\, |} = \frac{1}{1 + T_r}$$

is distributed in the beta form

$$B\left(\frac{n - r + 1}{2}, \frac{r}{2}\right)$$

in which case T_r has the distribution

$$\text{const.} \frac{T^{(r/2)-1}}{(1 + T_r)^{(n+1)/2}} dT$$

This shows that

$$\frac{n - r + 1}{r} T_r$$

can be referred to a variance ratio table with r and $(n - r + 1)$ degrees of freedom.

It was further shown that, if $d_{r+1}, \cdots, d_p$ are distributed independently of $d_1, \cdots, d_r$ and $E(d_{r+1}) = \cdots = E(d_p) = 0$, $E(d_i)$ being not necessarily zero when $i = 1, \cdots, r$, the statistic

$$\frac{|\, nw_{ij}\, |_p}{|\, nw_{ij} + d_i d_j\, |_p} \cdot \frac{|\, nw_{ij} + d_i d_j\, |_r}{|\, nw_{ij}\, |_r} = \frac{1 + T_r}{1 + T_p} = (U_{p-r,r} + 1)^{-1}$$

is distributed as $B[(n - p + 1)/2, (p - r)/2]$. This shows that

$$\frac{n + 1 - p}{p - r} U_{p-r,r} \qquad (7\text{b}.1.2)$$

can be used as a variance ratio with $(p - r)$ and $(n + 1 - p)$ degrees of freedom. The statistic T_p is calculated from the formula (7b.1.1) by using all the p variables.

All the tests of significance considered in this section depend on the use of the statistics defined in (7b.1.1) and (7b.1.2).

7b.2 Problems of a Single Sample

Student's test connected with pairs of observations admits generalization in two directions.

The first is to test whether the means of p correlated variables are the same on the basis of a sample of size N from a p-variate population. When the test shows differences in mean values, there arises the question of deciding whether an assigned contrast involving the p variates differs from the best contrast as determined from the data.

If x_{1i}, x_{2i}, $\cdots$, x_{pi} are the observations on the ith individual, then they may be replaced by a linear compound $z_i = l_1 x_{1i} + \cdots + l_p x_{pi}$ where l_i satisfy the condition $l_1 + \cdots + l_p = 0$. The problem of determining the best contrast reduces to that of determining the compounding coefficients l_1, $\cdots$, l_p such that the ratio of mean z to standard deviation of z is a maximum. An alternative method which has some practical advantage is as follows.

By arbitrary choice of constants we construct $(p - 1)$ independent linear combinations of the variables x_1, $\cdots$, x_p,

$$y_j = m_{1j} x_1 + \cdots + m_{pj} x_p$$

such that $\sum_i m_{ij} = 0$ for $j = 1, 2, \cdots, (p - 1)$. Choosing a linear compound of x with coefficients adding to zero is the same as choosing a linear compound of y without any restriction on the compounding coefficients. If the linear compound is

$$\lambda_1 y_1 + \lambda_2 y_2 + \cdots + \lambda_{p-1} y_{p-1}$$

then the quantity to be maximized is

$$v = \frac{(\lambda_1 \bar{y}_1 + \cdots + \lambda_{p-1} \bar{y}_{p-1})^2}{\Sigma\Sigma \lambda_i \lambda_j w_{ij}}$$

where

$$w_{ij} = \frac{1}{N - 1} \sum_{r=1}^{N} (y_{ir} - \bar{y}_i)(y_{jr} - \bar{y}_j)$$

Observing that only the ratios of λ are uniquely determinable, the equations giving λ may be written

$$\lambda_1 w_{1i} + \cdots + \lambda_{p-1} w_{p-1,i} = \bar{y}_i \qquad i = 1, 2, \cdots, (p - 1)$$

with the solution

$$\lambda_i = w^{1i} \bar{y}_1 + \cdots + w^{p-1,i} \bar{y}_{p-1} \qquad i = 1, 2, \cdots, (p - 1)$$

where the matrix (w^{ij}) is reciprocal to (w_{ij}). This supplies the best linear compound of y, which on transformation to x gives the best contrast determinable from the data.

The maximum value of v is given by

$$\Sigma \lambda_i \bar{y}_i = \Sigma\Sigma w^{ij}\bar{y}_i\bar{y}_j$$

If $T_{p-1} = N(\Sigma\Sigma w^{ij}\bar{y}_i\bar{y}_j)/(N-1)$, then, on the hypothesis that all x have the same mean value, the conditions required for the use of the statistic (7b.1.1) are satisfied so that

$$\frac{T_{p-1}(N-p+1)}{(p-1)}$$

can be used as a variance ratio with $(p-1)$ and $(N-p+1)$ degrees of freedom to test the above hypothesis.

The statistic T_{p-1} is invariant for all sets of coefficients chosen to construct y from x so that in any practical problem either conveniently or conventionally chosen linear contrasts of x may be used to define y.

To test whether the best contrast as determined from the data is in agreement with an assigned contrast $\xi_1 x_1 + \cdots + \xi_p x_p$ or $\eta_1 y_1 + \cdots + \eta_{p-1}y_{p-1}$ in terms of y, we proceed as follows.

The appropriate statistic for testing the significance of the assigned contrast is

$$T_1 = \frac{N(\eta_1\bar{y}_1 + \cdots + \eta_{p-1}\bar{y}_{p-1})^2}{(N-1)(\Sigma\Sigma\eta_i\eta_j w_{ij})}$$

where $T_1(N-1)$ is a variance ratio with 1 and $(N-1)$ degrees of freedom. The appropriate statistic for all the $(p-1)$ contrasts is T_{p-1}, considered before. The hypothesis specifies that all contrasts orthogonal to the assigned one have zero mean so that the conditions for the use of the statistic (7b.1.2) are satisfied. Hence

$$\frac{(N-p+1)}{(p-2)}\left\{\frac{1+T_{p-1}}{1+T_1} - 1\right\} \qquad .$$

can be used as a variance ratio with $(p-2)$ and $(N-p+1)$ degrees of freedom to test the above hypothesis.

The above test can be generalized to answer the problem whether a set of k assigned contrasts contain the best contrast. In this case the statistic

$$\frac{(N-p+1)}{(p-k-1)}\left\{\frac{1+T_{p-1}}{1+T_k} - 1\right\}$$

can be used as a variance ratio with $(p-k-1)$ and $(N-p+1)$ degrees of freedom.

Example 1.   The data of Table 7b.2α consist of weights of cork borings taken from the north (N), east (E), south (S), and west (W) directions of the trunk for 28 trees in a block of plantations.   The problem is to test whether the bark deposit varies in thickness and hence in weight in the four directions.   It was suggested that the bark deposit is likely to be uniform in N and S directions and also uniform but less so in E and W directions, so that $(N - E - W + S)$ can be taken as the best contrast.   This can, however, be tested from the given data as shown below.

TABLE 7b.2α.   Weights of Cork Borings (in Centigrams) in the Four Directions for 28 Trees

N	E	S	W	N	E	S	W
72	66	76	77	91	79	100	75
60	53	66	63	56	68	47	50
56	57	64	58	79	65	70	61
41	29	36	38	81	80	68	58
32	32	35	36	78	55	67	60
30	35	34	26	46	38	37	38
39	39	31	27	39	35	34	37
42	43	31	25	32	30	30	32
37	40	31	25	60	50	67	54
33	29	27	36	35	37	48	39
32	30	34	28	39	36	39	31
63	45	74	63	50	34	37	40
54	46	60	52	43	37	39	50
47	51	52	43	48	54	57	43

It has been found in similar studies that there exists a significant correlation between contrasts such as $(N - E)$ and $(S - W)$ so that the method of fitting constants for the four directions and the individual trees by the method of least squares is not appropriate.   The three contrasts arising out of the four weights may then be treated as three correlated variables, in which case the theory developed above is applicable.

It is interesting to observe that the individual weights in Table 7b.2α are exceedingly asymmetrically distributed.   This does not, however, invalidate the test so long as the contrasts are normally distributed. In fact, the distribution of the individual weights depends on the nature of plants and the variation between plants.   If the above condition is satisfied, it is not necessary that the individual weights should follow any distribution law of the known type. It may be sometimes necessary to make a transformation (such as log, square, or cube root) of the variables under consideration to ensure that the contrasts of the transformed variables are symmetrically distributed if the contrasts of the original variables are not so.

As observed earlier, the contrasts may be conveniently or conventionally chosen. In the above example we may choose the simple set of contrasts

$$y_1 = N - E - W + S \qquad y_2 = S - W \qquad y_3 = N - S$$

The mean values and estimates of variances and covariances based on 27 degrees of freedom for y_1, y_2, y_3 are

$$\bar{y}_1 = 8.8571 \qquad \bar{y}_2 = 4.5000 \qquad \bar{y}_3 = 0.8571$$

$$(w_{ij}) = \begin{bmatrix} 128.7200 & 61.4076 & -21.0211 \\ 61.4076 & 56.9259 & -28.2963 \\ -21.0211 & -28.2963 & 63.5344 \end{bmatrix}$$

The coefficients of the best linear function $\lambda_1 y_1 + \lambda_2 y_2 + \lambda_3 y_3$ are given by the equations

$$128.7200\lambda_1 + 61.4076\lambda_2 - 21.0211\lambda_3 = 8.8571$$

$$61.4076\lambda_1 + 56.9259\lambda_2 - 28.2963\lambda_3 = 4.5000$$

$$-21.0211\lambda_1 - 28.2963\lambda_2 + 63.5344\lambda_3 = 0.8571$$

Solving, $\lambda_1 = 0.05620$, $\lambda_2 = 0.04415$, $\lambda_3 = 0.05174$, so that the best contrast is

$$\lambda_1(N - E - W + S) + \lambda_2(S - W) + \lambda_3(N - S)$$

$$= 0.10794N - 0.05620E - 0.10035W + 0.04861S$$

or, by multiplying the coefficients by 10 (arbitrarily),

$$1.0794N - 0.5620E - 1.0035W + 0.4861S$$

The statistic for testing the hypothesis of equality of means is

$$T_{p-1} = \frac{N}{N-1}(\lambda_1\bar{y}_1 + \lambda_2\bar{y}_2 + \lambda_3\bar{y}_3) = \frac{28}{27}(0.740790) = 0.768226$$

$$T_{p-1}\frac{(N-p+1)}{(p-1)} = \frac{0.768226(28 - 4 + 1)}{3} = 6.4019$$

The quantity 6.4019 as a variance ratio with 3 and 25 degrees of freedom is significant at the 1% level so that the bark deposit cannot be considered uniform in the four directions.

The assigned contrast is represented by y_1. To test for its significance the statistic is

$$T_1 = \frac{N}{N-1} \frac{\bar{y}_1^2}{w_{11}} = \frac{28(8.8571)^2}{27(128.7200)} = 0.632020$$

The quantity $(N-1)T_1 = 17.0645$ as the variance ratio with 1 and 27 degrees of freedom is significant.

To test whether the assigned contrast agrees with that estimated from the data, the statistic U defined in (7b.1.2) has to be calculated.

$$\frac{N-p+1}{p-2} U_{2,1} = \frac{N-p+1}{p-2}\left(\frac{1+T_{p-1}}{1+T_1} - 1\right)$$

$$= \frac{25}{2}\left\{\frac{1.768226}{1.632020} - 1\right\} = 1.0431$$

This value as the variance ratio with 2 and 25 degrees of freedom is small so that the evidence supplied by the data is not sufficient to reject the assigned contrast as not the best, although the ratios of the coefficients in the estimated contrast depart considerably from those assigned.

Another problem connected with a single sample is to test for the significance of the departures of the observed mean values from those assigned. Let $\bar{x}_1, \cdots, \bar{x}_p$ be the mean values based on a sample of size N, and $\xi_1, \cdots, \xi_p$ the assigned values. If (w_{ij}) is the covariance matrix of $x_1, \cdots, x_p$ estimated on n degrees of freedom, then

$$\frac{n}{N} T_p = \Sigma\Sigma w^{ij}(\bar{x}_i - \xi_i)(\bar{x}_j - \xi_j)$$

The variance ratio with p and $(n+1-p)$ degrees of freedom to test the above hypothesis is

$$T_p \frac{(n+1-p)}{p} = \frac{N(n+1-p)}{np}\Sigma\Sigma w^{ij}(\bar{x}_i - \xi_i)(\bar{x}_j - \xi_j)$$

In many problems both the mean values and the covariance matrix are estimated from the same sample, in which case $n = N - 1$.

Example 2. Consider the covariance matrix

128.7200	61.4076	−21.0211
61.4076	56.9259	−28.2963
−21.0211	−28.2963	63.5344

estimated on 27 degrees of freedom and mean values 8.8571, 4.5000, 0.8571 based on 28 observations as in example 1 above. Suppose that it is required to test whether the calculated averages agree with the assigned values 5, 1, and −2. The deviations are

$$8.8571 - 5 = 3.8571 \qquad 4.5000 - 1 = 3.5000 \qquad 0.8571 + 2 = 2.8571$$

To evaluate the quadratic form

$$\Sigma\Sigma w^{ij} d_i d_j$$

we follow the form adopted in 1d.1 and sweep out the matrix.

Dispersion Matrix			Deviations
128.7200	61.4076	−21.0211	3.8571
	56.9259	−28.2963	3.5000
		63.5344	2.8571
			0

This gives the last pivotal quantity 0.6529 (with a negative sign) which is the value of the quadratic form. The variance ratio with 3 and (27 + 1 − 3) degrees of freedom is

$$\frac{28}{27} \frac{27 + 1 - 3}{3} (0.6529) = \frac{457.0300}{81} = 5.6423$$

which is significant on the 1% level, indicating departure from the expected.

The second generalization of Student's t is concerned with testing, on the basis of a sample of size N from a $2p$-variate population containing the variables $y_1, \cdots, y_p, y_{p+1}, \cdots, y_{2p}$ whether the mean values of y_i and y_{i+p} are the same for all i. The $2p$ variates can be reduced to p variates

$$z_1 = y_{p+1} - y_1 \qquad z_2 = y_{p+2} - y_2 \qquad \cdots \qquad z_p = y_{2p} - y_p$$

in which case the problem reduces to the one considered above. The variance ratio with p and $(N - p)$ degrees of freedom is

$$\frac{N}{N - 1} \frac{N - p}{p} \Sigma\Sigma w^{ij} \bar{z}_i \bar{z}_j$$

where (w_{ij}) is the dispersion matrix of $z_1, \cdots, z_p$ based on $(N - 1)$ degrees of freedom.

The test is useful in various situations. Suppose that we want to test for asymmetry of organisms. The sets $y_1, \cdots, y_p$ and $y_{p+1}, \cdots, y_{2p}$ will then correspond to the same measurements on the right and left sides of an organism. Another interesting study is whether the first born in a family differs from the second born. To illustrate the method, a random sample of 25 families has been chosen from Dr. G. P. Frets's data giving the head lengths and breadths of all sons and daughters in a large number of families in Germany. For effective

TABLE 7b.2β. The Measurements on the First and Second Adult Sons in a Sample of 25 Families (Data by G. P. Frets)

Head Length			Head Breadth		
First Son	Second Son	Differ- ence	First Son	Second Son	Differ- ence
191	179	12	155	145	10
195	201	− 6	149	152	− 3
181	185	− 4	148	149	− 1
183	188	− 5	153	149	4
176	171	5	144	142	2
208	192	16	157	152	5
189	190	− 1	150	149	1
197	189	8	159	152	7
188	197	− 9	152	159	− 7
192	187	5	150	151	− 1
179	186	− 7	158	148	10
183	174	9	147	147	0
174	185	−11	150	152	− 2
190	195	− 5	159	157	2
188	187	1	151	158	− 7
163	161	2	137	130	7
195	183	12	155	158	− 3
186	173	13	153	148	5
181	182	− 1	145	146	− 1
175	165	10	140	137	3
192	185	7	154	152	2
174	178	− 4	143	147	− 4
176	176	0	139	143	− 4
197	200	− 3	167	158	9
190	187	3	163	150	3
Mean difference		1.88			1.48

comparison, only adults of the same sex (say sons or daughters) have to be chosen.

The dispersion matrix of the differences estimated on 24 degrees of freedom is

$$\begin{pmatrix} 68.03 & 11.52 \\ 11.52 & 24.01 \end{pmatrix} \quad \text{with its inverse} \quad \begin{pmatrix} 0.015999 & -0.007677 \\ -0.007677 & 0.045332 \end{pmatrix}$$

$\Sigma\Sigma w^{ij}d_id_j$

$$= 0.015999(1.88)^2 - 2(0.007677)(1.88)(1.48) + 0.045332(1.48)^2$$

$$= 0.113121$$

$$\frac{N}{N-1}\frac{N-p}{p}(0.113121) = \frac{25}{24}\frac{23}{2}(0.1131) = 1.3548$$

This is not significant as a variance ratio with 2 and 23 degrees of freedom. There is no difference in the dimensions of the first son and the second as judged by the above sample. The method described above for such studies is quite general and can be applied to any number of characters.

7b.3   Mahalanobis' D^2 and Problems of Two Samples

Let N_1 and N_2 be the samples drawn from two populations, each characterized by p variates. The sample means for the ith character are represented by $\bar{x}_{i1}$ and $\bar{x}_{i2}$ for the first and second samples, respectively. The estimated value of the covariance is given by

$$(N_1 + N_2 - 2)w_{ij} = \sum_{t=1}^{N_1} (x_{i1t} - \bar{x}_{i1})(x_{j1t} - \bar{x}_{j1})$$

$$+ \sum_{t=1}^{N_2} (x_{i2t} - \bar{x}_{i2})(x_{j2t} - \bar{x}_{j2})$$

the right-hand expression being the sum of the corrected sums of products for two samples. Mahalanobis' (1936) distance between the two populations as estimated from the sample on the basis of the p characters is *

$$D_p^2 = \sum_1^p \sum_1^p w^{ij}(\bar{x}_{i1} - \bar{x}_{i2})(\bar{x}_{j1} - \bar{x}_{j2})$$

where (w^{ij}) is the reciprocal of (w_{ij}), $(i, j = 1, 2, \cdots, p)$. The exact distribution of D^2 on the hypothesis specifying real differences in mean

* The subscript p in the symbol D_p^2 denotes the number of characters used. The suffix may be omitted unless various D^2 values based on different sets or numbers of characters are to be kept distinct in any problem.

values is derived in 2d.2. To test the hypothesis specifying no difference in mean values of the p characters for the two populations, the statistic

$$\frac{N_1 N_2 (N_1 + N_2 - p - 1)}{p(N_1 + N_2)(N_1 + N_2 - 2)} D^2$$

can be used as a variance ratio with p and $(N_1 + N_2 - 1 - p)$ degrees of freedom.

As observed earlier, the above test can be derived in an interesting way suggested by R. A. Fisher. If the p measurements are replaced by a linear compound

$$y = l_1 x_1 + \cdots + l_p x_p$$

then the ratio of between to within variance of y from the two samples is

$$\frac{N_1 N_2}{N_1 + N_2} \frac{(l_1 d_1 + \cdots l_p d_p)^2}{\Sigma\Sigma l_i l_j w_{ij}}$$

Maximizing this, we find that the coefficients of the best linear function separating the two groups are obtained as solutions of the equations

$$l_1 w_{11} + l_2 w_{12} + \cdots = d_1 \mu$$

$$l_1 w_{21} + l_2 w_{22} + \cdots = d_2 \mu$$

$$\cdots \qquad \cdots \qquad \cdots$$

$$l_1 w_{p1} + l_2 w_{p2} + \cdots = d_p \mu$$

where μ is a constant. Observing that only ratios of l can be uniquely determined, we can replace μ by unity and solve the above equations. Multiplying the above equations by $l_1, l_2 \cdots$ and adding, we find

$$\Sigma\Sigma l_i l_j w_{ij} = l_1 d_1 + \cdots + l_p d_p = \Sigma\Sigma w^{ij} d_i d_j = D^2$$

The optimum ratio is then

$$\frac{N_1 N_2}{N_1 + N_2} \Sigma\Sigma w^{ij} d_i d_j = \frac{N_1 N_2}{N_1 + N_2} D^2$$

The significance of this can be tested as shown above.

Example. The following tables (7b.3α and 7b.3β), reproduced from Fisher (1938), give the mean values based on 50 observations each and the covariance based on $(50 + 50 - 2)$ degrees of freedom for four characters in two species of plants *Iris versicolor* and *Iris setosa*.

The solution of the equations (see Table 7b.6β)

$$l_1 w_{1i} + \cdots + l_4 w_{4i} = d_i \qquad i = 1, 2, 3, 4$$

is obtained as

$$l_1 = -3.0692 \qquad l_2 = -18.0006 \qquad l_3 = 21.7641 \qquad l_4 = 30.7549$$

so that the discriminant function is

$$-3.0692x_1 - 18.0006x_2 + 21.7641x_3 + 30.7549x_4$$

The value of D^2 is

$$l_1 d_1 + \cdots + l_p d_p = 103.2119$$

To test for the differences in mean values the statistic is

$$\frac{N_1 N_2 (N_1 + N_2 - 1 - 4)}{(N_1 + N_2)(N_1 + N_2 - 2)} \frac{D_4{}^2}{4} = \frac{50 \times 50 \times 95}{100 \times 98 \times 4} 103.2119$$

$$= \tfrac{95}{4} (26.3295) = 625.3256$$

which as a variance ratio with 4 and 95 degrees of freedom is significant.

TABLE 7b.3α.   Observed Mean Values Based on 50 Observations Each for the Two Species

Character	Iris versicolor	Iris setosa	Difference
Sepal length (x_1)	5.936	5.006	0.930
Sepal width (x_2)	2.770	3.428	−0.658
Petal length (x_3)	4.260	1.462	2.798
Petal width (x_4)	1.326	0.246	1.080

TABLE 7b.3β.   The Pooled Covariance Matrix (w_{ij}) Based on 98 Degrees of Freedom

	x_1	x_2	x_3	x_4
x_1	0.195340	0.092200	0.099626	0.033055
x_2	0.092200	0.121079	0.047175	0.025251
x_3	0.099626	0.047175	0.125488	0.039586
x_4	0.033055	0.025251	0.039586	0.025106

The method of evaluating the D^2 given above is useful because the best discriminating function is also found out during the process. This is useful in problems of classification as treated in the next chapter.

7b.4   Test for an Assigned Discriminant Function

In the last section the discriminant function for *Iris versicolor* and *Iris setosa* based on four measurements was found to be

$$-3.0692x_1 - 18.0006x_2 + 21.7641x_3 + 30.7549x_4$$

with the value of $D_4{}^2 = 103.2119$. Since the mean measurements for *versicolor* exceed those for *setosa* except in sepal width (x_2), a discriminant function of the type

$$x_1 - x_2 + x_3 + x_4$$

may be suggested. In such a case it might be of interest to know whether the discriminant function derived above is an improvement over the assigned simpler function. If the assigned function is represented by y, then

$$D_y^2 = \frac{(\bar{y}_1 - \bar{y}_2)^2}{V(y)}$$

where $\bar{y}_1$ and $\bar{y}_2$ are the mean values of y for the two species.

$$\bar{y} = \bar{x}_1 - \bar{x}_2 + \bar{x}_3 + \bar{x}_4$$

$$\bar{y}_1 - \bar{y}_2 = d_1 - d_2 + d_3 + d_4$$

$$= 0.930 - 0.658 + 2.798 + 1.080 = 5.466$$

$$V(y) = V(x_1) + V(x_2) + V(x_3) + V(x_4) -$$

$$2 \text{ cov } (x_1 x_2) + 2 \text{ cov } (x_1 x_3) + 2 \text{ cov } (x_1 x_4) +$$

$$2 \text{ cov } (x_3 x_4) - 2 \text{ cov } (x_2 x_3) - 2 \text{ cov } (x_2 x_4)$$

$$= w_{11} + w_{22} + w_{33} + w_{44} - 2w_{12} - 2w_{23} - 2w_{24} + 2w_{13}$$

$$+ 2w_{14} + 2w_{34}$$

$$= 0.482295$$

using the values of w_{ij} given in Table 7b.3β.

$$D_y^2 = \frac{29.8771}{0.482295} = 61.9479$$

To test whether the assigned discriminant function is in agreement with that derived from the data, the significance of the statistic

$$U = \frac{1 + N_1 N_2 D^2/(N_1 + N_2)(N_1 + N_2 - 2)}{1 + N_1 N_2 D_y^2/(N_1 + N_2)(N_1 + N_2 - 2)} - 1$$

$$\frac{1 + 26.3295}{1 + 15.8030} - 1 = 0.6265$$

has to be tested. The value of the statistic

$$\frac{U(N_1 + N_2 - 1 - 4)}{4 - 1} = \frac{0.6265 \times 95}{3} = 19.8392$$

as a variance ratio with 3 and 96 degrees of freedom is significant at the 1% level. This shows that the assigned function is not the best discriminant of the two species.

In general, if the assigned discriminant function is

$$y = a_1x_1 + \cdots + a_px_p$$

then

$$D_y{}^2 = \frac{(\bar{y}_1 - \bar{y}_2)^2}{V(y)}$$

where $V(y) = \Sigma\Sigma a_i a_j w_{ij}$. If w_{ij} are estimated on n degrees of freedom and the mean values are based on N_1 and N_2 observations for the two groups, then

$$U = \frac{1 + N_1 N_2 D_p{}^2/(N_1 + N_2)n}{1 + N_1 N_2 D_y{}^2/(N_1 + N_2)n} - 1$$

and

$$\frac{U(n - p + 1)}{p - 1}$$

can be used as a variance ratio with $(p - 1)$ and $(n - p + 1)$ degrees of freedom. This test is due to Fisher.

7b.5   Tests for Discriminant Function Coefficients

If four samples of sizes N_1, N_2, N_3, and N_4 from populations A, B, C, and E are available, we can test whether the discriminant functions between A, B and C, E are significantly different by an extension of the test criterion discussed above. It is a necessary condition of the test that the variances and covariances are identical in the four populations A, B, C, and E. No reasonably simple test can be constructed to establish the equivalence of the discriminant functions when this condition is not satisfied.

Let (w_{ij}) be the dispersion matrix based on $(N_1 + N_2 + N_3 + N_4 - 4)$ degrees of freedom. If $d_1, \cdots, d_p$ are the differences in mean values for A and B, and $d_1', \cdots, d_p'$ are those for C and E, the test for equality of discriminant functions and the *associated distances* is identical with the testing of the hypotheses

$$E(d_i) = E(d_i') \qquad i = 1, 2, \cdots, p$$

$$E(d_i) = E(-d_i') \qquad i = 1, 2, \cdots, p$$

The variance ratios with p and $n = (N_1 + N_2 + N_3 + N_4 - 3 - p)$

degrees of freedom for the two cases are

$$\frac{n}{p}\frac{f(N)}{n + p - 1}\Sigma\Sigma w^{ij}(d_i - d_i')(d_j - d_j')$$

and

$$\frac{n}{p}\frac{f(N)}{n + p - 1}\Sigma\Sigma w^{ij}(d_i + d_i')(d_j + d_j')$$

where

$$\frac{1}{f(N)} = \frac{1}{N_1} + \frac{1}{N_2} + \frac{1}{N_3} + \frac{1}{N_4}$$

The equality of discriminant functions is indicated if at least one of the statistics is not significant. Similar tests can be constructed for judging the differences in discriminant functions in parallel samples from two populations or between A, B and A, C.

If the equality of discriminant function coefficients are to be tested without considering the associated distance function, a suitable statistic is

$$g(N)\Sigma\Sigma w^{ij}(d_i - \lambda d_i')(d_j - \lambda d_j') \qquad (7b.5.1)$$

where

$$g(N) = \frac{1}{N_1} + \frac{1}{N_2} + \lambda^2\left(\frac{1}{N_3} + \frac{1}{N_4}\right)$$

and λ is chosen to minimize (7b.5.1). This minimum value may be used as χ^2 with $(p - 1)$ degrees of freedom when n is large.

Standard errors of discriminant function coefficients have been evaluated in an attempt to judge the significance of any single coefficient. There is some difficulty in this approach because discriminant function coefficients are not unique in the sense that they are the estimates of definite population parameters. What is unique is the ratio of any two coefficients, and an exact test is possible to test for an assigned ratio. For instance, if the ratio for the ith and jth characters is ρ, then we have to test whether the distance based on the $(p - 1)$ characters

$$x_1, \cdots, x_{i-1}, x_{i+1}, \cdots, x_{j-1}, x_{j+1}, \cdots, x_p, x_i + \rho x_j$$

is the same as that based on all the p characters

$$x_1, \cdots, x_p$$

The statistic is

$$U = \frac{1 + \dfrac{N_1 N_2}{(N_1 + N_2)(N_1 + N_2 - 2)}D_p^2}{1 + \dfrac{N_1 N_2}{(N_1 + N_2)(N_1 + N_2 - 2)}D^2_{p-1}} - 1$$

and to test for its significance

$$\frac{N_1 + N_2 - p - 1}{1} U$$

can be used as a variance ratio with 1 and $(N_1 + N_2 - p - 1)$ degrees of freedom.

7b.6   The Additional Information Supplied by Some Characters

Table 7b.6α gives the mean values of femur and humerus lengths of 20 Indian and 27 Anglo-Indian skeletons.

TABLE 7b.6α.   Mean Values of Femur and Humerus Lengths

	Sample Size	Mean Length of Femur	Humerus
Anglo-Indians	27	460.4	335.1
Indians	20	444.3	323.2
Difference		16.1	11.9

The pooled estimates (on 45 degrees of freedom) of standard deviations are 23.7 and 18.2 and of correlation 0.8675. The D^2 based on the femur alone is 0.4614, which yields a significant variance ratio 5.301 with 1 and 45 degrees of freedom. But the D^2 based on the two characters, femur and humerus lengths, is 0.4777, leading to the variance ratio 2.685 which is not significant on 2 and 44 degrees of freedom. Here appears to be a dangerous situation where the inclusion of an extra character is not beneficial in discriminating between two populations. This leads us to the problem of studying the nature and number of characters which may be of use in discriminating between the groups. The first step in such a study is to develop a test to judge the significance of the additional distance contributed by the inclusion of some extra characters. The addition of such characters which do not increase the distance between the groups in the population will weaken the test.

Even a small increase in distance will be helpful if the sample size is large. For instance, in the above example, with 10 more observations and an *equal division* of the sample size between the two groups, the observed D^2 would have been significant.

Two problems then arise: first to test whether the inclusion of some extra characters increases the distance in the population, and second to estimate the additional distance and determine for what sample size this addition is useful. There is yet another practical issue which is relevant in problems of the next chapter where a number of measurements are obtained for assigning an individual to one of two groups. The error committed in such a classification depends on the distance between the two groups, and an extra character added may increase the distance only by a trifle, in which case it may not be worth while to measure an extra character.

To solve the first problem let p be the number of basic characters to which are added q more characters. Let samples of sizes N_1 and N_2 be available for the two groups containing measurements on all the $p + q$ characters. If D^2_{p+q} is of the same order as D_p^2, then the ratio

$$R = \frac{1 + \dfrac{N_1 N_2}{(N_1 + N_2)(N_1 + N_2 - 2)} D^2_{p+q}}{1 + \dfrac{N_1 N_2}{(N_1 + N_2)(N_1 + N_2 - 2)} D_p^2}$$

is about unity. A high value of this ratio would indicate that D^2_{p+q} is significantly greater than D_p^2 so that the q characters supply some additional information. The actual test is to use

$$\frac{N_1 + N_2 - p - q - 1}{q} U_{q,p}$$

where $U_{q,p} = (R - 1)$ as a variance ratio with q and $(N_1 + N_2 - p - q - 1)$ degrees of freedom.

In the example of *Iris versicolor* and *Iris setosa* we might ask the question whether sepal and petal lengths alone are sufficient for discrimination. In other words, does the inclusion of widths increase the distance? For this we need the value of D^2 based on the lengths only. It is useful to obtain the corresponding discriminant function also. The successive evaluation of D^2's and discriminant functions can be carried out as illustrated in Table 7b.6β. This is essentially a method of pivotal condensation developed by Aitken (1933) but slightly modified to effect economy in entries.

The D_2^2 corresponding to lengths only is 76.7082, and $D_4^2 = 103.2119$, so that

$$U_{q,p} = \frac{1 + 50 \times 50(103.2119)/100 \times 98}{1 + 50 \times 50(76.7082)/100 \times 98} - 1$$

$$\frac{1 + 26.3295}{1 + 19.5684} - 1 = 0.3287$$

TABLE 7b.6β.   Pivotal Condensation Method for Obtaining Successive D^2 Values and Discriminant Functions $L(x)$

Dispersion Matrix (x_1, x_3, x_2, x_4)

Row No.	x_1	x_3	x_2	x_4	Difference in Means (d)	Sum Including the Indented	Check Excluding the Indented
01	0.1953	0.0996	0.0922	0.0331	0.930	1.3502	
02		0.1255	0.0472	0.0396	2.798	3.1099	
03			0.1211	0.0252	0.658	0.9437	
04				0.0251	1.080	1.2030	
05					0.000	3.1500	
10	1	0.509985	0.472094	0.169483	4.761904		6.913466
11	0.509985	0.074705	0.000179	0.022719	2.323714	2.931302	2.421317
12	0.472094		0.077573	0.009574	1.097047	0.537627	1.009721
13	0.169483			0.019490	0.922381	1.143647	0.974164
14 $L_1(x) =$	4.761904				$-\,4.428571 = -D_1^2$	$-\,2.482381$	2.279523
20	6.826638	1	0.002396	0.304116	31.105200		39.238350
21	0.470872	0.002396	0.077572	0.009519	1.102615	$-\,0.542256$	$-\,0.544652$
22	0.014389	0.304116		0.012581	0.215702	0.556307	0.252191
23 $L_2(x) =$	11.101250	31.105200			$-\,76.708160 = -D_2^2$	-57.609123	-88.714323
30	6.070128	0.030887	1	0.122712	14.214085		6.990358
31	-0.043393	0.303822	0.122712	0.011413	0.351006	0.745560	$-\,0.622848$
32 $L_3(x) =$	-4.408236	31.139256	-14.214085		$-\,92.380813 = -D_3^2$	-79.512872	-65.298787
40	-3.802068	26.620696	10.751950	1	30.754929		65.325507
41 $L_4(x) =$	-3.069247	21.764139	-18.000642	30.754929	$-103.211900 = -D_4^2$		102.517650

1. Rows 10, 20, 30, and 40 are the pivotal rows at each stage.

2. After sweeping out the first column, fill in the first column by the elements of the first pivotal row. These are indented as shown above. Retain these elements in sweeping out the second column at the second stage. In the reduced matrix fill up the second column by elements in the second pivotal row. Retain them at subsequent stages.

3. The sums in the last but one column are used in obtaining the elements of the check column at each stage of reduction.

4. At the stage of obtaining $L_i(x)$ and D_i^2 an additional check is available, because $L_{4i}(d) = D_i^2$. Thus from row 23, $11.101250(0.930)$ $+\ 31.105200(2.798) = 76.708160$, and so on.

5. If only successive values of D^2 are needed, as in the test for additional information, then the entries below the diagonal are unnecessary. One check column will do.

The variance ratio with 2 and $(N_1 + N_2 - p - q - 1) = 95$ degrees of freedom is

$$\tfrac{95}{2}(0.3287) = 15.6132$$

which is significant, showing that widths are useful in addition to the lengths. The additional distance in such a case is determined by

$$D^2_{p+q} - D_p{}^2 = 103.2119 - 76.7082 = 26.5037$$

A question may be asked as to why the difference $D^2_{p+q} - D_p{}^2$ could not be tested directly. The distribution of this difference involves the population value of the distance based on the first p characters, and unless this is known no exact test of significance can be made. On the other hand the statistic $U_{q,p}$, which also gives a comparison of the two D^2 values, is distributed in a simple manner, and there is not the problem of any nuisance parameter (5c.3). If the samples are large and the population value $\Delta_p{}^2$ of $D_p{}^2$ is not large, the distribution of the difference $D^2_{p+q} - D_p{}^2$ is independent of $\Delta_p{}^2$ to a large extent. In such a case

$$\left\{ \frac{N_1 + N_2 - p - 1}{N_1 + N_2 - 1} W_{q,p} \right\} \frac{N_1 + N_2 - p - q - 1}{q} \tag{7b.6.1}$$

can be used approximately as a variance ratio with q and $(N_1 + N_2 - p - q - 1)$ degrees of freedom, where

$$W_{q,p} = \frac{N_1 N_2}{(N_1 + N_2)(N_1 + N_2 - 2)} (D^2_{p+q} - D_p{}^2)$$

In the above example,

$$W_{q,p} = 26.3295 - 19.5684 = 6.7611$$

$$\tfrac{97}{99} \times \tfrac{95}{2}(6.7611) = \tfrac{95}{2}(6.6245) = 314.6637$$

which is a very high variance ratio compared to that obtained on the basis of $U_{q,p}$. The approximation here is very crude (it always overestimates significance), especially because $D_p{}^2$ happens to be very high.

Cochran and Bliss (1948) considered a situation where initial intelligent quotients (I.Q.) can be used as concomitant variables in studying the differences introduced by two types of training. For this it is suggested that a sample may be divided at random into two groups, each of which is required to take a different training. This means that with respect to initial I.Q. values the two groups can be regarded as having come from the same population so that an exact test based on $W_{q,p}$ is possible. The exact distribution of $W_{q,p}$, even in this case, is a bit complicated, but a good approximation to this is the variance ratio considered above (7b.6.1).

It is interesting to observe that $U_{q,p}$ in any case is distributed independently of the first p variables. The only condition needed for the test is that, given p measurements, the expected value of any other measurement is a linear combination of the first p. If this is so, it is not necessary that the first p variables be observed at random. If the problem is to test whether q additional characters discriminate between the two populations independently of a basic set, it might be profitable to select samples from the two populations such that they agree on the average, as far as possible, in the basic set of p characters. In the problem of Cochran and Bliss the initial I.Q. values may be used to effect such a division. The only test available in such a case is that based on $U_{q,p}$. If the sample is divided at random into two groups, the test based on $W_{q,p}$ is theoretically more accurate.

The following conclusions will be useful in studying the problems of this nature.

1. Whatever may be the number of characters chosen to discriminate between two populations, it is profitable to divide the samples equally between the two populations.

2. Unless the samples are large, it is not profitable to consider nearly related measurements in tests for discrimination.

3. To judge the significance of increase in distance due to the inclusion of q extra characters to a basic set of p, it is advantageous (from the point of view of the test) to choose the individuals from the two populations such that they may agree, as far as possible, in the average measurements of the basic set.

In 3f.3 some comments were made as to the applicability of a prediction formula found from one series for an individual of an unrelated series. Thus a question might be asked whether a prediction formula for cranial capacity deduced from the measurements on an Anglo-Saxon skull can be used to predict the capacity of an Indian skull, providing measurements on its length, breadth, and height. This is a very important problem because, in the absence of suitable data, it may be necessary to use the formula derived from a different series. As observed earlier, one condition may be that the internal relationships of the measurements should be the same for the two series, which means that the variances and covariances of the measurements should be the same. This requirement is very often satisfied with biometric material; the differences, when they exist, are quite small. This is not enough. It must be known that the two series are such that the whole distance between them should be capable of being explained by the differences in the characters used for prediction. In other words, if

$x_1, x_2, \cdots, x_p$ are the characters used for the prediction of a character y, then these measurements must be such that the additional distance due to y on eliminating $x_1, \cdots, x_p$ is theoretically zero. Only in such cases can a single formula be applicable for two series. This can be verified by the methods developed here. In fact the methods are applicable in a more general case requiring the prediction of more than one character with the help of a basic set.

7c Generalization of D^2 and the Large Sample Theory for Several Groups

Let there be k multivariate populations $A_1, A_2, \cdots, A_k$ from which samples of sizes $N_1, N_2, \cdots, N_k$ are available for $(p + q)$ characters. The common covariance matrix assumed to be known or estimated on a large number of degrees of freedom is represented by $(\alpha_{ij})_p$ for the first p characters and by $(\alpha_{ij})_{p+q}$ for all the $(p + q)$ characters. The inverse of $(\alpha_{ij})_p$ is represented by $(\alpha_p{}^{ij})$, and that of $(\alpha_{ij})_{p+q}$ by $(\alpha^{ij}{}_{p+q})$. Let $\bar{x}_{i1}, \bar{x}_{i2}, \cdots$, be the mean values of the ith character in the first, second, etc., populations.

It is shown in 2c.3 that the statistic,

$$V_{pk} = \sum_{i,j=1}^{p} \alpha_p{}^{ij} \sum_{r=1}^{k} N_r(\bar{x}_{ir} - \bar{x}_i)(\bar{x}_{jr} - \bar{x}_j)$$

where $\bar{x}_i = (\Sigma N_r \bar{x}_{ir})/(\Sigma N_r)$, can be used as χ^2 with $p(k - 1)$ degrees of freedom to test the hypothesis that the mean values are the same in all the k populations for these p characters. The statistic V is a suitable generalization of Mahalanobis' D^2 in its classical form.

When this test indicates differences in mean values it is in some problems necessary to test whether the observations on q additional characters supply independent information for discrimination. The statistic for testing the differences in means for all the $p + q$ characters is

$$V_{(p+q)k} = \sum_{i,j=1}^{p+q} \alpha^{ij}{}_{p+q} \sum_{r=1}^{k} N_r(\bar{x}_{ir} - \bar{x}_i)(\bar{x}_{jr} - \bar{x}_j)$$

which can be used as χ^2 with $(p + q)(k - 1)$ degrees of freedom. The $q(k - 1)$ additional degrees of freedom bring in the contribution

$$V_{(p+q)k} - V_{pk}$$

and the significance of this difference can be appropriately used to judge the significance of the information supplied by the additional characters. This difference can be used as χ^2 with $q(k - 1)$ degrees of freedom, as shown below.

The hypothesis that the new characters do not lead to further discrimination of the populations specifies that any linear function of the $(p + q)$ characters uncorrelated with each of the p characters has the same mean value for all the k populations. There are q such linear functions and, if they are treated as q variables, a χ^2 with $q(k - 1)$ degrees of freedom can be constructed to test the above hypothesis. The above method of taking the difference is only an alternative way of calculating this χ^2; for, $V_{(p+q)k}$ calculated from all the $(p + q)$ characters, being invariant under linear transformations of the variables, is equal to $V_{pk} + \chi^2$ calculated from the p original characters and the q linear functions chosen to be uncorrelated with each of the p characters.

In the above derivation it has been assumed that the variances and covariances are known, and the distributions are asymptotically true when they are estimated on a large number of degrees of freedom. When more than two populations are involved the pooled estimates of the covariances usually have a sufficiently large number of degrees of freedom to validate the use of the asymptotic distributions. More exact tests for cases involving small numbers of degrees of freedom are given in the next section.

7d   Tests with Wilks's Λ Criterion

7d.1   Analysis of Dispersion and the Theoretical Aspects of the Λ Criterion

In the univariate analysis of variance, tests of significance reduce to the comparison of two independently distributed mean squares. One of the mean squares is an unbiased estimate of the variance to which a single observation in any particular class is subject and is called the error variance. The other is an unbiased estimate only when the null hypothesis which is being tested is correct and may be called the mean square due to deviation from the hypothesis. The test depends only on the individual degrees of freedom of two mean squares.

When each sample supplies p mutually correlated variables, there are p total sums of squares and $p(p - 1)/2$ total sums of products which can be analyzed into various categories. This process, which involves the technique of analyzing the variances and covariances of multiple correlated variables, may be termed the analysis of dispersion. The term dispersion was originally used by P. C. Mahalanobis to indicate the scatter of a set of observations as measured by the variances and covariances. Following this terminology, the total dispersion may be said to be analyzed into dispersion due to various categories.

If we represent the total sums of products by the matrix $S = (S_{ij})$, then the analysis of dispersion consists in analyzing each element such as S_{ij}, according to the usual procedure, into various categories with the corresponding distribution of degrees of freedom. The dispersion due to any category supplies the sum of products (S.P.) matrix which on division by the degrees of freedom gives the mean product (M.P.) matrix. The S.P. matrix leading to unbiased estimates of the variances and covariances to which a single set of variables is subject is called the S.P. matrix due to error. This error matrix may be denoted by W with w as its degrees of freedom. In the analysis of dispersion the S.P. matrix due to any other category leads to unbiased estimates of variances and covariances only when the null hypothesis regarding that category is true. This may be called the S.P. matrix due to deviation from the hypothesis. If such a matrix is represented by Q with q as its degrees of freedom, then the problem of testing the null hypothesis consists in comparing the matrices $(1/w)W$ and $(1/q)Q$. The simultaneous comparison of the estimates of the variances and covariances appears to be a natural extension of the comparison of variances in the case of a single variate.

The appropriate test criteria for comparison may be obtained by extending the method of discriminant function analysis. A linear compound of the variables is taken, and the compounding coefficients are chosen such that the ratio of mean squares due to deviation from hypothesis and due to error for this variable is a maximum. The ratio f^2 which comes out as a root of the determinantal equation

$$\left| Q - \frac{q}{w} f^2 W \right| = 0$$

may be used as the appropriate test criterion. If $|\,W\,| \neq 0$, the number of non-zero roots of this equation is equal to the number of variables under consideration or q, the number of degrees of freedom of Q, whichever is smaller. An adequate comparison of $(1/q)Q$ and $(1/w)W$ must involve the tests of significance of all the roots. If $f_1, f_2, \cdots$ represent the various roots, it is easy to verify that

$$\left(1 + \frac{q}{w} f_1^2 \right) \left(1 + \frac{q}{w} f_2^2 \right) \cdots = \frac{|\,W + Q\,|}{|\,W\,|}$$

The ratio $|\,W\,|/|\,W + Q\,|$ denoted by Λ decreases as the magnitude of the roots increase, and a significantly small value of Λ may be taken as providing the significance of one or more of the roots. This is the underlying theory of the Λ criterion arrived at by Wilks (1932) by using the likelihood ratio method and later extended by Bartlett (1934) for general use in multivariate analysis.

However, this does not provide a satisfactory test, for when only one or a smaller number of roots than the total indicate real differences, their significance may be obscured by the use of the overall test. Its use can be recommended only in situations where small deviations from the hypothesis can be ignored.

7d.2 The Distribution of Λ and Its Practical Use

The following notations will be used throughout this and the subsequent sections.

TABLE 7d.2α.   Analysis of Dispersion for p Variables

Due to	D.F.	S.P. Matrix
(1) Deviation from hypothesis	q	Q
(2) Error	$n - q$	W
(3) Total	n	$W + Q$

$$\Lambda = \frac{|W|}{|W + Q|}$$

If the number of variables involved is p, then, assuming that the elements of W are distributed independently of those of Q, it is easy to derive the tth moment of Λ.

$$E(\Lambda^t) = \prod_{i=0}^{p-1} \frac{\Gamma\{\frac{1}{2}(n - i)\}\Gamma\{\frac{1}{2}(n - q - i) + t\}}{\Gamma\{\frac{1}{2}(n - q - i)\}\Gamma\{\frac{1}{2}(n - i) + t\}}$$

The tests based on the exact distributions given by Wilks (1932) and Nair (1939) for some particular cases obtained by a comparison of moments are reproduced below.

	Nature of the Test	
	Variance Ratio	Degrees of Freedom
$q = 1$, for any p	$\dfrac{1 - \Lambda}{\Lambda} \dfrac{n - p}{p}$	p and $(n - p)$
$q = 2$, for any p	$\dfrac{1 - \sqrt{\Lambda}}{\sqrt{\Lambda}} \dfrac{n - p - 1}{p}$	$2p$ and $2(n - p - 1)$
$p = 1$, for any q	$\dfrac{1 - \Lambda}{\Lambda} \dfrac{n - q}{q}$	q and $(n - q)$
$p = 2$, for any q	$\dfrac{1 - \sqrt{\Lambda}}{\sqrt{\Lambda}} \dfrac{n - q - 1}{q}$	$2q$ and $2(n - q - 1)$

For other values of p and q, the exact values of the probabilities can be obtained by the use of χ^2 tables alone. Defining

$$V = -m \log_e \Lambda = -\left(n - \frac{p+q+1}{2}\right) \log_e \Lambda$$

the distribution function of V can be obtained in the asymptotic form

$$P_{pq} + \frac{\gamma_2}{m^2}(P_{pq+4} - P_{pq}) + \frac{1}{m^4}$$

$$\times \{\gamma_4(P_{pq+8} - P_{pq}) - \gamma_2{}^2(P_{pq+4} - P_{pq})\} + \cdots$$

where P_{pq+r} is the distribution function of χ^2 with $(pq + r)$ degrees of freedom. If m is large, the first approximation consists in using V as χ^2 with pq degrees of freedom. For obtaining the second and third approximations the expressions for γ_2 and γ_4 are

$$\gamma_2 = \frac{pq}{48}(p^2 + q^2 - 5)$$

$$\gamma_4 = \frac{\gamma_2{}^2}{2} + \frac{pq}{1920}\{3p^4 + 3q^4 + 10p^2q^2 - 50(p^2 + q^2) + 159\}$$

In many practical problems the first approximation suggested by Bartlett can be used.

Defining the statistic

$$y = \Lambda^{1/s} \qquad s = \sqrt{\frac{p^2q^2 - 4}{p^2 + q^2 - 5}}$$

the distribution function of y can be written

$$B\left(\frac{ms}{2} + \lambda, r\right) + \frac{c\Gamma\left(\dfrac{ms}{2} + \lambda + r\right)}{\Gamma\left(\dfrac{ms}{2} + \lambda + r + 4\right)}\left[B\left(\frac{ms}{2} + \lambda, r + 4\right)\right.$$

$$\left. - B\left(\frac{ms}{2} + \lambda, r\right)\right] + \cdots$$

where

$$c = \frac{\Gamma(r+4)}{\Gamma(r)} \left\{ \frac{\gamma_4 s^4}{16r(r+1)(r+2)(r+3)} - \frac{(r-1)(5r-7)}{10 \times 16 \times 36} \right\}$$

$$r = \frac{pq}{2}$$

$$\lambda = -\frac{pq-2}{4}$$

and $B(t, u)$ is the distribution function of the beta variable. The first term above offers a powerful approximation, the second term being $O(1/m^4)$. In this case the statistic

$$\frac{1 - \Lambda^{1/s}}{\Lambda^{1/s}} \frac{ms + 2\lambda}{2r}$$

can be used as a variance ratio with $2r$ and $(ms + 2\lambda)$ degrees of freedom. The quantity $(ms + 2\lambda)$ need not be integral.

7d.3   Test of Differences in Mean Values for Several Populations

Let $A_1, A_2, \cdots, A_k$ be k populations from which samples of sizes $N_1, \cdots, N_k$ for p correlated variables are available. The disperison has to be analyzed into between and within populations. The S.P. matrix due to within populations (or the error) has $(N_1 + \cdots + N_k - k)$ degrees of freedom, and that due to between populations has $(k - 1)$ degrees of freedom. If these are represented by W and Q, then the statistic to be used for testing the differences in mean values is

$$V = -m \log_e \Lambda$$

$$\Lambda = \frac{|W|}{|W + Q|}$$

where

$$m = n - \frac{p+q+1}{2}$$

$$n = N_1 + \cdots + N_k - 1$$

$$q = k - 1$$

The exact probability of V's exceeding the observed value can be calculated as explained in 7d.2.

Example 1. Table 7d.3α gives the analysis of dispersion for the three characters, head length (x_1), height (x_2), and weight (x_3), measured on

140 schoolboys, of almost the same age, belonging to six different schools in an Indian city.

TABLE 7d.3α. Analysis of Dispersion

Dispersion Due to	D.F.		S.P. Matrix					
			x_1^2	x_2^2	x_3^2	x_1x_2	x_1x_3	x_2x_3
Between schools	5	(Q_{ij})	752.0	151.3	1,612.7	214.2	521.3	401.2
Within schools	134	(W_{ij})	12,809.3	1499.6	21,009.6	1003.7	2671.2	4123.6
Total	139	(S_{ij})	13,561.3	1650.9	22,622.3	1217.9	3192.5	4524.8

$$\Lambda = \frac{|W|}{|S|} = \frac{\begin{vmatrix} 12,809.3 & 214.2 & 521.3 \\ 214.2 & 1,499.6 & 401.2 \\ 521.3 & 401.2 & 21,009.6 \end{vmatrix}}{\begin{vmatrix} 13,561.3 & 1,217.9 & 3,192.5 \\ 1,217.9 & 1,650.9 & 4,524.8 \\ 3,192.5 & 4,524.8 & 22,622.3 \end{vmatrix}}$$

$$= \frac{10^{12}(0.176005)}{10^{12}(0.213628)}$$

$$-\log_e \Lambda = 0.193724$$

$$m = 139 - \tfrac{1}{2}(5 + 3 + 1) = 134.5$$

$$V = -m\log_e \Lambda = (134.5)(0.193724)$$

$$= 26.0559$$

Using V as χ^2 with $pq = 15$ degrees of freedom, the first approximation comes out as

$$P_{15} = 0.0375$$

The second term is

$$\frac{\gamma_2}{m^2}(P_{19} - P_{15})$$

where

$$\gamma_2 = \frac{29 \times 15}{48} \quad \text{and} \quad \frac{\gamma_2}{m^2} = \frac{29 \times 15}{48(134.5)^2} = 0.00050096$$

$$\frac{\gamma_2}{m^2}(P_{19} - P_{15}) = 0.00050096(0.1285 - 0.0375) = 0.00004574$$

This correction to the first approximation affects only the fourth decimal place so that correction is hardly necessary. The observed value of V is significant at the 5% level, showing thereby that boys of various schools differ in physique. This appears to be generally true since boys belonging to different social strata attend different schools.

To use the variance ratio approximation we find $2r = 15$, $s = 2.67$, $ms + 2\lambda = 352.61$. The variance ratio 1.77 with 15 and 352.61 degrees of freedom is significant at the 5% level.

7d.4 Internal Analysis of a Set of Variates

Let $x_1, \cdots, x_p, x_{s+1}, \cdots, x_{s+p}$ be $(s + p)$ correlated variables for which samples of sizes $N_1, \cdots, N_k$ are available from k populations. If the differences in mean values of these $(s + p)$ variables are to be tested for significance, then the method given in 7d.3 can be used. An important problem that arises in biometry is to test whether the variables, say $x_{s+1}, \cdots, x_{s+p}$, bring out further differences in populations when the differences due to $x_1, \cdots, x_s$ are removed.

It is apparent in problems of this nature that some of the variables in the set $x_1, \cdots, x_s$ might be in the nature of concomitant variables which have been observed in association with the dependent variables or which might have been chosen to have some specified values. An illustration of such an analysis is found in a problem where three dependent variables g, h, and i, corresponding to linear, parabolic, and cubic terms of growth curves of pig weights, are considered together with a concomitant variable w giving the initial weight of pigs. It was desired to test whether the variables h and i bring out further differences in food treatments when the differences due to g and w are eliminated. The problem is identical with that posed above, with g, w forming the first set and h, i the second set of variables.

There is a third set of problems in which it is desired to test whether the differences in k groups characterized by $(s + p)$ measurements can be explained by variations in s assigned linear functions of these measurements. If $y_1, \cdots, y_{s+p}$ are the $(s + p)$ variables and

$$L_1 = m_{1,1}y_1 + \cdots + m_{1,p+s}y_{p+s}$$

$$\cdot \quad \cdot \quad \cdot \quad \cdot \quad \cdot \quad \cdot \quad \cdot \quad \cdot \quad \cdot \quad \cdot \quad \cdot \quad \cdot \quad \cdot$$

$$L_s = m_{s,1}y_1 + \cdots + m_{s,p+s}y_{p+s}$$

are the assigned linear functions, then we can replace the $(s + p)$ variables $y_1, \cdots, y_{s+p}$ by $x_1, \cdots, x_{s+p}$, defined by

$$x_1 = L_1, \cdots \qquad x_s = L_s$$

$$x_{s+1} = m_{s+1,1}y_1 + \cdots + m_{s+1,s+p}y_{p+s}$$

$$\cdot \quad \cdot \quad \cdot \quad \cdot \quad \cdot \quad \cdot \quad \cdot \quad \cdot \quad \cdot \quad \cdot \quad \cdot \quad \cdot \quad \cdot \quad \cdot \quad \cdot$$

$$x_{s+p} = m_{s+p,1}y_1 + \cdots + m_{s+p,s+p}y_{p+s}$$

where the coefficients in $x_{s+1}, \cdots, x_{s+p}$ are chosen arbitrarily subject to the condition that the determinant $\lvert m_{ij} \rvert$, $[i, j = 1, 2, \cdots, (s + p)]$, is not zero. This latter condition ensures that the transformation from the y to the x leads to one-to-one correspondence. Once again, the problem is reduced to that of considering the differences in $x_{s+1}, \cdots,$ x_{s+p} when those due to $x_1, \cdots, x_s$ are removed. The proposed test is independent of the compounding coefficients used to define the set $x_{s+1}, \cdots, x_{s+p}$ so that, in any practical problem, they may be conveniently or conventionally chosen.

In all these cases, the problem is one of analyzing the dispersion of the variables $x_{s+1}, \cdots, x_{s+p}$ when the dispersion due to $x_1, \cdots, x_s$ is removed. This can be done by following the covariance technique suitable for p dependent variables and s independent variables as indicated in 3g.2.

Let

$$(S_{ij}) = (Q_{ij}) + (W_{ij}) \qquad i, j = 1, 2, \cdots, (s + p)$$

be the analysis of dispersion for all the $(s + p)$ variates due to deviation from hypothesis and error with the corresponding distribution of degrees of freedom as

$$n' = q + (n' - q)$$

The S.P. matrix due to error for the variables $x_1, \cdots, x_s$ to be eliminated is

$$\begin{bmatrix} W_{11} & \cdots & W_{1s} \\ \cdot & \cdot \cdot \cdot \cdot \cdot & \cdot \\ W_{s1} & \cdots & W_{ss} \end{bmatrix}$$

and its inverse is represented by

$$\begin{bmatrix} W^{11} & \cdots & W^{1s} \\ \cdot & \cdot \cdot \cdot \cdot \cdot & \cdot \\ W^{s1} & \cdots & W^{ss} \end{bmatrix}$$

The S.P. matrix due to error for $x_{s+1}, \cdots, x_{s+p}$ when corrected for $x_1, \cdots, x_s$, is given by $W(s+1, \cdots, s+p \mid 1, \cdots, s)$ or simply $W(p \mid s)$ where

$$
W(p \mid s) = \begin{bmatrix} W_{s+1,s+1} & \cdots & W_{s+1,s+p} \\ \cdot & \cdots & \cdot \\ W_{s+p,s+1} & \cdots & W_{s+p,s+p} \end{bmatrix}
$$

$$
- \begin{bmatrix} W_{1,s+1} & \cdots & W_{s,s+1} \\ \cdot & \cdots & \cdot \\ W_{1,s+p} & \cdots & W_{s,s+p} \end{bmatrix} \begin{bmatrix} W^{11} & \cdots & W^{1s} \\ \cdot & \cdots & \cdot \\ W^{s1} & \cdots & W^{ss} \end{bmatrix} \begin{bmatrix} W_{1,s+1} & \cdots & W_{1,s+p} \\ \cdot & \cdots & \cdot \\ W_{s,s+1} & \cdots & W_{s,s+p} \end{bmatrix}
$$

This form, which involves the evaluation of a triple product of matrices, appears to be conveneint for computation as illustrated in the next section. Another way of obtaining this matrix $W(p \mid s)$ is to start with the complete matrix (W_{ij}), $(i, j = 1, 2, \cdots, s, s+1, \cdots, s+p)$ and reduce it s times by the method of pivotal condensation starting from the element W_{11}. Replacing W by S, we have the formula for computing the S.P. matrix due to "deviation from hypothesis + error" for $x_{s+1}, \cdots, x_{s+p}$ when corrected for $x_1, \cdots, x_s$. If this is represented by $S(p \mid s)$, then the required criterion is

$$
\frac{W(p \mid s)}{S(p \mid s)}
$$

The degrees of freedom for $W(p \mid s)$ are $(n' - q - s)$, and that for $S(p \mid s)$ are $(n' - s)$, so that in standard notation the parameters associated with Λ are

$$
n = n' - s \qquad p = p \qquad q = q
$$

The test can be carried out as discussed in 7d.2.

7d.5   Barnard's Problem of Secular Variations in Skull Characters

The problem of measuring secular variations in skull characters considered by Barnard (1935) is of immense importance to the anthropologists. It is, however, of interest to examine the methods employed by her in the light of the latest developments in multivariate analysis. The two problems involved in her study are:

(i) The selection of a smaller number, out of seven skull characters, which give significant information, so far as is possible, as to changes taking place with time in four series of Egyptian skulls; and

(ii) The determination of an expression, linear in measurements, which characterizes most effectively an individual skull with respect to the progressive secular changes.

To answer problem (i), Barnard first chose basialveolar length and nasal height as two basic characters which, independently of each other, show significant variation in the four series. To choose further characters she considered the problem of testing the significance of the linear regression of the mean values of an added character with time (corresponding to the four series) when that part of the regression due to the two basic characters is removed. This meant the choice of characters with special reference to the average linear rate of change of the individual means with time. If the choice of characters is to be with reference to the complete nature of changes taking place with time, then what is needed is an internal analysis of the characters to decide whether the configuration of the four series as determined by several characters is the same as that indicated by a smaller number. Barnard's method should, of course, be preferred if the regressions were known to be linear. This can, however, be tested from the data.

Taking the four measurements

$$x_1 = \text{basialveolar length}$$

$$x_2 = \text{nasal height}$$

$$x_3 = \text{maximum breadth}$$

$$x_4 = \text{basibregmatic height}$$

the relevant data are summarized in Tables 7d.5α and 7d.5β, which give the means for the four series and the analysis of dispersion.

TABLE 7d.5α.   Means for the Four Series

	Series			
	I	II	III	IV
Character	$N_1 = 91$	$N_2 = 162$	$N_3 = 70$	$N_4 = 75$
x_1	133.582418	134.265432	134.371429	135.306667
x_2	98.307692	95.462963	95.857143	95.040000
x_3	50.835165	51.148148	50.100000	52.093333
x_4	133.000000	134.882716	133.642857	131.466667

TABLE 7d.5β.   Analysis of Dispersion (S. P. Matrix)

Dispersion due to

	Between 3 D.F.	Within 394 D.F.	Total 397 D.F.
x_1^2	123.180628	9661.997470	9785.178098
x_2^2	486.345863	9073.115027	9559.460890
x_3^2	100.411505	3938.320351	4088.731856
x_4^2	640.733891	8741.508829	9382.242720
x_1x_2	−231.375635	445.573301	214.197666
x_1x_3	87.305348	1130.623900	1217.929248
x_1x_4	−128.763994	2148.584210	2019.820216
x_2x_3	−107.505618	1239.221990	1131.716372
x_2x_4	125.313318	2255.812722	2381.126040
x_3x_4	−137.580764	1271.054662	1133.473898

Example 1.   Do the characters x_3 and x_4 show significant variation in the four series independently of the variation due to the characters x_1 and x_2?

The method developed in 7d.4 is directly useful in this problem.   The S.P. matrix within for the basic characters x_1 and x_2 is

$$\begin{pmatrix} W_{11} & W_{12} \\ W_{21} & W_{22} \end{pmatrix} = \begin{pmatrix} 9661.997470 & 445.573301 \\ 445.573301 & 9073.115027 \end{pmatrix}$$

Its inverse is

$$\begin{pmatrix} W^{11} & W^{12} \\ W^{21} & W^{22} \end{pmatrix} = 10^{-4} \begin{pmatrix} 1.037332 & -0.050942 \\ -0.050942 & 1.104659 \end{pmatrix}$$

The within S.P. matrix for x_3, x_4 due to x_1, x_2 is given by the triple product

$$\begin{pmatrix} W_{13} & W_{23} \\ W_{14} & W_{24} \end{pmatrix} \begin{pmatrix} W^{11} & W^{12} \\ W^{21} & W^{22} \end{pmatrix} \begin{pmatrix} W_{13} & W_{14} \\ W_{23} & W_{24} \end{pmatrix}$$

$$= \begin{pmatrix} 1130.623900 & 1239.221990 \\ 2148.584210 & 2255.812722 \end{pmatrix} \begin{pmatrix} W^{11} & W^{12} \\ W^{21} & W^{22} \end{pmatrix} \begin{pmatrix} W_{13} & W_{14} \\ W_{23} & W_{24} \end{pmatrix}$$

$$= 10^{-4} \begin{pmatrix} 1109.703904 & 1311.321492 \\ 2113.879535 & 2382.450625 \end{pmatrix} \begin{pmatrix} W_{13} & W_{14} \\ W_{23} & W_{24} \end{pmatrix}$$

$$= \begin{pmatrix} 287.967620 & 534.238796 \\ 534.238796 & 991.621041 \end{pmatrix}$$

The within S.P. matrix for x_3 and x_4 after correcting for x_1 and x_2 is

$$\begin{pmatrix} W_{33} & W_{34} \\ W_{34} & W_{44} \end{pmatrix} - \begin{pmatrix} W_{13} & W_{23} \\ W_{14} & W_{24} \end{pmatrix} \begin{pmatrix} W^{11} & W^{12} \\ W^{21} & W^{22} \end{pmatrix} \begin{pmatrix} W_{13} & W_{14} \\ W_{23} & W_{24} \end{pmatrix}$$

$$= \begin{pmatrix} 3938.320351 & 1271.054662 \\ 1271.054662 & 8741.508829 \end{pmatrix} - \begin{pmatrix} 287.967620 & 534.238796 \\ 534.238796 & 991.621041 \end{pmatrix}$$

$$= \begin{pmatrix} 3650.353731 & 736.815866 \\ 736.815866 & 7749.887788 \end{pmatrix} = W(2 \mid 2)$$

This has $394 - 2 = 392$ degrees of freedom. Similarly, $S(2 \mid 2)$ with $397 - 2 = 395$ degrees of freedom is

$$\begin{pmatrix} 3809.335190 & 611.798381 \\ 611.798381 & 8393.755848 \end{pmatrix}$$

$$\Lambda = \frac{\mid W(2 \mid 2) \mid}{\mid S(2 \mid 2) \mid} = \frac{0.27746934}{0.31600332} = 0.878058$$

$$V = -m \log_e \Lambda \qquad m = n - \frac{p + q + 1}{2} = 395 - \frac{2 + 3 + 1}{2} = 392$$

$$V = -392 \log_e (0.878058) = 51.39$$

This value of V with pq equal to 6 degrees of freedom is significant so that x_3 and x_4 may be considered as discriminating the series independently of x_1 and x_2.

The above method could be simplified by starting with the full matrices W and S and reducing them by the method of pivotal condensation. The four pivotal elements for W are

$$10^4 (0.966200, 0.905257, 0.365033, 0.760117)$$

and for S

$$10^4 (0.978518, 0.955477, 0.380933, 0.829550)$$

The value of $\mid W(2 \mid 2) \mid$ is the product of the last two pivotal elements

$$10^8 (0.365033)(0.760117) = 0.277469 \times 10^8$$

Similarly, $\mid S(2 \mid 2) \mid = 0.316003 \times 10^8$. Thus we obtain the same value of Λ as above.

Example 2. Taking the relative times between the series in the proportion 2:1:2, can the variation of the characters be accounted for by the linear regression of individual characters with time?

In order to obtain the regression with time, the values of t, the time variable, may be taken as -5, -1, 1, and 5 for the individuals of the first, second, third, and fourth series, respectively. The calculation of individual regressions involves the quantities,

$$\Sigma(t - \bar{t})^2 = 4307.66832$$

$$\Sigma x_1(t - \bar{t}) = \quad 718.76286 \qquad \Sigma x_3(t - \bar{t}) = -410.10194$$

$$\Sigma x_2(t - \bar{t}) = -1407.26075 \qquad \Sigma x_4(t - \bar{t}) = -733.42758$$

The matrix R with 1 degree of freedom giving the squares and products due to regression is given in Table 7d.5γ.

TABLE 7d.5γ.   Matrix R with 1 Degree of Freedom

	x_1	x_2	x_3	x_4
x_1	119.930358	−234.810812	68.428235	−122.377258
x_2	−234.810812	459.734449	−133.975163	−149.601596
x_3	68.428235	−133.975163	39.042852	− 69.824358
x_4	−122.377258	−149.601596	− 69.824358	124.874099

In the above table

$$R_{11} = \frac{\{\Sigma x_1(t - \bar{t})\}^2}{\Sigma(t - \bar{t})^2}$$

$$R_{12} = \frac{\{\Sigma x_1(t - \bar{t})\}\{\Sigma x_2(t - \bar{t})\}}{\Sigma(t - \bar{t})^2} \qquad \text{and so on}$$

With these results we analyze the dispersion of which a typical product $(x_1 x_2)$ is chosen below for illustration. To test the hypothesis that the regressions are linear we compare W and $Q + W$.

TABLE 7d.5δ.   Analysis of Dispersion

Due to	D.F.	S.P. Matrix $(x_1 x_2)$	
Regression	1	−234.810812	(R_{ij})
Deviation from regression *	2	3.435177	(Q_{ij})
Total (between series)	3	−231.375635	$(R_{ij} + Q_{ij})$
Within series	394	445.573301	(W_{ij})
Total	397	214.197666	(S_{ij})
Deviation from regression + Within series	396	449.008478	$(Q_{ij} + W_{ij})$

* Obtained by subtraction. The complete matrix $(Q_{ij} + W_{ij})$ obtained by the above method is given in Table 7d.5ε. This is the total S.P. matrix minus the matrix R due to regression.

TABLE 7d.5ϵ.   Matrix $(Q + W)$ with 396 Degrees of Freedom

x_1	x_2	x_3	x_4
9665.247740	449.008478	1149.501013	2142.197474
449.008478	9099.726441	1265.691535	2231.524444
1149.501013	1265.691535	4049.689004	1203.298256
2142.197474	2231.524444	1203.298256	9257.368621

$$\Lambda = \frac{|W|}{|Q + W|} = \frac{0.24269054 \times 10^{12}}{0.26873816 \times 10^{12}} = 0.90307436$$

$$V = - \left\{ 396 - \frac{2 + 4 + 1}{2} \right\} \log_e (0.90307436)$$

$$= 40.02$$

The χ^2 approximation has $p \times q = 2 \times 4$ degrees of freedom, since Q has 2 degrees of freedom and there are four variables. The result is significant so that the regressions cannot be considered linear.

This test can be extended to examine whether a parabolic regression with time can explain the differences in mean values. The matrix Q giving the deviation from regression has then 1 degree of freedom and R due to regression 2.

To determine the coefficients of a linear compound which characterizes most effectively the secular changes in progress, Barnard maximized the ratio of the square of unweighted regression of the compound with time. It is doubtful whether such a linear compound can be used to specify an individual skull most effectively with respect to progressive changes, since linear regression with time does not adequately explain all the differences in the four series.

References

AITKEN, A. C. (1933).   On fitting polynomials to weighted data by least squares. *Proc. Roy. Soc. Edin.*, **54**, 1.

BARNARD, M. M. (1935).   The secular variation of skull characters in four series of Egyptian skulls. *Ann. Eugen. London*, **7**, 89.

BARTLETT, M. S. (1934).   The vector representation of a sample. *Proc. Camb. Phil. Soc.*, **30**, 327.

BARTLETT, M. S. (1938).   Further aspects of the theory of multiple regression. *Proc. Camb. Phil. Soc.*, **34**, 33.

BARTLETT, M. S. (1947).   Multivariate analysis. *J.R.S.S. Suppl.*, **9**, 76.

COCHRAN, W. G., and C. I. BLISS (1948).   Discriminant functions with covariance. *Ann. Math. Stats.*, **19**, 151.

FISHER, R. A. (1936).   The use of multiple measurements in taxonomic problems. *Ann. Eugen. London*, **7**, 179.

FISHER, R. A. (1938).   The statistical utilization of multiple measurements.   *Ann. Eugen. London*, **8**, 376.

FISHER, R. A. (1939).   The sampling distribution of some statistics obtained from nonlinear regression.   *Ann. Eugen. London*, **9**, 238.

FRETS, G. P. (1921).   Heredity of head form in man.   Reprinted from *Genetica*, The Hague, Nijhoff, **3**.

HOTELLING, H. (1931).   The generalization of Student's ratio.   *Ann. Math. Stats.*, **2**, 360.

HOTELLING, H. (1936).   The relation between two sets of variates.   *Biom.*, **28**, 321.

HSU, P. (1939).   On the distribution of the roots of certain determinantal equations, *Ann. Eugen. London*, **9**, 250.

MAHALANOBIS, P. C. (1936).   On the generalized distance in statistics.   *Proc. Nat. Inst. Sci. (India)*, **12**, 49.

NAIR, U. S. (1939).   The application of moment functions in the study of distribution laws in statistics, *Biom.*, **30**, 274.

NEYMAN, J., and E. S. PEARSON (1928).   On the use and interpretation of certain test criteria for purpose of statistical inference, *Biom.*, **20A**, 175.

NEYMAN, J., and E. S. PEARSON (1931).   On the problem of k samples.   *Bull. Int. Acad. Cracovie*, **A**, p. 460.

PEARSON, E. S., and J. NEYMAN (1930).   On the problem of two samples.   *Bull. Int. Acad. Cracoie*, **A**, p. 73.

RAO, C. R. (1946).   Tests with discriminant functions in multivariate analysis.   *Sankhyā*, **7**, 407.

RAO, C. R. (1949).   On some problems arising out of discrimination with multiple characters.   *Sankhyā*, **9**, 343.

ROY, S. N. (1939). p-Statistics or some generalizations in analysis of variance appropriate to multivariate problems.   *Sankhyā*, **4**, 381.

WALD, A., and R. J. BROOKNER (1941).   On the distribution of Wilks' statistic for testing independence of several groups of variables.   *Ann. Math. Stats.*, **12**, 137.

WILKS, S. S. (1932).   Certain generalizations in the analysis of variance.   *Biom.*, **24**, 471.

WILKS, S. S. (1935).   On the independence of k sets of normally distributed statistical variables.   *Econom.*, **3**, 309.

WISHART, J. (1928).   The generalized product moment distribution in samples from a normal multivariate population.   *Biom.*, **20A**, 32.

CHAPTER 8

Statistical Inference Applied to Classificatory Problems

8a Tests of Null Hypotheses

8a.1 Problems in Biological Research

There are two types of problems confronted in biological research. The first is that of specifying an individual as a member of one of many groups to which he can possibly belong, as when a taxonomist has to assign an organism to its proper species or subspecies or an anthropologist is faced with the problem of sexing a skull or a jawbone. The second is the problem of classification of the groups themselves into some significant system based on the configuration of the various characteristics. The need of this is felt in the study of systematics and the evolution of species. A number of species or subspecies may have to be arranged in a hierarchical order showing the closeness of some and the distinctness of others. Such a representation superimposed on a geographical classification may, it is suggested, be of use in tracing the evolution of various species or subspecies.

The solution of these problems requires the development of a suitable theory of statistical inference and the formulation of some practical rules of procedure which the biologist can profitably use.

To start, it is useful to distinguish problems of discrimination from those of testing of hypotheses. Recently there has been a tendency to treat both these problems on an equal footing, and this has no doubt caused a good deal of confusion. In testing of hypotheses we have a clearly stated null hypothesis and a comparatively undefined set of alternatives. The emphasis is more on the null hypothesis, which may be rejected or provisionally accepted. When a null hypothesis is rejected no decision is made about the actual alternative hypothesis. But in problems of discrimination we have a class of alternative hypotheses out of which one has to be chosen. Although it is a question of rejecting the null hypothesis at a given risk in the former problem, it is a question

273

of balancing between wrong and correct decisions in the latter problem. Although the a priori probabilities have no place, even conceptually, in problems of testing a null hypothesis, they are essential for a satisfactory solution of the problems of discrimination. In all scientific investigations both problems are important.

8a.2 Null Hypotheses

Consider the following problem, which frequently crops up in biological research.

A specimen is observed, and it is desired to know, on the basis of some morphological measurements, whether it belongs to a previously classified group whose characteristics are either known or estimated from a sample of individuals from that group. In such a problem there are only two possibilities: the new find belongs either to a known group or to an unknown group. The alternatives to the specified one are obviously undefined. The new group might be one whose existence has yet to be established.

Thus, when a fossil is discovered the paleontologist inquires whether it is a specimen from a known collection. Such an inquiry is often made with the hope of obtaining a negative answer, in which case the fossil could be taken as a new specimen.

The investigator may not be successful in distinguishing a new specimen from a previous collection because the answer depends on the evidence supplied by the observed specimen. The only safeguard offered by a statistical test in such a case is that it checks the investigator from rushing to a hasty conclusion unless the evidence is strong enough. If specimens like the observed or differing to a greater extent than the observed from the characteristics of a known group form a reasonable proportion in the group, then the evidence for rejecting the null hypothesis cannot be considered conclusive. Only when this proportion is small can we take the risk of asserting that the observed specimen belongs to a new group. How small this proportion or level of significance should be depends on the risk involved in asserting that the null hypothesis is wrong when in fact it is true. The choice of level of significance is arbitrary in this sense,* but once it is fixed the rule of procedure is determined exactly. Thus it may be possible to refute any statement made about the observed specimen. Such an inference is possible only when some risk is allowed.

* It is not arbitrary in the sense that we are assuming one value when in fact it should be something else. It is one which is chosen by the investigator. Thus if the consequences of rejecting a true hypothesis involve a great loss it is reasonable to keep the level of significance as low as possible.

On the other hand, it is almost impossible to assert that the new find belongs to a specified group. To make such a statement we must ascertain whether the chance of the observed specimen's arising from any other group is small. This is clearly not possible when the alternative groups are undefined ones.

There is clearly no scope for the introduction of a priori probabilities in this case. However perfect our past knowledge may be about the species that have been already studied and their relative numbers, nothing can be said about the new species to be discovered. When these new species are considered as alternatives to a null hypothesis tested, there is no method of attaching a priori probabilities to the alternatives.

Sometimes the a priori probabilities are introduced not as objective quantities measured by observed frequencies but as measuring merely psychological tendencies. If this is so we need further rules of procedure for choosing the a priori probabilities themselves. One can recall the efforts made by Jeffreys (1948) in this connection. To remove some apparent contradictions in Bayes's postulate of equal ignorance, Jeffreys advocates the use of certain invariant functions of the parameters occurring in a probability distribution as a priori weights. Even here no argument is put forward for using particular invariant functions of the parameters. In fact, different choices lead to different results so that no objective theory could be built up on the lines of inverse probability.

To take another example, a geneticist inquires on the basis of observed data whether two factors are segregating independently. If he can disprove this with some confidence, then he acquires some basis on which to plan future experiments, to estimate the intensity of their linkage, and to study the relationship of the two factors under consideration with others. If data are not sufficiently numerous, loose linkages go undetected and it is only by repeated experimentation and accumulation of evidence supplied by other factors linked with the former that some definite conclusion can be arrived at.

The alternative to the hypothesis of independence in the above problem is linkage with all possible values of the recombination fraction (lying between 0 and 1). To the experimenter it is definite knowledge if he can disprove the hypothesis of independence. Only then will he proceed to inquire what the value of the recombination fraction is and try to obtain an estimate. To ask for a priori probabilities of the alternative recombination fractions before attempting to answer the problem posed is to believe that from previous experience the frequencies with which various recombination fractions occur can be deduced. But there may not be sufficient reason to believe that the frequencies so derived correspond to the total frequencies obtainable from all possible factors known and unknown.

In the problem of the paleontologist the alternatives are completely undefined whereas in the problem of the geneticist the alternatives are known, viz., that the recombination fraction lies between 0 and 1. But in both types of problems there is no scope for the introduction of a priori probabilities.

The null hypothesis is one which is chosen by the experimenter appropriate to his inquiry. When sufficient evidence gathers against this during the experimental work, he rejects it. He is not trying to balance between the evidences supplied by the data on the various alternatives.

Whether a particular null hypothesis is rejected or not, there is a class of null hypotheses which are not contradicted by the data at a given level of significance. Any hypothesis outside this class is rejected. The class of null hypotheses acceptable to the data supplies us with what may be called a fiducial set. When the hypotheses refer to the values of a parameter, the fiducial set will be in the nature of an interval called the fiducial interval (Fisher, 1947). The fiducial set of hypotheses may be asserted to contain the true hypothesis because the chance of its being left out is small (equal to the percentage level of significance chosen). Thus, although it is not possible to accept any single hypothesis, it is possible to restrict the scope of inquiry to only a subset of all possible alternatives. Any further discrimination among the alternatives in the fiducial set has necessarily to be based on insufficient evidence. No statement of confidence can be made about a single hypothesis chosen by any rule of procedure as the most appropriate for the data, and consequently such a procedure does not possess a scientific basis of inference.

If the problem needs the choice of a single hypothesis, then what should be the nature of the answer? We might try to formulate a rule of procedure which selects a hypothesis which is as near as possible to the true hypothesis and which in large samples differs very little from the true one with probability approaching certainty. The procedure of choosing that hypothesis which maximizes the likelihood, advocated by Fisher, conforms to the above requirement to a large extent. Thus the two methodological problems, testing of hypothesis and estimation, admit neat solutions independent of the probabilities a priori.

As an example for the determination of the fiducial interval, consider a sample $x_1, \cdots, x_n$ from a normal population. If μ is the true mean value, then

$$t = \frac{\bar{x} - \mu}{s/\sqrt{n}}$$

is distributed as t with $(n - 1)$ degrees of freedom. All values of μ not acceptable to the data at the 5% level of significance satisfy the inequality

$$\left| \frac{\bar{x} - \mu}{s/\sqrt{n}} \right| \geq t_{5\%}$$

where $t_{5\%}$ is the 5% significant value of t. This gives two values

$$\bar{x} - \frac{st_{5\%}}{\sqrt{n}} \quad \text{and} \quad \bar{x} + \frac{st_{5\%}}{\sqrt{n}}$$

beyond which all values of μ are incompatible with the observed data. In such a case we could assert subject to a small risk that the true value of μ lies in the above interval.

Similarly, if the fiducial interval for σ^2 is needed, then two equations are considered:

$$\frac{(n - 1)s^2}{\sigma^2} = \chi_1^2 \quad \text{and} \quad \frac{(n - 1)s^2}{\sigma^2} = \chi_2^2$$

giving

$$\sigma_1^2 = \frac{(n - 1)s^2}{\chi_1^2} \quad \text{and} \quad \sigma_2^2 = \frac{(n - 1)s^2}{\chi_2^2}$$

where (χ_1^2, χ_2^2) is the critical interval given in Table 6a.1α for χ^2 with $(n - 1)$ degrees of freedom.

8a.3   Power Function of Neyman and Pearson

Various attempts have been made to build up a consistent theory from which all tests of significance can be deduced as solutions to precisely stated mathematical problems. It is difficult to argue whether such a theory exists or not, but formal theories leading to a clear understanding of the problems are nonetheless important. One such theory, contributed by Neyman and Pearson (1933), is an important development because it unfolded the various complex problems in testing of hypotheses and led to the construction of general theories in problems of discrimination, sequential tests, etc.

Any rule of procedure by which we can reject or accept a given hypothesis H_0 consists in a division of all possible samples into two groups, one opposed to H_0 and the other not unfavorable to it. Whenever a sample of the first category occurs, we reject the hypothesis H_0. As observed earlier, the frequency of the samples in this category, when H_0 is true, ought to be small so that the chance of rejecting the hypothesis when it is true is small. Let this chance be fixed as α (a small assigned quantity). Corresponding to any procedure such as the above, there is a frequency with which the samples of the first category appear under a different hypothesis H. This frequency, denoted by $\beta(H)$, is called the power of the test procedure associated with an alternative hypothesis H.

This function $\beta(H)$ is fundamental in the theory of Neyman and Pearson. It gives us the frequency with which various alternative hypotheses could be detected, or, to be more exact, the frequency with which the hypothesis H_0 is rejected when a different hypothesis H is true. If the sample is to be given a fair chance of rejecting H_0, when it is not true, the division of the samples must be such that the frequency of those in the first category is as high as possible under any different hypothesis. To start with, let us determine the maximum possible frequency of detection associated with a given alternative hypothesis.

Let $f_H(x)$ denote the probability density of the observations x under any hypothesis H. The sample observations $x_1, \cdots, x_n$ may be represented by a point in a space of n dimensions, in which case the rule of procedure suggested above results in a division of the space into two regions, w for rejecting the hypothesis and the rest for not favoring any alternative. Then, for a given H, what is w such that

$$\int_w f_{H_0}(x) \, dv = \alpha \qquad \text{(an assigned quantity)} \qquad (8a.3.1)$$

and

$$\int_w f_H(x) \, dv \qquad \text{is a maximum?}$$

Applying the result of lemma A1 in Appendix A, we find the best region w_0 is defined by

$$f_H \geq \lambda f_{H_0} \qquad \text{inside } w_0$$

and

$$f_H \leq \lambda f_{H_0} \qquad \text{outside } w_0$$

in which case the maximum $\beta(H)$ is

$$\beta(H) = \int_{w_0} f_H(x) \, dv$$

where λ is determined to satisfy 8a.3.1.

We are in a happy situation if the same region w_0 makes $\beta(H)$ a maximum for all H. In this situation w_0 is independent of H, and the knowledge of any particular alternative H which may be true does not help us in improving the test. The w_0 satisfying this property is said to be a *uniformly most powerful* critical region, and when this exists the test procedure is above criticism since nothing has been assumed about the alternatives. The existence of such tests can be easily verified because in this case the boundary of the critical region, $f_H/f_{H_0} =$ constant, can be expressed without the use of any unknown quantities entering in f_H.

Example 1. Consider n independent observations from a normal distribution $N(\mu, \sigma^2)$. Let the null hypothesis be $\mu = \mu_0$.

$$f_H = c \exp \left\{ \frac{-\Sigma(x_i - \mu)^2}{2\sigma^2} \right\}$$

$$f_{H_0} = c \exp \left\{ \frac{-\Sigma(x_i - \mu_0)^2}{2\sigma^2} \right\}$$

$$\log \frac{f_H}{f_{H_0}} = \frac{\mu - \mu_0}{\sigma^2} (x_1 + \cdots + x_n) + \frac{\mu_0^2 - \mu^2}{2\sigma^2}$$

The relationship

$$\log \frac{f_H}{f_{H_0}} \geq \log \lambda$$

reduces to

$$\bar{x}(\mu - \mu_0) \geq k$$

or

$$\bar{x} \geq k_1 \quad \text{if } \mu > \mu_0$$
$$\bar{x} \leq k_2 \quad \text{if } \mu < \mu_0$$

A uniformly most powerful test exists only when it is known that the alternative value μ is greater or smaller than the assigned value μ_0. The test simply depends on the distribution of the mean, $\bar{x}$, on the null hypothesis. The distribution of $\bar{x}$ is

$$c \exp \left[\frac{-n(\bar{x} - \mu_0)^2}{2\sigma^2} \right] d\bar{x}$$

which involves another parameter σ^2 so that the test can be carried out only when the hypothetical value of the standard deviation is known. When it is not known, a suitable device is necessary to make the test independent of σ.

Example 2. The best region for testing the hypothesis H_0 against a single alternative H is bounded by the surface of a constant value of a function of the minimal set of sufficient statistics.

When a set of sufficient statistics $T_1, T_2, \cdots, T_k$ exists,

$$f_H = P(T \mid H)P(x \mid T)$$

and

$$f_{H_0} = P(T \mid H_0)P(x \mid T)$$

and hence the ratio f_H/f_{H_0} is equivalent to $P(T \mid H)/P(T \mid H_0)$ which is a function of $T_1, \cdots, T_k$ only.

Example 3.   The probability of r successes in n trials of a binomial population with proportion p is

$$\binom{n}{r} p^r q^{n-r}$$

If the null hypothesis is $p = p_0$, then $\log (f_H/f_{H_0}) \geq \log \lambda$ reduces to

$$r \left\{ \log \frac{p}{p_0} - \log \frac{q}{q_0} \right\} \geq k$$

or

$$r \geq k_1 \quad \text{if} \quad p \geq p_0$$

and

$$r \leq k_2 \quad \text{if} \quad p \leq p_0$$

so that the uniformly most powerful test exists only when it is known that the alternative is greater or smaller than the assigned value.

In this example it is presumed that the best test is offered by the ratio f_H/f_{H_0}, even when the stochastic variable is discontinuous.   The difficulty arises owing to the fact that there may not exist a λ such that the probability that $f_H \geq \lambda f_{H_0}$ is exactly equal to the assigned value, the percentage level of significance.   The setup appropriate for discrete probability densities is to determine a class of events E such that

$$P_{H_0}(E) \leq \alpha \quad \text{an assigned value} \qquad (8a.3.2)$$

and

$$P_H(E) \quad \text{is a maximum}$$

The class of events so determined constitutes the critical set, and the happening of any event in this set disproves the null hypothesis.   It is easy to see that in the case of continuous distributions the equality relation in (8a.3.2) is attained.   Under the new setup the events in the critical set are those for which the ratio $(f_H/f_{H_0}) \geq \lambda$, where λ is the minimum value such that the total probability of the events on the null hypothesis does not exceed α.   The proof is similar to that in the case of continuous distributions.

8a.4   Locally Most Powerful Unbiased Tests

Uniformly most powerful tests exist very rarely so that in most cases there will not be a single region which is the best for all alternative hypotheses.   As a first step in making the test independent of the alternative hypotheses, Neyman and Pearson introduced the concept of the locally most powerful unbiased test, applicable to cases where the hypothesis is specified by the value of a parameter occurring in the probability distribution. Assuming differentiation under the integral sign, the solution depends on the existence of a region w such that

$$\int_w f(x \mid \theta_0) \, dv = \alpha \tag{8a.4.1}$$

$$\int_w f'(x \mid \theta_0) \, dv = 0 \tag{8a.4.2}$$

and

$$\int_w f''(x \mid \theta_0) \, dv \qquad \text{is a maximum} \tag{8a.4.3}$$

θ_0 is the value of the parameter under the null hypothesis.

It follows from the lemma in A1 (Appendix A) that a region w_0 inside which

$$f''(\theta_0) \geq k_1 f(\theta_0) + k_2 f'(\theta_0)$$

outside which

$$f''(\theta_0) \leq k_1 f(\theta_0) + k_2 f'(\theta_0)$$

where k_1 and k_2 are determined to satisfy the conditions (8a.4.1) and (8a.4.2), maximizes the integral in (8a.4.3).

This ensures maximum power only for alternatives in the immediate neighborhood of the null hypothesis. This is not a good solution unless the power is quite high for alternatives more distant from the null hypothesis also. In fact, if a locally most powerful test has a very low power beyond a certain range near the null hypothesis, no investigator would be tempted to use it. There is no provision in the method of derivation of a locally powerful test to safeguard against this. This method therefore cannot be considered as general but can be regarded only as a means by which test criteria can be derived for possible comparison with any other offered test procedure.

Example 1. The locally most powerful test for the null hypothesis $\sigma = \sigma_0$ is defined by

$$s^2 \geq s_1{}^2 \qquad \text{and} \qquad s^2 \leq s_2{}^2$$

such that

$$\left(\frac{ns_1{}^2}{\sigma_0{}^2}\right)^{n/2} e^{-ns_1{}^2/2\sigma_0{}^2} = \left(\frac{ns_2{}^2}{\sigma_0{}^2}\right)^{n/2} e^{-ns_2{}^2/2\sigma_0{}^2}$$

and

$$\int_0^{s_2{}^2} P(s^2) \, ds^2 + \int_{s_1{}^2}^{\infty} P(s^2) \, ds^2 = \alpha$$

where

$$P(s^2) = \text{const. } e^{-ns^2/2\sigma^2}(s^2)^{(n-2)/2}\, ds^2$$

and s^2 is the estimate of σ^2 based on n degrees of freedom.

Example 2. Among locally unbiased tests the power for *any* alternative value σ is greatest in the above case.

Example 3. What is the locally unbiased most powerful test for a given ratio of two hypothetical variances estimated from two independent samples from normal populations.

[Hint: Start with the variance ratio F distribution on n_1, n_2 degrees of freedom, assuming a hypothetical ratio ρ. The best test leads to the condition that a quadratic expression in F is greater than zero, so that the test is $F \geq F_1$ and $F \leq F_2$. To determine the relation between F_1 and F_2, express the condition of unbiasedness. This leads to a condition of the form $F_1/(1 + cF_1)^d = F_2/(1 + cF_2)^d$.]

Example 4. Prove that among locally unbiased tests the test derived in example 3 is uniformly most powerful.

The test derived in examples 1 and 2 is used in Chapter 6 in testing whether a calculated variance is in agreement with an assigned value. The test derived in examples 3 and 4 is useful in testing whether two estimated variances are equal in their expectation. In Chapter 6, a different test based on the L statistic was used. But these two are equivalent.

8a.5 Test for a Finite Number of Alternatives

Consider a null hypothesis H_0 and a set of alternatives H_1, H_2, $\cdots$. Let the power of the best possible test for H_0 when H_i is the only alternative be denoted by $\gamma_i(\alpha)$, where α denotes the level of significance. Any region w suggested as the critical region for testing H_0 will have

$$\int_w f_i\, dv = \beta_i(\alpha)$$

as the power for the alternative H_i. In no case can β exceed γ, but there may exist a single region such that $\beta_i = \gamma_i$ for all i, in which case a uniformly most powerful test exists.

If this is not so, various alternatives have been suggested. One is to choose a region which maximizes the minimum β (Neyman and Pearson, 1933). Such a procedure may give undue preference to the hypotheses nearer * to the null hypothesis. It may be felt that a method

* A hypothesis H_i can be said to be nearer than H_j to H_0 if $\gamma_i < \gamma_j$. With this concept a suitable distance function between two hypotheses can be defined as shown in Chapter 9.

which effectively controls the errors of not accepting a nearer hypothesis when it is true will be good enough for distant hypotheses.

On the other hand, we may take the view that in the course of experimentation it is necessary to detect a distant hypothesis as early as we can. If, in fact, a distant hypothesis were true and the critical region had been so chosen as to give this hypothesis the maximum possible power, then it could be discovered with the minimum possible number of observations. If a nearer hypothesis were true, a larger experiment would be necessary to detect it. In such a case the experimenter might consider himself unlucky on the choice of his subject or might regard the consequences of accepting H_0 when, in fact, an alternative close to it is true as less serious than when the alternative is distant.

A compromise solution may be suggested if the experimenter can assign a priori probabilities for the various alternatives. This means that he has a knowledge of a series of similar experiments and the frequencies of various types of alternatives. When such a knowledge is imperfect or if the experimenter is not sure that the particular experiment he is conducting belongs to the same group of experiments that have been conducted before, no unique solution is possible. In the absence of any information about the a priori probabilities, as a compromise between the two views of maximizing the minimum power or giving more weight to distant hypotheses, the following solution is suggested.

The critical region w is chosen such that the common ratio

$$\frac{\beta_1(\alpha)}{\gamma_1(\alpha)} = \frac{\beta_2(\alpha)}{\gamma_2(\alpha)} = \cdots$$

is a maximum where β and γ are as defined above. This method supplies a system of weights to be attached to the powers due to various alternatives, the weights being the individual maximum powers. This region has the following two properties.

(*i*) The distant hypotheses have necessarily more power than the nearer hypotheses.

(*ii*) The individual maximum powers are now reduced in the same proportion with the provision that this proportion is as small as possible.

If $f_0, f_1, f_2, \cdots$ denote the probability densities for the hypotheses $H_0, H_1, H_2, \cdots$, then the region satisfying the above requirements is deducible from the lemma proved in Appendix A4. The inside of this region w is defined by

$$f_0 \leq \lambda_1 f_1 + \lambda_2 f_2 + \cdots$$

where λ_1, λ_2, $\cdots$ are determined from the relations

$$\int_w f_0 \, dv = \alpha \qquad (8a.5.1)$$

and

$$\frac{1}{\gamma_1} \int_w f_1 \, dv = \frac{1}{\gamma_2} \int_w f_2 \, dv = \cdots \qquad (8a.5.2)$$

The solution deduced above is not useful in practice because of the difficulty in evaluating the constants. It may be convenient to consider the region complementary to

$$f_0 \geq \mu_i f_i \qquad (8a.5.3)$$

as the critical region, the quantities μ_1, μ_2, $\cdots$ being determined to satisfy the relations (8a.5.1) and (8a.5.2).

8a.6 Tests When the Alternatives Are Continuous

The foregoing theory could be extended to the case where the alternatives can be specified by parameters with continuous variation. The following definitions will be useful.

A region w which gives equal power to all hypotheses equidistant, i.e., having the same power of detection from the null hypothesis, is called the distance power region. A test based on a distance power region w_0 is said to be uniformly the best distance power test if:

(i) The size of the region w_0 with respect to the null hypothesis is α (an assigned value).

(ii) w_0 is a distance power region.

(iii) For any specified alternative hypothesis the power associated with the region w_0 is not less than the power for any other region satisfying requirements (i) and (ii).

Let Δ denote the distance of a hypothesis H from H_0, the null hypothesis. Then a distance power region satisfies the condition

$$\int_w f_H \, dv = \phi(\Delta) \qquad \text{a function of } \Delta \text{ only}$$

If the parameters entering in the alternative hypothesis are denoted symbolically by θ and in the null hypothesis by θ_0, then

$$\int_w f(\theta) \, dv = \phi(\Delta) \qquad \text{and} \qquad \int_w f(\theta_0) = \alpha \qquad (8a.6.1)$$

Let us define the inside of the region by

$$f(\theta_0) \leq \int_{\Delta = \text{const.}} \lambda(\theta)f(\theta) \, ds \cdots \tag{8a.6.2}$$

where the integral is taken over the surface Δ = constant. Let there exist a positive function $\lambda(\theta)$ such that the conditions (8a.6.1) are satisfied. The region w_0, if it exists, is the best distance power region for alternatives on the surface Δ = constant. This follows from the lemma in Appendix A4 extended to an infinite set of alternatives. If the relationship (8a.6.2) is independent of the alternative used, then we obtain a uniformly best distance power test. It is seen that the region (8a.6.2) is the same as the region which has the best average power for alternatives on the surface Δ = constant and for an assigned a priori probability density $\lambda(\theta)$ of the parameters. Although in the theory of average power tests there is no justification for choosing a particular type of the density function $\lambda(\theta)$ on which the test generally depends, the function $\lambda(\theta)$ is suitably determined in constructing distance power tests. The determination of such a function, even if its existence is known, may be a difficult task. Once it is determined by trial or otherwise, the optimum property of the test is immediately established.

It is of interest to examine the critical region obtained by extending the results in (8a.5.3) to the case of alternative hypotheses specified by parameters with continuous variation. The outside of such a critical region is defined by

$$f(\theta_0) \geq \lambda(\theta, \Delta)f(\theta)$$

for all θ on the surface $\Delta(\theta) = \Delta$, where Δ is the specified distance of the alternative from the null hypothesis. If, owing to considerations of symmetry, the function $\lambda(\theta, \Delta)$ could be replaced by a function of Δ only, then the critical region is the outside of the envelope of the surfaces

$$\frac{f(\theta_0)}{f(\theta)} = \text{const.}$$

for variations in θ on the surface $\Delta(\theta) = \Delta$. This is the likelihood ratio test developed by Neyman and Pearson (1928).

Example 1. Let $x_1, \cdots, x_n$ be n independent normal variates having zero mean on the null hypothesis. For any alternative hypothesis specifying the mean of x_i as μ_i, the best test is

$$\mu_1 x_1 + \cdots + \mu_n x_n \geq k$$

and the associated power is a function of $\mu^2 = \mu_1^2 + \cdots + \mu_n^2$. So we can define the distance of the alternative hypothesis from the null by μ^2.

The best distance power test, if it exists, is given by

$$e^{-\Sigma x_i{}^2/2\sigma^2} \leq \int_{\mu^2} e^{-\Sigma(x_i-\mu_i)^2/2\sigma^2} f(\mu_1, \cdots, \mu_n)\, d\mu_1 \cdots d\mu_n$$

$f(\mu_1, \cdots, \mu_n)$ can be chosen to be a constant, in which case because of symmetry between x and μ the test reduces to

$$\Sigma x_i{}^2 \geq k$$

which is a distance power test, the distribution of $\Sigma x_i{}^2$ being that of a noncentral χ^2 involving only the parameter μ^2.

Example 2. Following the method of example 1, construct a distance power test to examine whether p correlated variables have assigned mean values. This leads to Hotelling's T with a known dispersion matrix, in which case T has a χ^2 distribution.

When the variances and covariances are not known in examples 1 and 2 above, a slightly different technique has to be followed. The best region, besides satisfying the above property, must be *similar* to the sample space with respect to the unknown variances and covariances. That is, the integral of the probability density over such a region is equal to a constant α, *whatever* may be the value of the variances and covariances. We shall not enter into the mathematics of the construction of similar regions but simply note that all the univariate and multivariate tests considered in the earlier chapters are all best distance power tests.

8b Problems of Discrimination

8b.1 The General Problem

We now come to a group of problems where a priori probabilities are needed for a satisfactory solution and the null hypothesis does not play a prominent part but is sometimes posed to arrive at a decision subject to a small risk.

Thus when a question is asked whether a skull or a jawbone belonged to a male or a female, there are evidently two alternative hypotheses and one has to be chosen. Here a procedure is needed by which the individual specimen can be assigned to one or the other of the groups. In any such rule of procedure, errors are inevitable unless the ranges of measurements for the two groups are completely different.

We first answer the following problem. Suppose an individual is drawn from a mixed population consisting of two distinct groups of individuals in the ratio $\pi_1:\pi_2$, $(\pi_1 + \pi_2 = 1)$. If α_1 is the chance of wrongly classifying an individual of the first group by following any rule of procedure, and α_2 the corresponding chance for the second group, then the probability of wrongly classifying an individual chosen at random is $(\pi_1\alpha_1 + \pi_2\alpha_2)$. Evidently that procedure is the best which minimizes this error.

If the individual admits p measurements, then we need a division of the p dimensional space into two regions, R_1 and R_2, such that when the point representing the p measurements falls in R_1 the individual is assigned to the first group, and otherwise to the second. If $f_1(x \mid \theta_1)$ and $f_2(x \mid \theta_2)$ represent the probability densities, then the chance of committing an error is

$$\pi_1 \int_{R_2} f_1 \, dv + \pi_2 \int_{R_1} f_2 \, dv$$

We need such a division for which the above value is a minimum. Following a lemma given in Appendix A2, we find that the best regions are

$$R_1 \quad \cap \quad \pi_1 f_1 \geq \pi_2 f_2$$

$$R_2 \quad \cap \quad \pi_2 f_2 \geq \pi_1 f_1$$

where the symbol $\cap$ stands for "defined by." This supplies a mutually exclusive division of the space into two regions, R_1 and R_2. The case where the equality occurs can be decided by considering the corresponding relationship when one measurement (chosen at random from the available p) is omitted.

If, in any problem, there is scope for the introduction of a risk function specifying the loss incurred in a wrong classification, then the best solution which minimizes the expected risk can be determined as follows. Let r_1 be the loss resulting in assigning an individual of the first group to the second, and r_2 of the second to the first. Then the expected loss is

$$\pi_1\alpha_1 r_1 + \pi_2\alpha_2 r_2$$

The best solution is

$$R_1 \quad \cap \quad \pi_1 r_1 f_1 \geq \pi_2 r_2 f_2$$

$$R_2 \quad \cap \quad \pi_2 r_2 f_2 \geq \pi_1 r_1 f_1$$

8b.2 The Discriminant Function of R. A. Fisher

In the cases considered in the above section it is seen that the boundary separating the two regions in the space is defined by a constant value of the likelihood ratio. If the probability densities are multivariate normal with the same dispersion matrix (α_{ij}) and mean values, $\mu_{11}, \cdots,$

μ_{p1} and μ_{12}, $\cdots$, μ_{p2}, for the first and second groups, then the likelihood ratio or its logarithm is

$$\Sigma\Sigma\alpha^{ij}[(x_i - \mu_{i1})(x_j - \mu_{j1}) - (x_i - \mu_{i2})(x_j - \mu_{j2})]$$

where the matrix (α^{ij}) is reciprocal to (α_{ij}). Simplifying the above expression, the surface of a constant likelihood ratio can be expressed

$$\sum_{i=1}^{p} (\alpha^{1i}d_1 + \cdots + \alpha^{pi}d_p)x_i = \text{const.} \qquad (8b.2.1)$$

where $d_j = \mu_{j1} - \mu_{j2}$, $(j = 1, 2, \cdots, p)$. The regions in the p dimensional space are thus separated by a hyperplane whose equation is (8b.2.1) for a suitably determined constant. An individual for whom the value of the left-hand function exceeds the constant value chosen is assigned to the first group and when it is smaller he is assigned to the second group.

The linear function of the measurements deduced above is called the discriminant function, first introduced by R. A. Fisher, who suggested the following computational procedure.

If there is only one character, then the problem of classification is very simple; all individuals with the value of that character exceeding a suitably determined value could be assigned to one group, and the rest to the other. The multiple character case is reduced to that of a single variate by replacing the several measurements by a suitably chosen linear compound. If $x_1, x_2, \cdots, x_p$ are the measurements, then an arbitrary linear compound is $l_1x_1 + \cdots + l_px_p$. The coefficients $l_1, \cdots, l_p$ may be chosen such that the linear compound affords the maximum discrimination between the two groups.

The function $l_1x_1 + \cdots + l_px_p$ has the variance

$$\Sigma\Sigma\alpha_{ij}l_il_j \qquad (8b.2.2)$$

and the square of the difference in mean values of this compound for the two groups is

$$(l_1d_1 + \cdots + l_pd_p)^2 \qquad (8b.2.3)$$

The coefficients may be chosen such that the difference in mean values is a maximum, subject to the condition that the variance (8b.2.2) is a constant (say, unity). This is also equivalent to maximizing the ratio of (8b.2.3) to (8b.2.2) without any condition on the compounding coefficients. Introducing a Lagrangian multiplier λ and differentiating the expression

$$\Sigma\Sigma l_il_jd_id_j - \lambda\Sigma\Sigma\alpha_{ij}l_il_j$$

we obtain the equations

$$l_1\alpha_{11} + l_2\alpha_{12} + \cdots + l_p\alpha_{1p} = kd_1$$

$$l_1\alpha_{21} + l_2\alpha_{22} + \cdots + l_p\alpha_{2p} = kd_2$$

$$\cdot \qquad \cdots \qquad \cdot \qquad \cdot$$

$$l_1\alpha_{p1} + l_2\alpha_{p2} + \cdots + l_p\alpha_{pp} = kd_p$$

where $k = (l_1d_1 + \cdots + l_pd_p)/\lambda$. Observing that the above equations can supply only ratios of $l_1, \cdots, l_p$, we may substitute $k = 1$ and solve the above equations. The final values of $l_1, \cdots, l_p$ may be adjusted by multiplying each of them by a constant θ where

$$\theta^2 \Sigma\Sigma l_i l_j \alpha_{ij} = 1$$

This is unnecessary because the constant separating the values of the discriminant function for classification into the two groups can be adjusted suitably. The linear equations obtained above have the solutions

$$l_i = \alpha^{1i}d_1 + \cdots + \alpha^{pi}d_p \qquad i = 1, 2, \cdots, p$$

thus giving the same linear function derived as the ratio of the two likelihoods. Thus Fisher's linear discriminant function is the best for classification when the distributions are multivariate normal and the dispersion matrices are the same. If the dispersion matrices are different, then the likelihood ratio surface is defined by the quadratic expression

$$\Sigma\Sigma\{\alpha^{ij}(x_i - \mu_{i1})(x_j - \mu_{j1}) - \beta^{ij}(x_i - \mu_{i2})(x_j - \mu_{j2})\} = \text{const.}$$

where (α^{ij}) and (β^{ij}) are the inverses of the dispersion matrices corresponding to the two populations.

8b.3   Some Difficulties in the Use of the Best Discriminating Solution

The elegant solution obtained in 8b.1 has many limitations so far as the practical applications are concerned.

(i) The parameters occurring in the probability distributions are not usually known. The only solution is to obtain their best possible estimates and substitute them for the unknown values in setting up the discriminant function. This introduces some additional errors in classification, depending on the paucity of the available material for the estimation of the parameters.

(ii) The a priori probabilities explicitly occurring in the best solution may not be known, and in some cases they may not be estimable from the available data.

(iii) In any problem the finite number of alternatives into which an observed individual has to be classified is assigned by the investigator. In some cases, such as sexing, there are only two alternatives possible. But in general it may be necessary to test whether the a priori information that an individual belongs to one of the given groups is correct or not. Only when the a priori information is ascertained to be correct can we proceed to decide to which of the given groups he is likely to belong.

(iv) Even by following the best procedure of classification it may not be possible to assert with confidence that any individual has been correctly classified. Can any provision be made to identify at least those cases which are less likely to be misclassified?

(v) Suppose that it is known that an individual has been taken at random from only one group and it is not known whether it is the first or the second group. Should he be treated in the same way as an individual drawn from a mixed population?

(vi) What is the nature of a risk function in biometric investigations?

(vii) Suppose that some quick decisions are needed. Is there any simple method of arriving at a discriminating function which is a good approximation to the ideal one?

These problems are discussed in the following sections with suitable illustrations.

8b.4 Uncertainty of the A Priori Information That One of the Alternatives Is Correct

For discriminatory analysis it must be known that an individual belongs to one or the other of two groups. Such knowledge has to be inferred from external evidence; the association of artcrafts with a burial sometimes provides it for skeletal remains. In questions of sexing bones, the chances of identification are limited to two possibilities, male and female. However, where the external evidence is slight or equivocal, the assignment of an individual to one of two groups may be subject to another kind of error, viz., the wrong assumption that he belongs to one of the two groups when, in fact, he comes from a third unknown group. In the absence of any definite knowledge about the nature of the third group, we may have to examine by means of the internal evidence supplied by the measurements on the individual whether he could be considered as belonging to either of the two groups; that is, we examine whether there is any evidence to suggest that the individual could not have come from one or other of the two groups. Consider the following problem.

In August, 1939, a relatively complete male human skeleton was recovered from the ditch of an Iron Age camp on Highdown Hill, Goring by Sea, in the course of excavations conducted under the auspices of the Worthing Archaeological Society. Fragments associated with the bones suggest that the burial could not have taken place later than the very beginning of the Iron Age in Sussex, about 500 B.C. The camp went out of use not later than 250 B.C., and the remains themselves can be assigned to a 500 B.C. "invasion" horizon. It is doubtful, however, whether their owner was a Bronze Age "defender" or an Iron Age "invader." The principal question to be considered in the present context is whether the Highdown skull is more likely to have belonged to a Bronze Age or to an Iron Age population.

An attempt is made here to answer this problem by utilizing the published data concerning the Bronze Age and the Iron Age represented by Romano-British crania from Maiden Castle. The characteristics of these groups have been computed from scanty material, so that the conclusion regarding the Highdown skull cannot be treated as final. This example has been chosen merely to illustrate the method.

In solving the problem whether the Highdown skull belongs to the Bronze Age or to the Iron Age, we can test separately the two null hypotheses: (1) it belongs to the Bronze Age, and (2) it belongs to the other group. If neither of the two hypotheses can be rejected on the 5% level, there is sufficient justification to proceed with the problem of assigning the skull to one of the two groups.

It must be noted that in such a procedure we are not testing the combined null hypothesis that the specimen belongs to one or the other of the groups at the 5% level. Of the 5% of the rejected cases under one hypothesis, some are accepted under the second hypothesis so that when the 5% level is used for the two hypotheses separately we will be judging the combined null hypothesis at a lower level.

An adjustment could be made in the test procedure to correct this by defining the critical region (of rejection)

$$\Sigma\Sigma\alpha^{ij}(x_i - \mu_{i1})(x_j - \mu_{j1}) \geq c$$

$$\Sigma\Sigma\alpha^{ij}(x_i - \mu_{i2})(x_j - \mu_{j2}) \geq c$$

where (α^{ij}) is the reciprocal of the dispersion matrix (α_{ij}); μ_{i1}, μ_{i2}, are mean values for the two groups; x_1, x_2, $\cdots$ are the measurements on the individual; and c is chosen such that the total density of the region is α (the assigned value) *for each of the probability distributions.* The existence of c satisfying the above condition follows from symmetry. It is difficult to find its actual value. In practice the procedure outlined earlier of testing the two hypotheses separately may be followed.

Table 8b.4α gives the mean values of male English Bronze Age (Morant, 1926) and Maiden Castle (Goodwin and Morant, 1940) cranial measurements.

TABLE 8b.4α. Measurements on the Highdown Skull: Mean Values of Bronze Age and Maiden Castle Series

Character	Highdown Skull	Bronze Age	Maiden Castle
L	198.2	184.5 (45) *	188.6 (23)
B	148.1	149.9 (89)	140.8 (24)
H'	142.0	134.9 (25)	137.1 (22)
G'H	72.4	69.1 (30)	72.4 (14)
GB	95.8	98.0 (11)	95.2 (18)
NH,L	48.2	49.1 (13)	51.9 (16)

* The figures in parentheses indicate numbers on which the averages are based.

L = head length from the glabella in the median sagittal plane.
B = head breadth on the parietal bones perpendicular to L.
H' = head height from the basion to the bregma.
$G'H$ = upper facial height from nasion to the alveolare.
GB = bimaxillary breadth between the zygomaxillaria.
NH,L = nasal height from the nasion to the left nariale.

In the present problem, since only a few of the Bronze Age standard deviations have been published and none are available for the Maiden Castle, the variance-covariance matrix obtained from a long series of Farringdon Street (English male) crania measured by Hooke (1926) is used in the analysis. Such a procedure is not strictly correct, but as observed elsewhere the dispersion matrix remains sensibly constant, provided that the series are not completely unrelated. Since we are using it only to construct the coefficients of the discriminant function, slight variations in the elements of the dispersion matrix do not matter.

To study this problem in some detail and to judge the importance of the various characters used for discrimination it is advantageous first to obtain a set of uncorrelated functions of the original variables. This can be easily obtained by using the dispersion matrix with a unit matrix appended to it and reducing the dispersion matrix by the method of sweep out as shown in Table 8b.4β. The theoretical discussion associated with this procedure is treated in Appendix B.

TABLE 8b.48. Pivotal Condensation Method for the Construction of Transformation to an Uncorrelated Set

Row No.	L	B	H'	G'H	GB	NH,L	L	B	H'	G'H	GB	NH,L		Sum Check
01	41.73	10.78	7.76	3.87	9.63	6.79	1						= Y_1	81.56
02		34.81	7.70	12.08	6.64	6.12		1						79.13
03			25.60	3.89	1.37	4.51			1					51.83
04				19.80	3.87	9.48				1				53.99
05					37.94	4.35					1			64.80
06						9.73						1		41.98
10	1	0.25533	0.18596	0.09274	0.23077	0.16271	0.02396						= Y_2	1.95447
11		32.0252	5.6953	11.0803	4.1523	4.3660	−0.2583	1						58.0608
12			24.1569	3.1703	−0.4208	3.2474	−0.1859		1					36.6633
13				19.4411	2.9769	8.8503	−0.0927			1				46.4262
14					35.7177	2.7831	−0.2307				1			45.9784
15						8.6252	−0.1627					1		28.7091
20		1	0.17784	0.34599	0.12966	0.13633	−0.00806	0.03122					= Y_3	1.81297
21			23.1440	1.1998	−1.1592	2.4709	−0.1400	−0.1778	1					26.3379
22				15.6074	1.5402	7.3397	−0.0034	−0.3459		1				26.3379
23					35.1793	2.2170	−0.1972	−0.1296			1			38.4504
24						8.0300	−0.1275	−0.1363				1		20.7937
30			1	0.05184	−0.05009	0.10676	−0.00605	−0.00768	0.04321				= Y_4	1.13800
31				15.5452	1.6003	7.2116	0.0039	−0.3367	−0.0518	1				24.9725
32					35.1212	2.3407	−0.2042	−0.1385	0.0501		1			39.7696
33						7.7662	−0.1125	−0.1173	−0.1068			1		17.9818
40				1	0.10294	0.46391	0.00025	−0.02166	−0.00333	0.06433			= Y_5	1.60644
41					34.9565	1.5983	−0.2046	−0.1038	0.0554	−0.1029	1			37.1988
42						4.4207	−0.1143	0.0389	−0.0828	−0.4639		1		6.3968
50					1	0.04572	−0.00585	−0.00297	0.00158	−0.00294	0.02861		= Y_6	1.06415
51						4.3476	−0.1049	0.0436	−0.0853	−0.4592	−0.0457	1		4.6960

1. The elements below the diagonal are omitted because the matrices at all stages are symmetrical.

2. The rows 10, 20, 30, 40, 50 represent the pivotal rows at each stage of reduction. Following each pivotal row is the reduced matrix. The first row in the reduced matrix is given the pivotal row in that row. The reduced matrix supplies a linear function of the variables whose variance is the pivotal element (underlined) in that row. Thus Y_1, Y_2, Y_3, Y_4, Y_5, and Y_6 have 41.73, 32.0252, 23.1440, 15.5452, 34.9565, and 4.3476 as their variances.

3. The computations can be compactly represented by omitting the matrix for functions of original variables and accommodating the figures below the diagonal in the left-hand matrix as shown in Table 7b.6β.

Obtaining the expressions for Y_1, Y_2, $\cdots$, Y_6 from Table 8b.4β and dividing them by the corresponding standard deviations, we obtain the following uncorrelated transformed variables with unit variances.

$$y_1 = \quad 0.1548L$$

$$y_2 = -0.0456L + 0.1767B$$

$$y_3 = -0.0291L - 0.0369B + 0.2079H'$$

$$y_4 = \quad 0.0010L - 0.0854B - 0.0131H' + 0.2536G'H$$

$$y_5 = -0.0346L - 0.0176B + 0.0094H' - 0.0174G'H + 0.1691GB$$

$$y_6 = -0.0503L + 0.0209B - 0.0409H' - 0.2202G'H - 0.0219GB + 0.4796NH,L$$

TABLE 8b.4γ.   Values of Transformed Characters

	Highdown Skull (1)	Bronze Age Mean (2)	Maiden Castle Mean (3)	Difference (2) − (3) (4)	D^2 $\Sigma(4)^2$ (5)	$\dfrac{D}{2}$ (6)	Probability of Error (7)
y_1	30.681	28.561	29.195	−0.634	0.402	0.317	0.375
y_2	17.131	18.074	16.279	1.795	3.624	0.952	0.171
y_3	18.289	17.145	17.819	−0.674	4.078	1.009	0.156
y_4	4.051	3.140	4.729	−1.589	6.603	1.285	0.099
y_5	6.810	7.615	7.124	0.491	6.844	1.307	0.095
y_6	− 7.606	− 5.479	− 5.287	−0.192	6.881	1.312	0.095

To test whether the Highdown skull belongs to the Bronze Age we calculate the sum of squares of differences:

$$\chi^2 = (30.681 - 28.561)^2 + (17.131 - 18.074)^2 + \cdots$$

$$+ (-7.606 + 5.479)^2$$

$$= 12.694$$

which can be used as χ^2 with 6 degrees of freedom if the Bronze Age means and dispersion matrix have been obtained from a large sample. On the other hand, if the Bronze Age means are based on a sample of size N and the dispersion matrix is estimated on f degrees of freedom, then

$$F = \chi^2 \frac{(f + 1 - p)N}{fp(N + 1)}$$

can be used as a variance ratio with p and $(f + 1 - p)$ degrees of freedom, p being the number of characters. For the purposes of the above example we shall treat the mean values and dispersion matrix as known so that the χ^2 test can be used. The value 12.694 is just significant on the 5% level.

Similarly, the χ^2 for the Highdown skull and the Maiden Castle series is

$$(1.486)^2 + (0.852)^2 + \cdots + (-2.319)^2 = 9.091$$

which has a probability of more than 15%. By this criterion the Highdown skull could be assigned to the Maiden Castle series. Since χ^2 is only just significant in the other case, we might construct the discriminant function and decide the issue.

Since all y are *uncorrelated*, we can very easily construct the discriminant function. For instance, the one based on the first three values of y is

$$-0.634y_1 + 1.795y_2 - 0.674y_3$$

where the coefficients are the differences in mean values of y for the Bronze Age and the Maiden Castle series. The discriminant function based on y_1, y_2, y_3, y_4 is obtained by adding $-1.589y_4$ to the above expression, and so on. The discriminant function with all the characters is

$$-0.634y_1 + 1.795y_2 - 0.674y_3 - 1.589y_4 + 0.491y_5 - 0.192y_6$$

which has the mean values

$$-4.300 \quad \text{and} \quad 2.581$$

for the Maiden Castle and the Bronze Age series, with the middle value -0.859. Suppose we follow the procedure of assigning all individuals with values of the discriminant function above -0.859 to the Bronze Age, and all others to the Maiden Castle series. Then the error in classification corresponds to the area above -0.859 for a normal distribution with mean -4.300 and variance

$$D^2 = (-0.634)^2 + (1.795)^2 + \cdots + (-0.192)^2 = 6.881$$

which is the sum of squares of the discriminant function coefficients. The normal deviate with zero mean and unit standard deviation is

$$\frac{4.300 - 0.859}{\sqrt{6.881}} = \frac{3.441}{\sqrt{6.881}} = \frac{\sqrt{6.881}}{2} = \frac{D}{2} = 1.312$$

with a probability of about 0.095, which is the error of wrong classification associated with any group. The value of the discriminant function for the Highdown skull is -2.661 which assigns him to the Maiden Castle series.

In Table 8b.4γ the probability of error in using the first $i = 1, 2, \cdots,$ 6 characters is given in column (7). It is seen that the probability of error decreases with the increase in the number of characters, although such a decrease is inappreciable in some cases. For instance, the addition of the last character NH,L leading to the calculation of y_6 does not add much, the decrease in error being very small, less than 2 in 1000 or so.

The evaluation of the discriminant function coefficients and the tests of significance used above are easily carried out with the use of transformed variates. An alternative way is to adopt the computational scheme of Table 7b.6β in Chapter 7 where successive values of D^2 and the discriminant functions were obtained. The variance of the discriminant function (treated as a linear combination of the measurements) is D^2. This is useful in computing the frequencies of wrong classification.

8b.5 The Doubtful Region

In using the discriminant function in the example of 8b.4, the critical value separating the individuals of the two groups was obtained as the middle value of the mean values of the function for the two groups. The frequency of wrong classification for any group is 9.5%. Suppose that an individual is drawn at random from two such populations (considered above) mixed in the proportions $\pi_1 : \pi_2$. The probability of wrong assignment of an individual in such a case is

$$\pi_1(0.095) + \pi_2(0.095) = 0.095$$

which is the same as that for a single group. This is not, however, the minimum possible error when π_1 and π_2 are known, the minimum being associated with the section

$$\lambda = \frac{L_1 + L_2}{2} + \log_e \pi_2 - \log_e \pi_1 \qquad (8b.5.1)$$

where L_1 and L_2 are the mean values of the discriminant function L for the two groups, the higher value being associated with the first group. If $L > \lambda$, then the individual is assigned to the first group; otherwise to the second. Suppose that $\pi_1 : \pi_2 :: 1 : 2$, then

$$\lambda = -0.859 + 0.693 = -0.166$$

in which case the errors of wrong classifications for the two groups are

$$\alpha_1 = 0.15 \quad \text{and} \quad \alpha_2 = 0.05$$

giving a total error

$$\pi_1\alpha_1 + \pi_2\alpha_2 = \frac{(0.15 + 0.10)}{3} = 0.08 \quad \text{nearly}$$

Although the error is nearly 8%, the error of misclassification for an individual of the first group is as high as 15%, so that an individual assigned to the second group cannot be asserted to belong to the second group since his chances of belonging to the first group are as high as 15%.

Consider another situation where a doctor wants to discriminate between two types of neurotic, psychopaths and obsessionals, on the basis of some tests. If the test scores of properly diagnosed neurotics are available, then, assuming that the ratio of the two types of patient admitted into the hospital in the past represents the ratio in the general population, the doctor can set up the criterion (8b.5.1). By following this procedure he can minimize the number of cases of wrong diagnosis.

But in problems like this the groups overlap to a large extent so that even by following the best procedure the percentage of wrong classifications remains quite high. By increasing the number of characters this percentage could be made smaller and smaller but not always below an irreducible minimum because of the correlations between the characters.

Furthermore, a stage may be reached at which the cost involved in further examination will not be commensurate to the reduction in the number of wrong classifications. But, subject to a given cost, the indicators * can be chosen so as to minimize the number of wrong classifications. Thus one has to balance between the errors committed and the time or money available.

By following this procedure it may be difficult to assert that an individual belongs to one group or the other unless the groups are well separated, in which case the proportion of wrong classifications will be low. On the other hand, one may take the view that, whatever may be the basis of judgment, in some cases it should be possible to give a decisive answer (subject to a small risk) whereas in others no decision or only provisional decisions can be made. The latter group comprises the doubtful cases which need further examination.

---

* For instance, there are two types of jaundice which are difficult to distinguish. One calls for a surgical treatment; the other for medical treatment. A discriminant function based on two biochemical tests is used in practice to ensure a greater certainty of diagnosis for far less laboratory work.

Cases also arise where the question asked is whether a selected individual can be asserted to belong to one particular group out of a given number of possibilities. Consider the problem of the Highdown skull. The grave findings associated with the skull excavated from the "invasion horizon" do not give any conclusive evidence as to whether the skull belonged to a Bronze Age "defender" or to an Iron Age "invader." It may or may not be possible to give a definite answer in such a problem. The case has to be judged on its individual merits, with consideration given to the probability of the individual's having come from one group or the other.

Sitting on the fence is a scientific attitude if it means looking for further evidence and better methods of judgment to be able to give a definite answer.

Consider a doctor who has a routine method of diagnosing a disease or discriminating among a number of diseases. Although by following this procedure he commits the least possible errors, he would like to be more confident about his diagnosis in some selected cases. If the routine method does not give him sufficient assurance, he may supplement it by further tests.

For any specially chosen case like this or for an individual find such as the Highdown skull, the rule of procedure suggested should necessarily be independent of the a priori probabilities used in the general problem of discrimination. First, such a priori probabilities may not be available; in the case of the Highdown skull it is not possible to know the proportions of the Bronze and the Iron Age cranial population. Second, even if such knowledge is available from previous experience, this is not strictly applicable in a case not chosen at random from a mixed population. For instance, the proportions applicable to the Highdown skull may depend on the numbers of Bronze and Iron Age warriors who went down fighting and not on the general proportion.

Thus a problem involving only one individual must be distinguished from a problem in which a number of individuals have to be classified into a given number of groups by means of suitable criteria. The latter supplies a provisional answer to the former, but for definite answers suitable criteria have to be developed.

Let us suppose that for the best solution of assigning individuals to the first group if

$$\pi_1 f_1(x \mid \theta_1) \geq \pi_2 f_2(x \mid \theta_2)$$

and to the second group if

$$\pi_2 f_2(x \mid \theta_2) \geq \pi_1 f_1(x \mid \theta_1)$$

the expected proportions of wrongly classified individuals of the first
and second groups are α_1 and α_2, respectively. If α_1 and α_2 are small,
then we can assert for any given individual that he is rightly classified.
Otherwise we may follow the procedure of assigning an individual to
the first group if

$$f_1(x \mid \theta_1) \geq A f_2(x \mid \theta_2)$$

to the second if

$$f_1(x \mid \theta_1) \leq B f_2(x \mid \theta_2)$$

and remain in doubt if

$$A f_2(x \mid \theta_2) > f_1(x \mid \theta_2) > B f_2(x \mid \theta_2)$$

The quantities A and B are chosen such that the probabilities of
wrong decisions are *at assigned levels*. The diagram below (Figure 1)
shows the nature of the decisions that could be made after ascertaining
the value of the ratio or its logarithm.

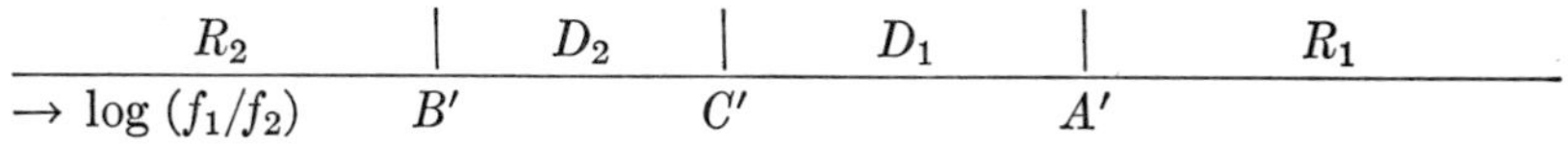

R_2		D_2		D_1		R_1
$\rightarrow \log (f_1/f_2)$	B'		C'		A'	

$$B' = \log_e B \qquad A' = \log_e A \qquad C' = \log_e \pi_2 - \log, \pi_1$$

FIGURE 1

In the region R_2 the individual can be asserted (at a given risk) to
belong to the second group; in D_2 he can be provisionally assigned to
the second group; and similarly for R_1 and D_1. In doubtful cases it
may be possible to measure more characters and thus bring in further
evidence to decide the issue.

In the example of the Highdown skull with $\pi_1 = \frac{1}{3}$ and $\pi_2 = \frac{2}{3}$, it
has already been shown that the point of section is -0.166 so that if
the discriminant value exceeds -0.166 the individual is assigned to the
Bronze Age. The point corresponding to the 5% level of errors for the
Maiden Castle series is

$$-4.300 + 1.645D = 0.016 \qquad D = 2.624$$

so that unless the discriminant value exceeds 0.016 an individual cannot
be asserted to belong to the Bronze Age, although provisionally he will
be put in the Bronze Age as soon as the value exceeds -0.166. Similarly, the 5% value for the Bronze Age is

$$2.581 - 1.645D = -1.735$$

and unless the value of the discriminant function is below -1.735 the individual cannot be asserted to belong to the Maiden Castle series. The value for the Highdown skull is -2.661 so that he can be confidently assigned to the Maiden Castle series.

8b.6 Resolution of a Mixed Series into Two Gaussian Components

In the previous sections were considered problems of determining the group to which an individual belongs when the distributions in the alternative groups are known. There may arise cases where a collection of individuals is observed but no information is available as to the distributions in the groups from which they have arisen or the proportion of mixture. The general problem is then to determine the characteristics of the various groups and also the proportion of mixture from the available set of measurements. This information may be finally used to specify the group of each individual, if necessary.

Considering only two groups in which a certain character is distributed normally, the statistical problem reduces to that of estimating from the observed frequency distribution the two mean values μ_1, μ_2, standard deviations σ_1, σ_2, and the proportion of mixture π. The estimation of these five parameters by the method of moments was discussed by Pearson (1894). The estimates depend on a suitably chosen root of a nonic (ninth-degree equation) constructed from the first five moments of the observed frequency distribution.

In many problems it is reasonable to suppose that $\sigma_1 = \sigma_2$, in which case there are only four parameters to be estimated. If the method of moments is followed, the first four moments are sufficient, for it has been shown that the estimates depend on the negative root of a simple cubic equation constructed from the first four moments. In practice, where large numbers are involved, the estimates obtained by the method of moments, though not efficient, may serve the purpose at hand. Where higher efficiency is aimed at, the estimates have to be found by the method of maximum likelihood. The numerical computations involved in this method are very complicated.

Whatever the method of estimation employed, the numerical computations become much simpler when the standard deviations are assumed to be equal. The simplifying assumption may introduce bias in the estimates when, in fact, the standard deviations differ. Such estimates are, however, more accurate than those obtained without this assumption when the bias in any estimate is smaller than its standard error. If the mean values and the proportion of mixture are to be estimated with a higher precision, small differences in the standard deviations can be ignored.

Estimation by the Method of Moments. The rule of estimating the parameters by the method of moments consists in equating the moments as calculated from the observations to functions of parameters representing the moments in the population. Since the expectations of calculated moments are not the same as the moments in the population, this method might introduce a little bias in the estimating equations. This bias can be avoided by equating the calculated moments to their expected values. Instead of this, we can choose the system of k-statistics of Fisher (defined in *Statistical Methods for Research Workers*) and equate them to their expectations which are the cumulants of the distribution. If s_2, s_3, and s_4 are the second, third, and fourth moments about the mean, and s_1 the first moment about the origin, as calculated by the usual method, the first four k-statistics derivable from them are given by

$$k_1 = s_1$$

$$k_2 = \frac{n}{(n-1)} s_2$$

$$k_3 = \frac{n^2}{(n-1)(n-2)} s_3$$

$$k_4 = \frac{n^2}{(n-1)(n-2)(n-3)} \{(n+1)s_4 - 3(n-1)s_2{}^2\}$$

If the moments are calculated from grouped data with class interval h, the quantities $\frac{1}{12} h^2$ and $\frac{1}{120} h^4$ have to be subtracted from the expressions for k_2 and k_4, respectively.

If p, m_1, m_2, and s denote the estimates of π, μ_1, μ_2, and σ, the common standard deviation, then the estimating equations by this method are

$$1 = p + q$$

$$k_1 = pm_1 + qm_2$$

$$k_2 = s^2 + pd_1{}^2 + qd_2{}^2$$

$$k_3 = pd_1{}^3 + qd_2{}^3$$

$$k_4 = pd_1{}^4 + qd_2{}^4 - 3(pd_1{}^2 + qd_2{}^2)^2$$

where $q = 1 - p$, $d_1 = m_1 - k_1$, and $d_2 = m_2 - k_1$. From the definition $x = d_1 d_2$, the value of x is obtained as the negative root of the cubic

$$x^3 + \tfrac{1}{2}k_4 x + \tfrac{1}{2}k_3{}^2 = 0$$

If x is the required root, then d_1 is given by the negative root of the quadratic

$$d_1^2 + \frac{k_3}{x} d_1 + x = 0$$

and d_2 by $-(k_3/x) - d_1$. The estimates m_1, m_2, p, and s are given by

$$m_1 = k_1 + d_1 \qquad m_2 = k_1 + d_2$$

$$p = \frac{d_2}{(d_2 - d_1)} \qquad s^2 = k_2 + x$$

The fundamental cubic equation

$$x^3 + \tfrac{1}{2}k_4 x + \tfrac{1}{2}k_3^2 = 0$$

introduced above has a single negative root greater than $(-k_2)$. The best method of determining the root is to start with a trial value and obtain the correction by Newton's method of approximation. Since the equation is in a reduced form with the coefficient of x^2 absent, it is easy to guess the root correct to the nearest integer. If x_1 stands for the trial value, then the additive correction δx_1 is given by

$$\left[3x_1^2 + \frac{k_4}{2} \right] \delta x_1 = -x_1^3 - \frac{1}{2}k_4 x_1 - \frac{1}{2}k_3^2$$

The process is repeated until the expression on the right-hand side becomes very small. The data of Table 8b.6α give the frequency distribution of heights of 454 plants of two different types grown on the same

TABLE 8b.6α. The Frequency Distribution of Height in Centimeters for 454 Plants

Class Interval	Frequency
7.5–8.5	3
9.5	9
10.5	21
11.5	40
12.5	59
13.5	76
14.5	79
15.5	69
16.5	46
17.5	30
18.5	13
19.5	7
20.5	2
	454

plot. The plants are indistinguishable except at the flowering stage. The problem is to estimate the mean height of the two types of plant, their common standard deviation, and the proportion of mixture.

The values of cumulants after adjustment for grouping are

$$k_1 = -0.244493 \qquad \text{about 14 as the origin}$$

$$k_2 = 4.975963$$

$$k_3 = 0.728751$$

$$k_4 = -5.314741$$

$$\tfrac{1}{2}k_4 = -2.657370 \qquad \tfrac{1}{2}k_3{}^2 = 0.265539$$

The fundamental cubic is

$$x^3 - 2.657370x + 0.265539 = 0$$

Taking -1.65 as a trial root, we find the correction δx is given by

$$[3(1.65)^2 - 2.657370]\, \delta x = -(-1.65)3 + 2.657370(-1.65) - 0.265539$$

$$5.510130\, \delta x = -0.158074$$

$$\delta x = -0.0286878$$

Similarly, the second correction is 0.000707 so that the second approximation is $-1.678688 + 0.000707 = -1.677981$. The quadratic giving d_1 is

$$d_1{}^2 - 0.434302d_1 - 1.677981 = 0$$

which yields the negative root

$$d_1 = -1.096293$$

$$d_2 = 1.096293 + 0.434302 = 1.530595$$

The estimates of m_1 and m_2 about 14 as the origin are

$$m_1 = -1.096293 - 0.244493 = -1.340786$$

$$m_2 = 1.530595 - 0.244493 = 1.286102$$

$$p = \frac{d_2}{(d_2 - d_1)} = 0.582665$$

$$q = (1 - p) = 0.417335$$

$$s^2 = 4.975963 - 1.677981 = 3.297982$$

$$s = 1.816035$$

This completes the estimation of the four parameters by the method of moments.

The expressions for standard errors of these estimates are very complicated, but it appears that the estimate of the proportion of mixture will have the highest percentage of error whereas the estimates of means and standard deviation will be fairly reliable in large samples.

A good deal of caution is needed in resolving a mixed series.

(i) It must be ascertained that the population is a mixture of two homogeneous groups only.

(ii) Departure of the individual distributions from the Gaussian type introduces serious errors in the estimates.

(iii) Samples must be large enough for a successful resolution into two components.

8b.7 Sexing of Osteometric Material

In anthropometric work the problem of sexing often arises. The sex of an excavated skull or jawbone can be ascertained with a high chance of success if the associated pelvis is also found. Sometimes the sex of the skeleton may be determined by external evidence such as beads and other ornaments found buried with the body. Anthropologists of the "trained eye" school claim that a skull can be properly sexed by anatomical appreciation. In such cases, the conclusions may be marred by a subjective bias unless the features of the specimen examined are so striking as to leave the question of its identity in little doubt.

In any case two types of situations have to be faced. Some skeletal remains can be definitely sexed, but how can the other bones belonging to the same series be sexed? All those bones which have been sexed supply the basic material with which suitable discriminant functions can be constructed. The sex proportion can also be ascertained from the basic material. The problem, then, reduces to the simplest one of discrimination between two groups when the individual distributions and the a priori probabilities are known.

It may be necessary to obtain discriminant functions based on different sets and subsets of characters to suit the various bones which have to be sexed. For instance, a skull may be in a broken condition so that only the length and breadth of the cranium can be measured. A decision is then made with the help of a discriminant function based on length and breadth of the cranium only. Some skulls may admit facial and nasal measurements as well, in which case the discriminant function based on all these measurements has to be used. The method of transformed characters and the construction of discriminant functions adopted in 8b.5 are very useful in this connection, provided that the order in which the characters are added is suitably determined. For instance, consider the five measurements of the cranium: length (L), breadth (B), frontal breadth (B'), height (H'), and circumference (S). The order here is obviously L, B, B', H', and S, for there may be some skulls providing measurements on L, B, and B' alone and not on the rest, whereas skulls admitting the measurements of H' and S must necessarily supply the measurements L, B, and B'.

We have another situation when adequate material is not available for the construction of the discriminant function. Then an approximate function can be tried, the simplest of which is of the type

$$\pm \frac{x_1}{\sigma_1} \pm \frac{x_2}{\sigma_2} \pm \cdots$$

where $+$ or $-$ is chosen according as the male mean for x_i is greater or smaller than the female mean. The values of the standard deviations $\sigma_1, \sigma_2, \cdots$ of $x_1, x_2, \cdots$ need not be known exactly. Values from any related series can be used because what is important is the relative order of the various standard deviations. This formula does not make use of the actual mean values but only of their inequality relationship. We shall term the above expression as the "general size factor."

In the problem of sexing, the size factor can be conveniently employed because the inequalities relating to various measurements of the male and female are known. Most of the linear measurements have higher values for males, whereas angles and some indices have higher values for females. The series of values of the size factor calculated for each specimen to be sexed can first be arranged in decreasing order of magnitude and then divided in a given sex ratio assigning the higher values to males and the smaller ones to females.

Some difficulty arises when the sex ratio is unknown. The series of size factor values may then be treated as in 8b.6 for resolution into two Gaussian components. This supplies the sex ratio and other constants which may be useful in setting up the best procedure for discrimination based on a single characteristic, viz., the size factor, or only the sex ratio may be used to divide the series into males and females, as suggested above.

As observed earlier, the resolution into Gaussian components is not always a happy proposition because the estimation involves the calculated higher moments which are subject to large standard errors. An alternative procedure is as follows.

First we observe that the standard deviation of the size factor σ^2 for a homogeneous group (either ♂♂ or ♀♀) can be obtained from any related series. If k_2, k_3 are the second and third cumulants of the mixed series of the size factor, then the estimating equations are

$$p_1 d_1 + p_2 d_2 = 0$$

$$d_1 d_2 = -(k_2 - \sigma^2)$$

$$d_1 + d_2 = \frac{k_3}{(k_2 - \sigma^2)}$$

$$p = \frac{d_2}{(d_2 - d_1)}$$

where $d_1 = m_1 - k_1$ and $d_2 = m_2 - k_1$, as defined before. The use of the fourth moment is avoided by this procedure, but it remains to be seen what error is committed by choosing a wrong σ. Consider the previous example with

$$k_1 = -0.244493 \qquad k_2 = 4.975963 \qquad k_3 = 0.728751$$

Assuming three different values

$$\sigma^2 = 4, \quad 3.297982, \quad 3$$

the equations are

$$d_1 d_2 = -0.975963, \quad -1.677981, \quad -1.975963$$

$$d_1 + d_2 = \quad 0.746699, \quad 0.434302, \quad 0.368808$$

with solutions

$$d_1 = -0.682753, \quad -1.096293, \quad -1.233329$$

$$d_2 = \quad 1.429452, \quad 1.530595, \quad 1.602137$$

$$p = \quad 0.676758, \quad 0.582665, \quad 0.565035$$

of which the middle one corresponds to the solution already obtained. It appears that p is stable for small variations in σ.

Another method is to avoid the calculation of even the third moment but to use the median instead. The computations will be slightly heavier.

If the mean values are available, then a better approximation to the discriminant function is

$$k_1 x_1 + k_2 x_2 + \cdots + k_p x_p$$

where $k_i = d_i / \sigma_i^2$, d_i being the difference in mean values of the ith character. This is exactly the discriminant function when the correlations are neglected.

Example 1.   Construct the discriminant function, assuming differences d_1, d_2, $\cdots$, d_p in the mean values and a correlation matrix with all correlations equal to a constant value r.   The function can be expressed in terms of two linear functions of the variables

$$P = \frac{x_1}{\sigma_1} + \frac{x_2}{\sigma_2} + \cdots + \frac{x_p}{\sigma_p}$$

and

$$Q = k_1 x_1 + \cdots + k_p x_p$$

where

$$k_i = \frac{d_i}{\sigma_i^{\,2}}$$

The second factor is called the shape factor by Penrose (1947) who uses a slightly different form.

Example 2.   Consider a correlation matrix of the type

$$\left(\begin{array}{c|c} A & B \\ \hline B & C \end{array} \right)$$

where A and C are two equicorrelation matrices and B is a matrix with all its elements constant.   Here the discriminant function depends on two sets of size and shape factors and on another factor which may be called the bipolar factor.

8b.8   The Problem of Three and More Groups

In 8b.5 it is seen that, if measurements on a certain number of characters are available for two groups, it is possible to construct a discriminant function which affords the maximum discrimination between them.   This function is useful in assigning with a certain degree of confidence an individual or individuals to one or the other of the two groups to which they are known to belong.   In taxonomic problems there arise cases where an individual specimen is known to belong to one of three or more groups and has to be assigned to its proper group.   Thus a plant may have to be specified as *Iris versicolor*, *Iris setosa*, or *Iris verginica*.   This problem is approached by the extension of the discriminant function analysis developed with special reference to two groups.

The General Theory for Three Groups.   Let the probability densities in the three groups be represented by $f_1(x, \theta_1)$, $f_2(x, \theta_2)$, $f_3(x, \theta_3)$, where x stands for the available set of measurements and θ for the parameters. First we shall consider the general problem of classifying a collection of individuals drawn from a mixed population containing individuals of the three groups in the proportions, π_1, π_2, π_3, $(\pi_1 + \pi_2 + \pi_3 = 1)$.

Any individual I characterized by p measurements can be represented by a point in a p-dimensional space. The problem of classifying an observed collection of individuals is the same as the division of the space into three mutually exclusive regions, R_1, R_2, R_3, with the rule of procedure of assigning an individual I, represented by a point in R_i, to the ith group. If the probability that an individual of the ith group will fall in R_i is β_i, then the expected value of the proportion of wrong classifications is

$$\alpha = 1 - (\pi_1\beta_1 + \pi_2\beta_2 + \pi_3\beta_3)$$

The errors will be a minimum for that choice of regions R_1, R_2, R_3 for which $\pi_1\beta_1 + \pi_2\beta_2 + \pi_3\beta_3$ is a maximum. Such regions, if they exist, may be termed the "best possible" regions. The following theorem establishes the existence and nature of the best possible regions.

Theorem 1. The regions defined by ($\cap$)

$$R_1 \quad \cap \quad \pi_1 f_1 \geq \pi_2 f_2, \quad \pi_1 f_1 \geq \pi_3 f_3$$

$$R_2 \quad \cap \quad \pi_2 f_2 \geq \pi_1 f_1, \quad \pi_2 f_2 \geq \pi_3 f_3$$

$$R_3 \quad \cap \quad \pi_3 f_3 \geq \pi_1 f_1, \quad \pi_3 f_3 \geq \pi_2 f_2$$

constitute the best possible system of mutually exclusive regions.

The result follows from the lemma proved in Appendix A2. It is interesting to observe that this solution is the same as that obtained from Bayes's theorem on posterior probabilities.

If every individual is equally likely to be drawn from any group, the best regions are

$$R_1 \quad \cap \quad f_1 \geq f_2, \quad f_1 \geq f_3$$

$$R_2 \quad \cap \quad f_2 \geq f_1, \quad f_2 \geq f_3$$

$$R_3 \quad \cap \quad f_3 \geq f_1, \quad f_3 \geq f_2$$

These regions may be used for classifying an observed collection of individuals when nothing is known about π_1, π_2, π_3, the proportions of mixture. This is the maximum likelihood method in the problem of classification. We choose that hypothesis for which the likelihood is a maximum.

By adopting this procedure the probability of an individual of the first group being rightly assigned is $\int_{R_1} f_1 \, dv = \beta_1$, and the probabilities of the individuals of the second and third groups being wrongly assigned to the first group are

$$\alpha_{12} = \int_{R_1} f_2 \, dv \quad \text{and} \quad \alpha_{13} = \int_{R_1} f_3 \, dv$$

Since, in $R_1, f_1 \geq f_2, f_1 \geq f_3$, it follows that

$$\beta_1 \geq \text{the greater of } \alpha_{12} \quad \text{and} \quad \alpha_{13}$$

If α_{12} and α_{13} are small, we can assert with some confidence that an individual falling in R_1 is correctly classified. If they are not small, it is pertinent to inquire whether there exists a region C_1 such that

$$\int_{C_1} f_1 \, dv \quad \text{is a maximum}$$

subject to the conditions that

$$\int_{C_1} f_2 \, dv \quad \text{and} \quad \int_{C_1} f_3 \, dv$$

are both not greater than a quantity α_1, chosen to be small, say 0.01 or 0.05. If an observed specimen falls in such a region, then the hypothesis that it belongs to the second or the third groups may be rejected, in which case it is assigned to the first group. The existence and nature of such regions are established by theorem 2.

Theorem 2. Region C_1 satisfying the condition

$$\int_{C_1} f_1 \, dv \quad \text{is a maximum}$$

subject to the restrictions

$$\alpha_1 \geq \int_{C_1} f_2 \, dv \quad \text{and} \quad \int_{C_1} f_3 \, dv$$

is defined by

$$f_1 \geq af_2 + bf_3$$

where a and b are suitably chosen.

The proof of this theorem follows from the lemma of Neyman and Pearson given in Appendix A1. To apply this lemma consider two quantities α_{12}, α_{13}, both less than the assigned quantity α_1, and choose a region such that

$$\int_w f_1 \, dv \quad \text{is a maximum}$$

subject to the conditions

$$\int_w f_2 \, dv = \alpha_{12} \qquad \int_w f_3 \, dv = \alpha_{13}$$

The inside of such a region is defined by

$$f_1 \geq a'f_2 + b'f_3$$

where a' and b' are properly chosen. Let the maximized value of $\int_w f_1 \, dv$, which is evidently a function of α_{12}, α_{13}, be represented by $\beta(\alpha_{12}, \alpha_{13})$. This is not, in general, an increasing function of α_{12} and α_{13}; therefore the maximum value is not necessarily attained when $\alpha_{12} = \alpha_{13} = \alpha_1$. If, now, the function $\beta(\alpha_{12}, \alpha_{13})$ is maximized with respect to α_{12}, α_{13}, subject to the conditions α_{12}, $\alpha_{13} \leq \alpha_1$, we obtain two values, $\alpha_{12}{}^0$, $\alpha_{13}{}^0$, corresponding to the optimum solution. Denoting the values of a', b', corresponding to $\alpha_{12}{}^0$, $\alpha_{13}{}^0$, by a, b, the required region may be written $f_1 \geq af_2 + bf_3$, which proves theorem 2.

It is easy to see that at least one of the values $\alpha_{12}{}^0$, $\alpha_{13}{}^0$ coincides with the boundary value α_1. Consider the best region corresponding to α_{12}, α_{13} with both less than α_1. If $\alpha_{12} \geq \alpha_{13}$, it is always possible to add a region in which $f_2 \geq f_3$ so that α_{12} is increased to α_1, and α_{13} to a value $\leq \alpha_1$. If this is not possible, a region in which $f_2 \leq f_3$ can be added such that at least one value, α_{12} or α_{13}, reaches the value α_1. The value of $\beta(\alpha_{12}, \alpha_{13})$ is increased in any case.

Having obtained regions R_1 and C_1 as given in theorems 1 and 2, we may specify an individual falling in the C_1 region as belonging to the first group, and an individual falling in $D_1 = R_1 - C_1$ as likely to belong to the first group. Regions R_2, C_2 and R_3, C_3 can be similarly constructed.

If the proportions π_1, π_2, π_3 considered in theorem 1 are known, then region C_1 is determined by

$$f_1 \geq a(\pi_2 f_2 + \pi_3 f_3)$$

where a is chosen such that $\int_{C_1} (\pi_2 f_2 + \pi_3 f_3) = \alpha_1 \pi_1$ and so on. The position is shown in Figure 2.

A certain amount of simplification results if the best region C_1 is replaced by

$$C_1' \quad \cap \quad f_1 \geq Af_2, \quad f_1 \geq Bf_3$$

where A and B are chosen such that

$$\int_{C_1'} f_1 \, dv \quad \text{is a maximum}$$

subject to the conditions

$$\int_{C_1'} f_2 \, dv \leq \alpha_1 \qquad \int_{C_1'} f_3 \, dv \leq \alpha_1$$

This region is not the best possible, but it is likely to be a good approximation.

In some situations it may be necessary to find regions R_1, R_2, R_3 such that the errors of classification are the same for each group or are to be

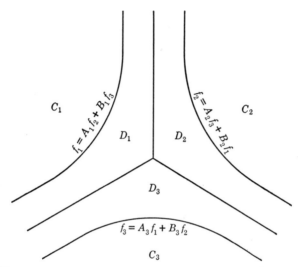

FIGURE 2. The division of the space for six possible decisions.

in given ratios $\rho_1 : \rho_2 : \rho_3$. The existence and nature of such regions are established by the following theorem.

Theorem 3. The system of regions

$$R_1 \quad \cap \quad af_1 \geq bf_2, \quad af_1 \geq cf_3$$

$$R_2 \quad \cap \quad bf_2 \geq cf_3, \quad bf_2 \geq af_1$$

$$R_3 \quad \cap \quad cf_3 \geq af_1, \quad cf_3 \geq bf_2$$

where a, b, c are suitably chosen, are the best possible if the errors of classification for the three groups are to be in an assigned ratio.

Let R_1', R_2', R_3' be any other set of regions for which the errors of classification are in the assigned ratio. The region common to R_i' and

R_j is represented by R_{ij}. Then

$$a \int_{R_1'} f_1 \, dv = \int_{R_{11}} af_1 \, dv + \int_{R_{12}} af_1 \, dv + \int_{R_{13}} af_1 \, dv$$

$$\leq a \int_{R_{11}} f_1 \, dv + b \int_{R_{12}} f_2 \, dv + c \int_{R_{13}} f_3 \, dv$$

Similar relationships can be set up, starting with $\int_{R_2'} bf_2 \, dv$ and $\int_{R_3'} cf_3 \, dv$. The errors of classification with respect to the systems R_1, R_2, R_3 and R_1', R_2', R_3' may be represented by $\alpha\rho_1$, $\alpha\rho_2$, $\alpha\rho_3$ and $\alpha'\rho_1$, $\alpha'\rho_2$, $\alpha'\rho_3$, respectively, $\rho_1 : \rho_2 : \rho_3$ being the assigned ratio. Writing down the values of integrals in the above three relationships and adding,

$$(1 - \rho_1\alpha')a + (1 - \rho_2\alpha')b + (1 - \rho_3\alpha')c$$

$$\leq (1 - \rho_1\alpha)a + (1 - \rho_2\alpha)b + (1 - \rho_3\alpha)c$$

or

$$-\alpha'(a\rho_1 + b\rho_2 + c\rho_3) \leq -\alpha(a\rho_1 + b\rho_2 + c\rho_3)$$

i.e., $\alpha' \geq \alpha$, since a, b, and c are positive quantities by definition. This proves the result of theorem 3.

The quantities a, b, c are to be determined from the relations

$$\frac{1}{\rho_1} \int_{R_2+R_3} f_1 \, dv = \frac{1}{\rho_2} \int_{R_1+R_3} f_2 \, dv = \frac{1}{\rho_3} \int_{R_1+R_2} f_3 \, dv$$

Von Mises (1945) considers the problem of classification which minimizes the maximum error. For any system of regions R_1, R_2, R_3, the errors associated with the three groups are

$$\alpha_1 = 1 - \int_{R_1} f_1 \, dv \qquad \alpha_2 = 1 - \int_{R_2} f_2 \, dv \qquad \alpha_3 = 1 - \int_{R_3} f_3 \, dv$$

The set of regions for which the maximum α is a minimum is recommended by Von Mises for possible use in problems of classification. It is first easy to see that for such regions

$$\alpha_1 = \alpha_2 = \alpha_3$$

for, if an inequality relationship is true, say $\alpha_2 > \alpha_3$, it is possible to reallocate the regions R_2 and R_3 such that α_2 is decreased and α_3 is increased, thus reducing the maximum α. No improvement is possible by this method when $\alpha_1 = \alpha_2 = \alpha_3$, in which case we can choose the regions with the help of theorem 3 to minimize this common value, i.e., when $\rho_1 = \rho_2 = \rho_3$.

The minimax requirement is to some extent unrealistic. Consider a situation where two of the three groups are close together and the other is quite distant. If the individuals of the distant group are considered, the chance of misclassification should be small whereas the chance of error for any one of the closer groups should be high. No compromise is served by equalizing these errors. As observed earlier the maximum likelihood solution can be used when nothing is known about the a priori probabilities. When these regions are used, the requirement stated above is automatically satisfied. Also, there does not exist any other set of regions which is uniformly better than this set in the sense that the errors are smaller for each group.

Theorem 2 led us to the construction of 4 mutually exclusive regions with the help of which an observed specimen can be assigned either to a particular group or to none. In some problems it may be necessary to construct a system of 7 regions, 3 for assigning an observed specimen to particular groups, 3 others for specifying it as belonging to one of two of the groups, and the remaining one for making no decision. To construct these regions we set up three regions w_1, w_2, w_3 for not accepting respectively the first, the second, and the third groups, as the possible ones from which the observed specimen has arisen. The boundary surfaces of these regions determine by mutual intersection the required system of 7 regions. The region outside w_1, w_2, w_3 is the doubtful region; the intersection of w_i and w_j is the region for specifying an individual belonging to the kth group, $(k \neq i \neq j)$; and the region outside w_i, w_j but inside w_k is for either the ith or the jth group. Some methods of constructing regions w_1, w_2, w_3 are discussed below.

Regions w_i when π_1, π_2, π_3 are known: If π_1, π_2, π_3 considered in theorem 1 are known, then region w_1 is such that

$$\int_{w_1} \pi_1 f_1 \, dv = \alpha_1 \quad \text{(a small assigned quantity)}$$

and

$$\int_{w_1} (\pi_2 f_2 + \pi_3 f_3) \, dv \quad \text{is a maximum}$$

The boundary surface of such a region is

$$\pi_1 f_1 \leq a(\pi_2 f_2 + \pi_3 f_3)$$

where the constant a is suitably determined. Similarly, w_2 and w_3 can be constructed.

Regions w_i independent of any a priori information: Consider the region w_1' such that

$$\int_{w_1'} f_1 \, dv = \alpha_1$$

and

$$\int_{w_1'} f_2 \, dv = \int_{w_1'} f_3 \, dv = \beta \quad \text{is a maximum}$$

Having determined β, it is possible to construct the region w_1 such that

$$\int_{w_1} f_1 \, dv = \alpha_1$$

$$\int_{w_1} f_i \, dv = \beta \qquad i \neq 1$$

$$\int_{w_1} f_j \, dv \quad \text{is a maximum} \qquad j \neq i$$

where $i = 2$ if

$$\int_{w_1} f_2 \, dv \leq \int_{w_1} f_3 \, dv$$

and $i = 3$ otherwise. The boundary surface of such a region is of the form

$$f_1 \leq af_2 + bf_3$$

where a and b are suitably determined.

There is an alternative method of constructing w_1, w_2, w_3 which may be useful in some practical situations. Let β_2 and β_3 be the maximum values of

$$\int_{u_2} f_2 \, dv \qquad \text{and} \qquad \int_{u_3} f_3 \, dv$$

subject to the conditions

$$\int_{u_2} f_1 \, dv = \alpha_1 \qquad \int_{u_3} f_1 \, dv = \alpha_1$$

where u_2 and u_3 are the regions corresponding to the maxima. Region w_1 may be determined such that

$$\int_{w_1} f_1 \, dv = \alpha_1$$

and

$$\frac{1}{\beta_2} \int_{w_1} f_2 \, dv = \frac{1}{\beta_3} \int_{w_1} f_3 \, dv \quad \text{is a maximum}$$

The boundary surface of such a region is again of the form

$$f_1 \leq af_2 + bf_3$$

where a and b are suitably determined.

Denoting the populations or possible alternatives by H_1, H_2, H_3, the rule of procedure is as indicated in Figure 3.

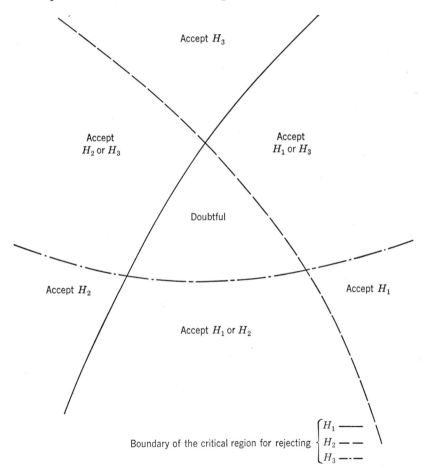

FIGURE 3.   Division of the space for seven possible decisions.

8b.9   Application to Multivariate Normal Populations

For multivariate normal populations the probability density for the rth group is

$$f_r = \text{const. exp} -\tfrac{1}{2}\{\Sigma\Sigma\lambda^{ij}(x_i - \mu_{ir})(x_j - \mu_{jr})\}$$

The surfaces of constant likelihood ratios are defined by

$$\sum_j \{\sum_i \lambda^{ij}(\mu_{ir} - \mu_{is})\}x_j = \text{const.}$$

$$r, s = 1, 2, 3$$

These surfaces can also be defined in terms of what may be called linear discriminant scores defined in terms of the constants for the rth group only.

$$L_r = \sum_j (\sum_i \lambda^{ij}\mu_{ir})x_j - \tfrac{1}{2}\Sigma\Sigma\lambda^{ij}\mu_{ir}\mu_{jr}$$

$$r = 1, 2, 3$$

A constant likelihood ratio corresponds to a constant difference in the discriminant scores. If the a priori probabilities are π_1, π_2, π_3 for the three groups, then the rule of procedure is to assign an observed individual to that group for which

$$L_r + \log_e \pi_r$$

is a maximum.

Example 1. The scores in three tests, A, B, and C, of 256 army recruits classified by their neurotic condition have the mean values as given in Table 8b.9α.

TABLE 8b.9α.   Mean Scores of Neurotic Groups (Rao and Slater, 1949)

Group	Sample Size	Mean Score A	Mean Score B	Mean Score C
Anxiety state	114	2.9298	1.1667	0.7281
Hysteria	33	3.0303	1.2424	0.5455
Psychopathy	32	3.8125	1.8438	0.8125
Obsession	17	4.7059	1.5882	1.1176
Personality change	5	1.4000	0.2000	0.0000
Normal	55	0.6000	0.1455	0.2182

The dispersion matrix within the groups and its reciprocal are given below.

	Within Dispersion Matrix (λ_{ij}) A	B	C	Reciprocal (λ^{ij}) A	B	C
A	2.300851	0.251578	0.474169	0.543234	-0.200195	-0.420813
B	0.251578	0.607466	0.035774	-0.200195	1.725807	0.055767
C	0.474169	0.035774	0.595094	-0.420813	0.055767	2.012357

For any group the linear discriminant score is

$$l_1 A + l_2 B + l_3 C - \tfrac{1}{2}(l_1 m_1 + l_2 m_2 + l_3 m_3)$$

where

$$l_1 = \lambda^{11} m_1 + \lambda^{12} m_2 + \lambda^{13} m_3$$

$$l_2 = \lambda^{21} m_1 + \lambda^{22} m_2 + \lambda^{23} m_3$$

$$l_3 = \lambda^{31} m_1 + \lambda^{32} m_2 + \lambda^{33} m_3$$

m_1, m_2, m_3 are the mean values of A, B, C, and the elements λ^{ij} belong to the reciprocal of the dispersion matrix. For the anxiety state group

$$m_1 = 2.9298 \qquad m_2 = 1.1667 \qquad m_3 = 0.7281$$

$$l_1 = \quad 0.5432(2.9298) - 0.2002(1.1667) - 0.4208(0.7281) = 1.0515$$

$$l_2 = -0.2002(2.9298) + 1.7258(1.1667) + 0.0558(0.7281) = 1.4676$$

$$l_3 = -0.4208(2.9298) + 0.0558(1.1667) + 2.0124(0.7281) = 0.2975$$

$$\tfrac{1}{2}(l_1 m_1 + l_2 m_2 + l_3 m_3) = \tfrac{1}{2}\{1.0515(2.9298) + \cdots\} = 2.5047$$

Hence the discriminant score for the anxiety state is

$$L = 1.0515 A + 1.4676 B + 0.2975 C - 2.5047$$

For purposes of classification the expression to be calculated is $L + \log_e \pi$, where π denotes the relative frequency of cases of anxiety state. The discriminant scores involving the relative frequencies are given in Table 8b.9β.

The present data are not a representative sample of officers serving in the Army and the Navy. The sample of neurotic officers has not been exposed to any known bias, and the proportions between the numbers in the various groups may be fairly representative; but the number of normal officers is grossly under-represented. It seems impossible to obtain a reliable general estimate of the risk that a man will be referred to a hospital for the treatment of a neurosis while he is serving in the Army or the Navy as an officer; but the indications are that, even under conditions of very severe stress, it is not more than 2 to 3 per cent. For proportional representation over 100 times as many normal cases should have been reported.

In Table 8b.9β the formulae have been given in terms of general relative frequencies and also for the particular values realized in the sample although they are subject to systematic as well as to chance errors. The formulae are unsuitable for practical use unless reliable estimates of the relative frequencies are available.

TABLE 8b.9β.   The Linear Discriminant Scores for Various Groups

Group	Coefficients of Measurements			Constant Term	
				(a) In Terms of General Proportion	(b) For Proportions from Present Data *
	A	B	C		
Normal	0.2050	0.1431	0.1947	$-0.0931 + \log_e \pi_1$	-1.6311
Personality					
change	0.7204	0.0649	-0.5780	$-0.5107 + \log_e \pi_2$	-4.4465
Anxiety state	1.0515	1.4676	0.2974	$-2.5047 + \log_e \pi_3$	-3.3137
Hysteria	1.1678	1.5679	-0.1081	$-2.7139 + \log_e \pi_4$	-4.7626
Psychopathy	1.3599	2.4641	0.1336	$-4.9182 + \log_e \pi_5$	-6.9977
Obsession	1.7680	1.8611	0.3573	$-5.8375 + \log_e \pi_6$	-8.5495

* $\pi_1 = 0.21484$, $\pi_2 = 0.01953$, $\pi_3 = 0.44531$, $\pi_4 = 0.12891$, $\pi_5 = 0.12500$, π_6 = 0.06641.

Given the measurements A, B, C of an individual, we calculate the linear discriminant scores $L_1 \cdots L_6$, corrected for a priori probabilities, and assign him to the group for which his score is highest. If the a priori probabilities are not known, the maximum likelihood method leads to the rule of assigning an individual to that group for which L is highest.

Example 2.   Table 8b.9γ gives the statistical constants for three groups of individuals measured by D. N. Majumdar. These groups are considered again in Chapter 9 where the constants for all available characters are given.

TABLE 8b.9γ.   Statistical Constants for Three Groups

Mean Values

Group	Stature (St)	Sitting Height (SH)	Nasal Depth (ND)	Nasal Height (NH)
Brahmin	164.51	86.43	25.49	51.24
Artisan	160.53	81.47	23.84	48.62
Korwa	158.17	81.16	21.44	46.72

Dispersion Matrix

St	32.95	7.43	1.78	3.97
SH	.....	10.24	1.17	2.43
ND	.....	.....	3.06	1.78
NH	.....	.....	....	12.25

By inverting the dispersion matrix we can obtain the linear discriminant scores, as in the illustration of neurotic groups, and use them for classification. In order to determine the probabilities of wrong classification for each group it is necessary to go through a slightly complicated procedure. If there are only three groups, the four (in general, p) measurements can be replaced by two independent linear functions, given which the relative distributions in all the groups become identical. The problem is thus reduced to a two-variable case. The two independent functions can be obtained in a number of ways. One simple method is to calculate the discriminant functions for any two pairs of groups. The computational method is to write down the dispersion matrix with two appended columns:

| | Differences in Mean Values | | | |
	(St)	(SH)	(ND)	(NH)
Brahmin − Artisan	3.98	4.96	1.65	2.62
Artisan − Korwa	2.36	0.31	2.40	1.90

and reduce it, for solving equations (see 1d.1).

$$
\begin{array}{cccc|cc}
32.95 & 7.43 & 1.78 & 3.97 & 3.98 & 2.36 \\
 & 10.24 & 1.17 & 2.43 & 4.96 & 0.31 \\
 & & 3.06 & 1.78 & 1.65 & 2.40 \\
 & & & 12.25 & 2.62 & 1.90
\end{array}
$$

The two sets of solutions give the two discriminant functions for the pairs Brahmin, Artisan and Artisan, Korwa,

$$X = -0.0039St + 0.4301SH + 0.3293ND + 0.0819NH$$
$$Y = 0.0476St - 0.1036SH + 0.7679ND + 0.0486NH$$

and the discriminant function for Brahmin, Korwa is $X + Y$, which have the following mean values.

	X	Y	$X + Y$
Brahmin	49.1224	20.9406	70.0630
Artisan	46.2467	19.8706	66.1173
Korwa	45.1766	17.8551	63.0317

The discriminant function for Artisan − Korwa gives the rule for distinguishing Artisan from Korwa when

$$Y \geq \frac{19.8706 + 17.8551}{2} = 18.8628$$

Similarly, Artisan is distinguished from Brahmin when

$$X \leq \frac{49.1224 + 46.2467}{2} = 47.6845$$

Therefore, the maximum likelihood method of classification for Artisan is $Y \geq 18.8628$, $X \leq 47.6845$. Similarly, by considering the discriminant functions between Brahmin, Artisan and Brahmin, Korwa, the rule for Brahmin is

$$X \geq 47.6845 \qquad X + Y \geq 66.5473$$

For Korwa the rule is

$$Y \leq 18.8628 \qquad X + Y \leq 66.5473$$

obtained by considering the two discriminant functions separating Korwa from Artisan and Korwa from Brahmin. For instance consider an individual with

$$St = 162.00 \qquad SH = 84.00 \qquad ND = 24.00 \qquad NH = 49.00$$

The value of $X = 47.4129$, $Y = 19.8198$, and $X + Y = 67.2327$. Since

$$19.8198 > 18.8628 \qquad \text{and} \qquad 47.4129 < 47.6845$$

the individual is assigned to the Artisan group.

Figure 4 gives the two-dimensional chart for X and Y with respect to which the individuals can be classified. The point (X, Y) for the

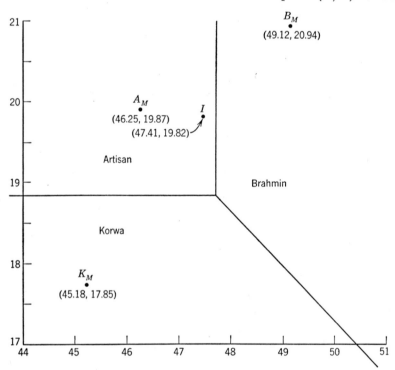

FIGURE 4. The regions separating the three groups.

observed individual is represented by I and the mean values by B_M, A_M, and K_M.

To determine the errors of classification we need find the variances and covariances of X and Y which can be simply obtained from the mean values.

$$V(X) = B_X - A_X = 49.1224 - 46.2467 = 2.8757$$

$$V(Y) = A_Y - K_Y = 19.8706 - 17.8551 = 2.0155$$

$$\text{cov } (X, Y) = A_X - K_X = 46.2467 - 45.1767$$

$$= B_Y - A_Y = 20.9406 - 19.8706 = 1.0700$$

$$V(X + Y) = V(X) + V(Y) + 2 \text{ cov } (X, Y)$$

$$= 2.8757 + 2.0155 + 2(1.0700) \quad = 7.0312$$

$$\text{cov } (X, X + Y) = V(X) + \text{cov } (X, Y)$$

$$= 2.8757 + 1.0700 \quad\quad\quad = 3.9457$$

$$\text{cov } (Y, X + Y) = V(Y) + \text{cov } (X, Y)$$

$$= 2.0155 + 1.0700 \quad\quad\quad = 3.0855$$

The correlation matrix of X, Y and $X + Y$ is

	X	Y	$X + Y$
X	....	0.4459	0.8810
Y		......	0.8200
$X + Y$			......
Standard deviation	1.69	1.42	2.65

The proportion of right classification for Brahmin is

$$P(X \geq 47.6845, X + Y \geq 66.5473)$$

which give the deviates

$$\frac{47.6845 - 49.1224}{1.69} \quad \text{and} \quad \frac{66.5473 - 70.0630}{2.65}$$

$$h = -0.85 \quad \text{and} \quad k = -1.33$$

The probability for $h > 0.85$, $k > 1.33$ and $r = 0.88$ is given in Part II of Pearson's tables for statisticians and biometricians. This value is approximately 0.085. The required probability for wrong classification is

$$P(h > 0.85) + P(k > 1.33) - P(h > 0.85, k > 1.33)$$

$$= 0.195 + 0.092 - 0.085 = 0.202$$

where the first two probabilities are obtained from univariate normal tables.

Similarly, for Korwa the deviates are

$$h = 0.71 \quad \text{and} \quad k = 1.33, \quad r = 0.82$$

and the probability for correct classification is

$$h \leq 0.71 \quad \text{and} \quad k \leq 1.33$$

The tabular value gives the probability 0.085 for $h > 0.71$ and $k > 1.33$. The probability for wrong classification is

$$P(h > 0.71) + P(k > 1.33) - P(h > 0.71, k > 1.33)$$
$$= 0.239 + 0.092 - 0.085 = 0.246$$

Similarly, for Artisan the deviates are

$$h = 0.85 \quad \text{and} \quad k = -0.71, \quad r = 0.45$$

and the probability for correct classification is

$$P(h < 0.85, k > -0.71)$$

Since one of the deviates is negative, the tabular entry for $h > 0.85$ and $k > 0.71$ has to be obtained, taking r to be negative. For $r = -0.44$ the value is 0.013. The probability for wrong classification is

$$P(h > 0.85) + P(k > 0.71) - P(h > 0.85, k > 0.71)$$
$$= 0.195 + 0.239 - 0.013 = 0.421$$

8b.10 Allocation of a Number of Individuals to Two or More Groups

Suppose that n_1 and n_2 posts have to be filled in the Navy and the Air Force, a candidate being chosen on the basis of his performance in a test. Assuming that the distribution of test scores for those who are fit for the Navy and the Air Force are available from past experience, how can this knowledge be used for the most efficient selection?

In the actual population the relative proportions of candidates suitable for the Navy may be different from $n_1 : n_2$. The procedure for selection must be such that, whatever may be the actual proportion in the population, the division of a sample of $(n_1 + n_2)$ individuals in the assigned ratio $n_1 : n_2$ should involve the least possible errors. A similar problem is the allocation of a given number of skulls into two sexes in a given ratio which is determined from some a priori considerations. This may be only an estimated proportion and hence may not represent the true sex ratio. Whatever criterion is chosen, some male skulls will be classified as female and vice versa. A procedure which gives the least value to the expected number of wrong classifications in either group may be regarded as the best one.

There may arise another situation. Two samples of sizes n_1 and n_2 drawn independently from the first and second groups may get mixed. The difference between the first and second problems is that in the latter every sample is known to consist of n_1 individuals from the first group and n_2 from the second whereas in the former no such information is available, the sample being drawn at random from a mixed population.

Solution to the First Problems. Let $x_1, \cdots, x_n$ represent the measurements on n individuals. As observed earlier, x_i will stand for all the available set of measurements on the ith individual. The probability of the set is

$$\prod_{i=1}^{n} [\pi_1 f_1(x_i) + \pi_2 f_2(x_i)]$$

Consider the following set of functions

$$\delta_i(x_1, \cdots, x_n), \, \delta_i'(x_1, \cdots, x_n) \qquad i = 1, \cdots, n$$

which can be represented simply as δ_i, δ_i', satisfying the conditions

$$\delta_i = 0 \text{ or } 1 \qquad \delta_i + \delta_i' = 1$$

and

$$\Sigma \delta_i = n_1 \qquad \Sigma \delta_i' = n_2$$

where n_1 and n_2 are the specified numbers. If the individual with measurements x_i is assigned to the first group when $\delta_i = 1$ and to the second when $\delta_i' = 1$, then the above set of functions constitutes a decision rule. The problem is then to construct the above functions such that the expected risk associated with this decision rule is a minimum. To calculate the expected risk we need know as a datum of the problem the loss of assigning an individual of one group to another. If r_{12} represents the loss in assigning an individual of the first group to the second and r_{21} the loss in the other case, then the quantity to be minimized is the expected value of

$$\sum_{1}^{n} (\delta_i a_{i1} + \delta_i' a_{i2}) \qquad (8b.10.1)$$

where

$$a_{i1} = \frac{r_{21} \pi_2 f_2(x_i)}{\pi_1 f_1(x_i) + \pi_2 f_2(x_i)} \qquad a_{i2} = \frac{r_{12} \pi_1 f_1(x_i)}{\pi_1 f_1(x_i) + \pi_2 f_2(x_i)}$$

The expected loss will be a minimum if δ_i and δ_i' are chosen such that the expression (8b.10.1) has the least value. The problem is the same as that treated in lemma 2 of Appendix A5 leading to the solution

$$\delta_i = 1 \quad \text{if } a_{i1} + \mu_1 \leq a_{i2} + \mu_2$$

$$\delta_i' = 1 \quad \text{if } a_{i1} + \mu_1 \geq a_{i2} + \mu_2$$

where μ_1 and μ_2 are suitably chosen to satisfy the condition $\Sigma \delta_i = n_1$. Now $(a_{i1} - a_{i2}) \leq (\mu_2 - \mu_1)$ implies that

$$\frac{r_{21}\pi_2 f_2(x_i) - r_{12}\pi_1 f_1(x_i)}{\pi_1 f_1(x_i) + \pi_2 f_2(x_i)} \leq \mu$$

or

$$\frac{f_1(x_i)}{f_2(x_i)} \geq \lambda$$

so that the decision rule reduces to the evaluation of the likelihood ratios $\lambda_r = f_1(x_r)/f_2(x_r)$ and assigning all the individuals with highest n_1 values of the ratios to the first group and the rest to the second. Fortunately the decision rule is independent of the a priori probabilities and also the loss function.

Corresponding to every decision rule we can set up a density function of the observations by considering all individuals assigned to the first group as having been drawn at random from the first group and similarly for the second. By using lemma 1 in Appendix A5 we find that the best decision rule found above maximizes the corresponding probability density. As shown below this forms the basis on which the solution of the second problem depends.

Solution to the Second Problem. In this problem the mixture is known to consist of n_1 individuals drawn from the first group and n_2 from the second. The observations $x_1, \cdots, x_n$ could have arisen in $\binom{n}{n_1}$ ways, any subset of n_1 observations belonging to the first group. The probability density of the observations is equal to the sum of the densities associated with $\binom{n}{n_1}$ ways of splitting the sample. If $x_a, x_b, \cdots$ and $x_p, x_q, \cdots$ represent a division into two groups of sizes n_1 and n_2, then the probability density of the observations can be written as

$$P(x_1, \cdots, x_n) = \Sigma' f_1(x_a) f_1(x_b) \cdots f_2(x_p) f_2(x_q) \cdots \quad (8b.10.2)$$

where the summation is over $\binom{n}{n_1}$ such terms. Corresponding to any one of $\binom{n}{n_1}$ possible decision rules the loss relative to the given set of observations is $1/P(x_1, \cdots, x_n)$ times

$$\Sigma' l(a, b, \cdots; p, q, \cdots) f_1(x_a) f_1(x_b) \cdots f_2(x_p) f_2(x_q) \cdots \qquad (8b.10.3)$$

where $l(a, b, \cdots; p, q, \cdots)$ is the loss incurred in adopting a given decision rule when in fact x_a, x_b, $\cdots$ come from the first group and x_p, x_q, $\cdots$ from the second. The loss will generally be a function of the number of wrong classifications only. That decision rule for which the expression (8b.10.3) is the least is the best in the sense that it minimizes the expected loss. The solution depends on the evaluation of the expression (8b.10.3) for each of the $\binom{n}{n_1}$ decision rules, and this makes the application a little difficult in practice even when n is small.

As an alternative we may try to minimize the maximum loss incurred by following a decision rule. If we suppose that the loss function is proportional to the number of wrong classifications, then the maximum loss occurs when all the individuals in the smaller group are wrongly classified. With this assumption it can be shown that the division of the sample corresponding to the maximum probability density supplies the best possible solution to the problem. This solution may be referred to as the maximum likelihood solution; we consider the $\binom{n}{n_1}$ ways of splitting the sample as associated with $\binom{n}{n_1}$ different hypotheses concerning the individuals in the sample and choose that hypothesis which has the maximum likelihood.

To prove the property referred above, consider any other decision rule leading to a division

$$x_{a_1}, x_{a_2}, \cdots, x_{b_1}, x_{b_2}, \cdots \text{ and } x_{c_1}, x_{c_2}, \cdots, x_{d_1}, x_{d_2}, \cdots$$

of the sample into two groups of sizes n_1 and n_2 and compare with the division

$$x_{a_1}, x_{a_2}, \cdots, x_{c_1}, x_{c_2}, \cdots \text{ and } x_{b_1}, x_{b_2}, \cdots, x_{d_1}, x_{d_2}, \cdots$$

associated with the maximum density. The measurements classified in the same way by the two decision rules are represented by $x_{a_1}, x_{a_2}, \cdots$ for the first group and by $x_{d_1}, x_{d_2}, \cdots$ for the second group. By definition

$$\frac{f_1(x_{c_i})}{f_2(x_{c_i})} \geq \frac{f_1(x_{b_j})}{f_2(x_{b_j})} \qquad (8b.10.4)$$

and the same is true for the product of a number of ratios involving x_c and the product of the same number of ratios involving x_b.

Let $n_2 \leq n_1$ without loss of generality. In this case the maximum loss occurs, by following the first decision rule when

$$x_{c_1}, x_{c_2}, \cdots, x_{d_1}, x_{d_2}, \cdots \qquad (8\text{b}.10.5)$$

arise from the first group in which case a subset n_2 out of

$$x_{a_1}, x_{a_2}, \cdots, x_{b_1}, x_{b_2}, \cdots \qquad (8\text{b}.10.6)$$

arise from the second group. Let this subset be

$$x_{a_i}, x_{a_j}, \cdots, x_{b_p}, x_{b_q}, \cdots$$

By replacing the subscript c by b we obtain the corresponding situation for the proposed maximum likelihood decision rule. The difference between the above two probability densities associated with maximum errors for the two rules is, apart from a common multiplier, equal to

$$[f_1(x_{c_p})f_1(x_{c_q}) \cdots f_2(x_{b_p})f_2(x_{b_q}) \cdots - f_1(x_{b_p})f_1(x_{b_q}) \cdots f_2(x_{c_p})f_2(x_{c_q}) \cdots]$$

which is not less than zero according to (8b.10.4). By considering all subsets of n_2 observations out of (8b.10.6) we exhaust all possible ways in which the observations leading to maximum error according to the first rule can arise. To each such case there is a corresponding division leading to the maximum error for the proposed rule. But this division leads to a smaller probability density. The total chance of maximum error relative to the given set of observations is thus a minimum for the maximum likelihood decision rule.

The Problem of Three Groups. As in the case of two groups we consider two situations, firstly when the sample consists of n individuals observed at random from a mixed population and secondly when the sample is a mixture of n_1 individuals drawn from the first group, n_2 from the second, and n_3 from the third. The problem in either case is to select n_1 individuals for the first group, n_2 for the second, and n_3 for the third where $n_1 + n_2 + n_3 = n$.

Let $f_1(x)$, $f_2(x)$, $f_3(x)$ represent the probability densities of x for the three groups and π_1, π_2, π_3 the proportions of mixture in the general population. The loss in assigning a person to the ith group when, in fact, he belongs to the jth group is denoted by r_{ji}. The a posteriori risks in assigning an individual with measurements x_i to the first, second, and third groups are, respectively, equal to

$$a_{1i} = \frac{\pi_2 f_2(x_i) r_{21} + \pi_3 f_3(x_i) r_{31}}{b(x_i)}$$

$$a_{2i} = \frac{\pi_1 f_1(x_i) r_{12} + \pi_3 f_3(x_i) r_{32}}{b(x_i)}$$

$$a_{3i} = \frac{\pi_2 f_2(x_i) r_{23} + \pi_1 f_1(x_i) r_{13}}{b(x_i)}$$

where

$$b(x_i) = \pi_1 f_1(x_i) + \pi_2 f_2(x_i) + \pi_3 f_3(x_i)$$

Consider a set of functions

$$\delta_i = 0 \text{ or } 1 \qquad \delta_i' = 0 \text{ or } 1 \qquad \delta_i'' = 0 \text{ or } 1 \qquad \delta_i + \delta_i' + \delta_i'' = 1$$

such that

$$\Sigma \delta_i = n_1 \qquad \Sigma \delta_i' = n_2 \qquad \Sigma \delta_i'' = n_3$$

They define a decision rule if the individual with measurements x_i is assigned to the first group when $\delta_i = 1$, to the second when $\delta_i' = 1$, and to the third when $\delta_i'' = 1$. The a posteriori risk for such a selection procedure is

$$\sum_1^n (\delta_i a_{1i} + \delta_i' a_{2i} + \delta_i'' a_{3i})$$

The best decision rule is one that minimizes the above expression. This is exactly the problem solved in lemma 2 of Appendix A5. The best solution is

$$\delta_i = 1 \qquad \text{when } a_{1i} + \lambda_1 \leq a_{2i} + \lambda_2, \ a_{1i} + \lambda_1 \leq a_{3i} + \lambda_3$$

$$\delta_i' = 1 \qquad \text{when } a_{2i} + \lambda_2 \leq a_{1i} + \lambda_1, \ a_{2i} + \lambda_2 \leq a_{3i} + \lambda_3$$

$$\delta_i'' = 1 \qquad \text{when } a_{3i} + \lambda_3 \leq a_{1i} + \lambda_1, \ a_{3i} + \lambda_3 \leq a_{2i} + \lambda_2$$

where λ_1, λ_2, λ_3 are determined such that $\Sigma \delta_i = n_1$, $\Sigma \delta_i' = n_2$, and $\Sigma \delta_i'' = n_3$. As it stands, the problem of determination of λ_1, λ_2, λ_3 appears to be complicated. There is a geometrical device which is helpful in the solution of the problem. In higher dimensional cases involving four or more groups the geometrical method cannot be applied.   For three groups we replace a_{1i}, a_{2i}, a_{3i} by two coordinates

$$X_i = a_{1i} - a_{2i} \qquad Y_i = a_{1i} - a_{3i}$$

and represent the n points (X_i, Y_i) on a two-dimensional chart with rectangular axes.   The problem is to determine a point (X_0, Y_0) on this chart such that the regions formed by the lines $X = X_0$, $Y = Y_0$ and $Y - Y_0 = X - X_0$ contain the requisite number of points.   This

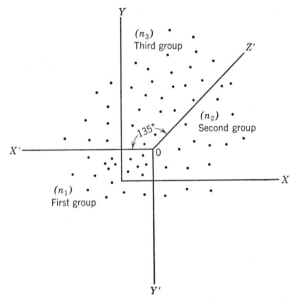

FIGURE 5.   The arrangement of three thin rods leading to the required division.

can be done by moving three thin rods $0X'$, $0Y'$, $0Z'$ fixed at the point 0 as shown in Figure 5, with $0X'$ and $0Y'$ parallel to the X and Y axes, and arrive at the required division by trial and error.   It will help in this process if the numbers falling in the three regions are recorded for a few positions of the frame with the frame marked on the chart.

   To solve the second problem when the sample consists of a mixture of n_1 individuals drawn from the first group, n_2 from the second, and n_3 from the third we can set up the total risk relative to the given set of observations for each of $n!/n_1!n_2!n_3!$ possible decision rules and choose that rule for which the risk is a minimum.   This is very difficult in practice so that a simplified procedure is needed.   As before we may choose that decision rule which leads to a division of the sample with the maximum probability density.   This rule possesses an important property that the probability of the maximum number of wrong classifications for any one group is as small as possible.

The method of arriving at the required division is first to obtain the quantities

$$a_{1i} = \log f_1(x_i) \qquad a_{2i} = \log f_2(x_i) \qquad a_{3i} = \log f_3(x_i)$$

$$i = 1, \cdots, n$$

and plot the points

$$X_i = a_{2i} - a_{1i} \qquad Y_i = a_{3i} - a_{1i}$$

and proceed geometrically as in Figure 5. For this division the probability density will be a maximum.

The problems treated in 8b fit in with the general decision function theory developed by Wald (1949).

8c Discriminant Function for Selecting Genetically Desirable Types

8c.1 Prediction Formula for the Genotypic Value

When quantitative characters are involved, it is considerably difficult to select genetically desirable types in breeding work because heritable differences are to some extent masked by non-heritable or environmental variations. The problem then arises as to what is the best indicator of the genotypic value of any individual line. Suppose the desired quality in the plant is yield. The observed yield is no doubt a good measure, but, if the factors influencing the yield affect to some extent other observable characters of the plant, then these latter characters can also be used in assessing the strength of factors responsible for yield. This can also be looked on as a problem of prediction: How can the genotypic value with respect to some characteristic be predicted when measurements on a number of observable characters are available?

This problem can be extended further to cases where the quality of a line is determined not by a single character but by a given linear compound of the genotypic values corresponding to a number of characteristics. The coefficients of the linear compound are fixed by the relative worth of these characters in assessing the quality of the line as a whole.

Thus, in poultry, the annual number of eggs laid (x_1), the size of the egg (x_2), and the age at maturity (x_3) are some of the important factors to be considered. To what extent these can be combined in a breed depends on the genetic relationships among these characters, and in any breeding program best use should be made of the available material.

If ψ_1, ψ_2, ψ_3 represent the genotypic values of the three characters mentioned above, the breeder's interest is in the value of a linear compound $a_1\psi_1 + a_2\psi_2 + a_3\psi_3$ which corresponds to the commercial value of the bird for properly chosen values of the compounding coefficients. For instance, Panse (1946) considers three sets of weights of which one is

$$a_1 = 8 \qquad a_2 = 5 \qquad a_3 = -2$$

These weights depend on the relative importance to be attached to each of these characters and are assigned by the animal breeder. The cash return from each bird depends on the number of eggs laid and also on the size of the egg. The age at maturity is also important when the cost of feeding the bird in the period from its hatching to the date of laying the first egg is considered. For this reason the age at maturity is given a negative weight. The highest weight is given to the annual number of eggs laid.

To estimate the above linear compound it may be useful, as observed earlier, to consider other characters in which the animal breeder is not directly interested. In the material on poultry analyzed by Panse (1946) the body weight (x_4) is also available and the best predictor may be written as

$$b_0 + b_1\bar{x}_1 + \cdots + b_4\bar{x}_4$$

where $\bar{x}_1$, $\bar{x}_2$, $\bar{x}_3$, and $\bar{x}_4$ are the mean values for a sire. In fact, any number of extraneous characters can be considered in building up the prediction formula, and it is not necessary that the formula be linear in the measurements although linearity introduces a great simplification in actual computation. To determine these coefficients, Smith (1936) maximized the regression between the two linear compounds $a_1\psi_1 + a_2\psi_2 + a_3\psi_3$ and $b_1\bar{x}_1 + b_2\bar{x}_2 + b_3\bar{x}_3 + b_4\bar{x}_4$, which is equivalent to minimizing the sum of squares with due weights

$$\Sigma n_r(a_1\psi_{1r} + a_2\psi_{2r} + a_3\psi_{3r} - b_0 - b_1\bar{x}_{1r} - \cdots - b_4\bar{x}_{4r})^2$$

where n_r is the sample size on which the mean values $\bar{x}_{1r}$, $\cdots$, $\bar{x}_{4r}$ are based for the rth sire and ψ_{1r}, ψ_{2r}, ψ_{3r} are the genotypic values for the rth sire.

The minimizing equations for b_1, b_2, b_3, and b_4 are

$$b_1B_{11} + b_2B_{12} + b_3B_{13} + b_4B_{14} = a_1G_{11} + a_2G_{12} + a_3G_{13}$$

$$b_1B_{21} + b_2B_{22} + b_3B_{23} + b_4B_{24} = a_1G_{21} + a_2G_{22} + a_3G_{23}$$

$$b_1B_{31} + b_2B_{32} + b_3B_{33} + b_4B_{34} = a_1G_{31} + a_2G_{32} + a_3G_{33}$$

$$b_1B_{41} + b_2B_{42} + b_3B_{43} + b_4B_{44} = a_1G_{41} + a_2G_{42} + a_3G_{43}$$

where B_{ij} is the sum of products between sires and

$$G_{ij} = \Sigma n_r(\psi_{ir} - \bar{\psi}_i)(\bar{x}_{jr} - \bar{x}_j)$$

$$\bar{\psi}_i = \frac{\Sigma n_r \psi_{ir}}{\Sigma n_r} \quad \text{and} \quad \bar{x}_j = \frac{\Sigma n_r \bar{x}_{jr}}{\Sigma n_r}$$

The actual values of G_{ij} are not known, but their expected values are obtained from the equations

$$E(B_{ij}) = E(G_{ij}) + (k - 1)\sigma_{ij}$$

where σ_{ij} is the expected covariance between the ith and jth characters within a sire. If S_{ij} is the sum of products within a sire, then an estimate of G_{ij} is

$$wG_{ij} \sim wB_{ij} - (k - 1)S_{ij}$$

where w is the degrees of freedom within sires, and $(k - 1)$ the degrees of freedom between sires.

The analysis of sum of squares and products, the estimated values of G_{ij}, and other related values are given in Table 8c.1α.

TABLE 8c.1α. Analysis of Dispersion

Due to	Between (B_{ij}) $k - 1 = 14$ D.F.	Within (S_{ij}) $w = 201$ D.F.	$wB_{ij} - (k - 1)S_{ij}$ $= wG_{ij}$
x_1^2	6,476.4	67,797.3	352,594.2
x_2^2	982.10	2,440.14	163,240.14
x_3^2	37,422	317,982	3,070,074
x_4^2	335.16	3,660.21	16,124.22
x_1x_2	678.16	367.83	131,160.54
x_1x_3	− 6,043.8	− 35,898.6	− 712,223.4
x_1x_4	750.54	− 172.86	153,278.58
x_2x_3	825.86	404.01	160,341.72
x_2x_4	248.22	1,246.20	32,445.42
x_3x_4	708.12	− 1,370.82	161,523.60
$a_1x_1^2 + a_2x_1x_2 + a_3x_1x_3$	67,289.60	616,014.75	4,901,003.10 *
$a_1x_1x_2 + a_2x_2^2 + a_3x_2x_3$	8,684.06	14,335.32	1,544,801.58 *
$a_1x_1x_3 + a_2x_2x_3 + a_3x_3^2$	−119,065.10	−921,132.75	−11,036,226.60 *
$a_1x_1x_4 + a_2x_2x_4 + a_3x_3x_4$	5,829.18	7,589.76	1,065,408.54 *

* These quantities can be obtained in two ways: (i) directly from the G_{ij} values above, and also (ii) from B_{ij} and S_{ij} values of the linear compounds, thus providing a check. These form the right-hand expressions of the equations for b. Since only the ratios of b are important, these quantities are divided by 1000 and corrected to three decimal places to obtain the same order of figures as those in the equations.

The equations are

$$6476.4b_1 + 678.16b_2 - 6043.8b_3 + 750.54b_4 = 4901.003$$

$$678.16b_1 + 982.10b_2 + 825.86b_3 + 248.22b_4 = 1544.802$$

$$-6043.8b_1 + 825.86b_2 + 37{,}422b_3 + 708.12b_4 = -11{,}036.227$$

$$750.54b_1 + 248.22b_2 + 708.12b_3 + 335.16b_4 = 1065.409$$

yielding the solutions

$$b_1 = -0.16274 \qquad b_2 = 1.12795 \qquad b_3 = -0.41387 \qquad b_4 = 3.58233$$

Strangely, the character which is scored quite high has a negative co-efficient in the discriminant function, which leads us to suspect the reliability of the material. If, however, body weight, which has a suspiciously low variance, is omitted from consideration, the new weights are

$$b_1 = 0.33484 \qquad b_2 = 1.57346 \qquad b_3 = -0.27556$$

leading to the discriminant function

$$0.33484x_1 + 1.57346x_2 - 0.27556x_3$$

against a straight selection function

$$8x_1 + 5x_2 - 2x_3$$

It is seen that although the number of eggs is scored high in the latter function its selective value is not so high as that of the egg weight as shown by the calculated discriminant function.

First, it is necessary to test whether the genotypic value $a_1\psi_1 + a_2\psi_2 + a_3\psi_3$ is significantly different between the sires. An answer to this is provided by an analysis of the linear compound $a_1x_1 + a_2x_2 + a_3x_3$ between and within the sires, as shown in Table 8c.2α. The discriminant function obtained above is a better estimate of the genotypic value $a_1\psi_1 + a_2\psi_2 + a_3\psi_3$, and it is unnecessary to test whether the estimated function sufficiently discriminates between the sires. What is more important is the construction of an index to measure the advantages in selection by means of the discriminant function and also a test of its significance.

8c.2 The Genetic Advance

Let ψ be a characteristic as measured by a character x with mean μ and variance σ^2. Let the regression of ψ on x be β; then the expected value of ψ for a given x is

$$\bar{\psi} + \beta(x - \mu)$$

where $\bar{\psi} = E(\psi)$ for all x. If x is normally distributed, then the expected value of ψ for all x exceeding the upper qth part is

$$\frac{1}{q}\frac{1}{\sqrt{2\pi}\sigma}\int_{x_q}^{\infty}\{\bar{\psi} + \beta(x - \mu)\}e^{-(x-\mu)^2/2\sigma^2}\,dx = \bar{\psi} + \frac{\beta\sigma z}{q}$$

where z is the ordinate to the normal curve at x_q, the abscissa corresponding to the upper qth part of the normal curve.

Suppose that a large number of plant lines are available and a qth part of them is chosen for further propagation by the above method. The genetic advance then is

$$\frac{\beta\sigma z}{q}$$

and, since z/q is common for all selection procedures, the intensity of genetic advance depends on $\beta\sigma$, which is equivalent to $\mathrm{cov}(\psi x)/\sigma$.

For selection of poultry the values of the discriminant function at the mean values are calculated and the sires corresponding to the highest values are chosen. It is seen that, if the means are based on a large number of observations corresponding to each sire, then the prediction of the genotypic value is more accurate and consequently the genetic advance is higher, the maximum genetic advance being available when the mean values are known exactly. So in the problem of evaluation of the genetic advance it is required to know how much experimentation is contemplated to assess the value of each sire. Suppose that the mean values for each sire are based on a sample of size n. The genetic advance associated with any linear compound

$$c_1\bar{x}_1 + c_2\bar{x}_2 + c_3\bar{x}_3$$

is

$$\frac{\mathrm{cov}\,(a_1\psi_1 + a_2\psi_2 + a_3\psi_3,\, c_1\bar{x}_1 + c_2\bar{x}_2 + c_3\bar{x}_3)}{\sqrt{V(c_1\bar{x}_1 + c_2\bar{x}_2 + c_3\bar{x}_3)}}$$

The numerator has the expected value

$$c_1(a_1g_{11} + a_2g_{12} + a_3g_{13})$$

$$+ c_2(a_1g_{12} + a_2g_{22} + a_3g_{23})$$

$$+ c_3(a_1g_{13} + a_2g_{23} + a_3g_{33})$$

and the square of the denominator $V(c_1\bar{x}_1 + \cdots + c_3\bar{x}_3)$ is

$$\Sigma\Sigma c_i c_j g_{ij} + \frac{\Sigma\Sigma c_i c_j \sigma_{ij}}{n}$$

where σ_{ij} is the expected covariance between the ith and jth characters within the sires and g_{ij} is the covariance between the ith and jth genotypic values between the sires. The estimated values of g_{ij} and σ_{ij} are substituted in the above expressions. These estimates are obtained by a direct analysis of variance and covariance of the linear compound $c_1 x_1 + c_2 x_2 + c_3 x_3$ and the straight selection function $a_1 x_1 + a_2 x_2 + a_3 x_3$.

The mean square between sires (S_1) for any linear compound $c_1 x_1 + c_2 x_2 + c_3 x_3$ has the expectation

$$\lambda \Sigma\Sigma c_i c_j g_{ij} + \Sigma\Sigma c_i c_j \sigma_{ij}$$

where

$$\lambda = \frac{(\Sigma n_r - \Sigma n_r^2 / \Sigma n_r)}{(k - 1)}$$

In the above expression, n_1, n_2 $\cdots$ are the observations on the first, second, $\cdots$ sires. The mean square within sires (S_2) has the expectation $\Sigma\Sigma c_i c_j \sigma_{ij}$, so that

$$\Sigma\Sigma c_i c_j g_{ij} \sim \frac{(S_1 - S_2)}{\lambda}$$

Hence the variance of the mean of the linear compound based on n observations is

$$V(c_1\bar{x}_1 + c_2\bar{x}_2 + c_3\bar{x}_3) \sim \frac{S_1 - S_2}{\lambda} + \frac{\Sigma\Sigma c_i c_j \sigma_{ij}}{n}$$

Similarly,

$$\text{cov}\,(a_1\psi_1 + a_2\psi_2 + a_3\psi_3, c_1\bar{x}_1 + c_2\bar{x}_2 + c_3\bar{x}_3) = \frac{D_1 - D_2}{\lambda}$$

where D_1 and D_2 are the mean sums of products between and within sires for the two linear compounds, $a_1 x_1 + a_2 x_2 + a_3 x_3$ and $c_1 x_1 + c_2 x_2 + c_3 x_3$.

We shall illustrate the method for the linear compound determined above. The analysis of variance and covariance for the calculated function $b_1 x_1 + b_2 x_2 + b_3 x_3 = Y_1$ and the straight selection function $a_1 x_1 + a_2 x_2 + a_3 x_3 = Y_2$ is shown in Table 8c.2α.

TABLE 8c.2α. Analysis of Variance and Covariance of Y_1 and Y_2

	D.F.	$Y_1{}^2$ S.S.	M.S.	$Y_2{}^2$ S.S.	M.S.	Y_1Y_2 S.P.	M.P.
Between sires	14	7,112.875	508.0625	819,867.3	58,561.9	69,004.85	4928.92
Within sires	201	44,449.820	221.1433	6,842,060.1	34,040.1	482,649.77	2401.24
Difference			286.9192		24,521.8		2527.68
Difference / λ			20.791		1,776.948		183.166
Within sires / n			15.357		2,363.881		166.752
Total			36.148		4,140.829		349.918

(i) The values are obtained by the following formulae.

$7{,}112.875 = b_1(4901.003) + b_2(1544.801) + b_3(-11{,}036.227)$ (the values used in the equations for b from Table 8c.1α)

$44{,}449.820 = \Sigma\Sigma b_i b_j S_{ij}$

$819{,}867.3 \quad = a_1(67{,}289.60) \quad + a_2(8684.06) \quad + a_3(-119{,}065.10)$

$69{,}004.85 \quad = b_1(\quad) + b_2(\quad) + b_3(\quad)$

$6{,}842{,}060.1 \quad = a_1(616{,}014.75) + a_2(14{,}335.32) + a_3(-921{,}132.75)$

$482{,}649.77 \quad = b_1(\quad) + b_2(\quad) + b_3(\quad)$

(ii) The ratio of mean squares for Y_2 is $58{,}561.9/34{,}040.1 = 1.72$ which is on the 5% significant level for 14 and 201 degrees of freedom. Only when this is significant can we proceed to estimate the genotypic value.

The actual values of $n_1, n_2, \cdots, n_{15}$ available for $k = 15$ sires are not known in the above experiment. Let us suppose that the values are such that

$$\lambda = \frac{(\Sigma n_r - \Sigma n_r{}^2/\Sigma n_r)}{(k-1)} = 13.3$$

and let us find the genetic advance for the value of $n = 14.4$, which is the average size in the above example. As observed earlier, we can calculate the genetic advance for any n, depending on the intensity of experimentation.

The index of genetic advance for straight selection associated with $a_1 x_1 + a_2 x_2 + a_3 x_3$ is

$$\frac{\dfrac{\text{Difference}}{\lambda}}{\sqrt{\dfrac{\text{Difference}}{\lambda} + \dfrac{\text{Within}}{n}}} \text{ for } Y_2{}^2 = \frac{1776.9}{\sqrt{4140.83}} = 27.613$$

The numerator and denominator are both obtained from the column under $Y_2{}^2$ in Table 8c.2α. The expression for $b_1 x_1 + b_2 x_2 + b_3 x_3$ is

$$\frac{\dfrac{\text{Difference}}{\lambda}\ \text{for } Y_1 Y_2}{\sqrt{\left[\dfrac{\text{Difference}}{\lambda} + \dfrac{\text{Within}}{n}\right]\ \text{for } Y_1{}^2}} = \frac{183.166}{\sqrt{36.148}} = 30.467$$

so that the genetic advance is $\left(\dfrac{30.467}{27.613} - 1\right) 100 = 10.33\%$ higher for the discriminant function. It is difficult to test how far this observed increase is significant.

8d Problems of Optimum Selection

8d.1 A Single Predictor for Dichotomy

Birnbaum and Chapman (1950) considered a problem of selecting candidates on the basis of p admission scores $y_1, \cdots, y_p$. The object is to select those whose performance is expected to be better in the final test. The offered solution does not refer to a case where the scores of a number of individuals N have been observed but to a hypothetical set of individuals applying for the admission test. The former problem is often met with because the question asked is who out of a number of individuals whose admission scores *are available* should be admitted. Let the scores of N individuals be represented by

$$y_{11}, \ y_{21}, \ \cdots, \ y_{p1}$$
$$\cdot \qquad \cdot \qquad \cdots \qquad \cdot$$
$$y_{1N}, \ y_{2N}, \ \cdots, \ y_{pN}$$

To answer this problem we need to know the expected performance in the final test of an individual with the admission scores $y_{1i}, \cdots, y_{pi}$. Let this expected performance be

$$x_i = \phi(y_{1i}, \cdots, y_{pi})$$

which actually stands for the regression equation of the final performance on the initial scores. The regression function, which may be of any complicated type, supplies us with the expected performances $x_1, \cdots, x_N$ of the candidates, and these latter scores form the basis for selection. The regression function can be estimated on the basis of the previous information.

For instance, if a given number of k seats are available, then the best plan is to admit k candidates corresponding to the k largest values of x because this maximizes the expected performance under the condition that k have to be chosen.

A second alternative may be to admit as many as possible with the restriction that the expected average performance is not less than an assigned number x_0. The best plan is then to order the x scores in a decreasing order and find the cumulative averages from the top and admit all those for whom the cumulative average is greater than or equal to x_0. Obviously under such a selection procedure the maximum number is admitted subject to the condition that the expected average performance of the selected candidates is not less than x_0.

If the restriction is that the average performance of the chosen candidates should exceed a given value x_0 with a probability greater than β, then again we start with the highest score of x and go on adding the others in the decreasing order of x till the required probability remains greater than β. The calculations are not simple, however.

If we consider a hypothetical set of candidates, a situation that may arise when the statistician is asked to give a uniform rule for independent recruitment at various places without specifying the numbers to be selected from each place, then what is needed is the determination of a critical value x_h leading to the selection of all individuals with the expected x score (calculated on the basis of the admission y score) greater than or equal to x_h. For this the distribution of the expected score x as a function of y has to be studied. Let this be $f(x)$. If the criterion is that the maximum number of candidates has to be admitted subject to the condition that the expected average performance is not less than x_0, then x_h is determined from the formula

$$\int_{x_h}^{\infty} xf(x)\, dx = x_0 \int_{x_h}^{\infty} f(x)\, dx$$

in which case the expected proportion admitted is

$$\int_{x_h}^{\infty} f(x)\, dx$$

8d.2   The Problem of Differential Predictors

In the problem treated in 8b.10 it was assumed that the individuals belong to separate groups characterized by distinct distributions. What was needed there was the classification of a collection of individuals into the distinct groups to which they belong. But situations arise where an individual cannot be said to belong to a distinct group, as when we have to judge the relative usefulness of a person in two jobs, A and B. To give another instance, it may be necessary to determine on the basis of a student's score in an admission test whether he should be allowed to take a course in mathematics or physics. What we need in such cases is a set of predictors measuring the success of a candidate in various careers on the basis of the initial scores and decide on a profitable course of action. The general problem may be stated as follows.

Out of N applicants, n_1 have to be selected for the first job, n_2 for the second, $\cdots$, n_k for the kth, given their scores in some suitably designed tests. If the number of applications exceed the number of jobs to be filled, then the rest of the applications n_{k+1} have to be rejected. This problem arising out of a study by Brogden (1946) admits a neat solution by the use of lemmas in A5.

Let x_1, $\cdots$, x_p be the scores for p items of a test used to predict the success of a candidate in k careers. For a proper treatment of the problem it is necessary that success should be measurable quantitatively, in which case the success in two different jobs could be compared. For instance it may be possible to predict (if past records are available) on the basis of initial scores or to find out by direct practical tests, if possible, how much worth of goods a person can produce in various types of jobs. If it is the admission of a student into one of various alternative courses, the success may be measured by the number of marks (properly standardized) the student is expected to secure at the end of the course on the basis of the initial score. These quantities measuring a person's success in k given situations are represented by $s_1(x)$, $s_2(x)$, $\cdots$, $s_k(x)$ which are necessarily functions of the initial scores x_1, $\cdots$, x_p. Let there be N applicants whose success scores are given below, with a zero column representing the success score when the applicant is not selected for any job.

$$s_{11}, \ s_{21}, \ \cdots, s_{k1}, \ 0$$

$$\cdot \quad \cdot \quad \cdots \quad \cdot \quad \cdot$$

$$s_{1N}, \ s_{2N}, \ \cdots, s_{kN}, \ 0$$

Let us choose n_1 values from the first column, n_2 from the second, $\cdots$ and n_{k+1} from the last, such that the sum of all these values is a maximum. The method of determining these values is given in A5. The candidates corresponding to the n_i values chosen from the ith column are selected for the ith job. The candidates corresponding to n_{k+1} zero values from the last column are not chosen for any job.

Appendix A

A1   A Lemma of Neyman and Pearson

Let F_0, F_1, $\cdots$, F_m be a set of integrable functions defined in the whole space of $(x_1 \cdots x_n)$ and w any region such that

$$\int_w F_i \, dv = C_i \qquad i = 1, 2, \cdots, m \tag{A1.1}$$

where dv stands for the volume element $dx_1 \cdots dx_n$ and C_i are assigned constants. Let w_0 be a region within which

$$F_0 \geq k_1 F_1 + \cdots + k_m F_m \tag{A1.2}$$

and outside which

$$F_0 \leq k_1 F_1 + \cdots + k_m F_m \tag{A1.3}$$

where k_i are determined such that w_0 satisfies (A1.1).

The lemma states that for any region w satisfying (A1.1) the following relationship holds.

$$\int_w F_0 \, dv \leq \int_{w_0} F_0 \, dv$$

Let the common part of the regions w and w_0 be denoted by ww_0. The region $w - ww_0$ is the part of w not common to w_0. From condition (A1.1) it follows that

$$\int_{w - ww_0} F_i \, dv = \int_{w_0 - ww_0} F_i \, dv \tag{A1.4}$$

Consider the difference

$$\Delta = \int_{w_0} F_0 \, dv - \int_w F_0 \, dv = \int_{w_0 - ww_0} F_0 \, dv - \int_{w - ww_0} F_0 \, dv$$

$$\geq \int_{w_0 - ww_0} (\Sigma k_i F_i) \, dv - \int_{w - ww_0} (\Sigma k_i f_i) \, dv$$

$$= 0 \qquad \text{due to (A1.4)}$$

Hence the lemma is proved.

A2   A Generalization of the Neyman-Pearson Lemma

(i) Let R_1', R_2', $\cdots$ be a set of mutually exclusive regions covering the whole space such that with respect to the integrable functions g_1,

$g_2, \cdots$ the values

$$\int_{R_i'} g_j \, dv = s_{ji} \tag{A2.1}$$

are constant.

(ii) Consider the system of regions ($\cap$ = defined by)

$$R_k \quad \cap \quad F_k \leq F_s \quad s = 1, 2, \cdots$$
$$k = 1, 2, \cdots \tag{A2.2}$$

where

$$F_k = \phi_k + \lambda_{k1} g_1 + \lambda_{k2} g_2 + \cdots$$

ϕ_k being some assigned functions. We now prove that the value of the integral

$$\int_{R_1'} \phi_1 \, dv + \int_{R_2'} \phi_2 \, dv + \cdots$$

subject to the conditions in (A2.1) is a minimum for the set of regions defined in (A2.2).

The intersection of the regions R_i and R_j' is represented by R_{ij}. It follows from definition that

$$\int_{R_1} F_1 \, dv \leq \int_{R_{11}} F_1 \, dv + \int_{R_{12}} F_2 \, dv + \cdots$$

Writing down the above relationship for all R_i and adding, we obtain

$$\int_{R_1} F_1 \, dv + \int_{R_2} F_2 \, dv + \cdots \leq \int_{R_1'} F_1 \, dv + \int_{R_2'} F_2 \, dv + \cdots$$

or

$$\int_{R_1} \phi_1 \, dv + \int_{R_2} \phi_2 \, dv + \cdots + \Sigma\Sigma\lambda_{ij} s_{ji}$$
$$\leq \int_{R_1'} \phi_1 \, dv + \int_{R_2'} \phi_2 \, dv + \cdots + \Sigma\Sigma\lambda_{ij} s_{ji}$$

because of the conditions in (A2.1). The above result is established.

Suppose that the sum

$$\int_{R_1} \phi_1 \, dv + \int_{R_2} \phi_2 \, dv + \cdots$$

has to be maximized. Then the regions are

$$R_1 \quad \cap \quad F_1 \geq F_2, F_1 \geq F_3, \cdots$$
$$R_2 \quad \cap \quad F_2 \geq F_1, F_2 \geq F_3, \cdots$$
$$\cdot \qquad \cdots \qquad \cdots$$

Suppose that no conditions such as (A2.1) are specified. Then the regions are

$$R_1 \quad \cap \quad \phi_1 \geq \phi_2, \phi_1 \geq \phi_3, \cdots$$

$$R_2 \quad \cap \quad \phi_2 \geq \phi_1, \phi_2 \geq \phi_3, \cdots$$

$$\cdot \qquad \cdots \qquad \cdots \qquad \cdots$$

A3   A Slight Variation of Lemma A1

Let $F_0, F_1, \cdots, F_m$ be a set of integrable functions such that, with respect to a positive function $p(x) \leq 1$,

$$\int_S F_i p(x) \, dv = C_i \qquad i = 1, \cdots, m \tag{A3.1}$$

over the *whole* space S.

Consider the special form of the function $p(x)$

$$p(x) = 0 \qquad \text{when } F_0 \leq k_1 F_1 + \cdots + k_m F_m \tag{A3.2}$$

$$= 1 \qquad \text{when } F_0 \geq k_1 F_1 + \cdots + k_m F_m$$

where $k_1, \cdots, k_m$ are determined to satisfy the condition (A3.1). Out of all $p(x)$ the integral

$$\int_S F_0 p(x) \, dv$$

is a maximum for the special form chosen in (A3.2).

Let D be a region inside which $F_0 \geq k_1 F_1 + \cdots + k_m F_m$ and outside which the reverse relation holds. For any general $p(x)$

$$\int_S F_0 p(x) \, dv = \int_D F_0 p(x) \, dv + \int_{S-D} F_0 p(x) \, dv$$

$$\leq \int_D F_0 p(x) \, dv + \int_{S-D} (\Sigma k_i F_i) p(x) \, dv$$

$$= \int_D F_0 p(x) \, dv + \int_S (\Sigma k_i F_i) p(x) \, dv - \int_D (\Sigma k_i F_i) p(x) \, dv$$

$$= \int_D F_0 p(x) \, dv + \int_D (\Sigma k_i F_i)[1 - p(x)] \, dv$$

$$\leq \int_D F_0 p(x) \, dv + \int_D F_0 [1 - p(x)] \, dv = \int_D F_0 \, dv$$

A4   A Lemma on Power Functions

Let $f_1, f_2, \cdots$ be a finite number of probability densities alternative to f_0 which is specified by the null hypothesis. Let w be any region satisfying the conditions

$$\int_w f_0 \, dv = \alpha \qquad (A4.1)$$

and

$$\frac{1}{a_1} \int_w f_1 \, dv = \frac{1}{a_2} \int_w f_2 \, dv = \cdots \qquad (A4.2)$$

where $a_1, a_2, \cdots$ are positive assigned quantities.

Out of all regions satisfying the conditions A4.1 and A4.2, the region w_0

Inside which $f_0 \leq \lambda_1 f_1 + \lambda_2 f_2 + \cdots$

Outside which $f_0 \geq \lambda_1 f_1 + \lambda_2 f_2 + \cdots$

where $\lambda_1, \lambda_2, \cdots$ are determined such that the above conditions are satisfied, gives the highest common value to the quantities in (A4.2).

Proof. Let β and β_0 be the common values (A4.2) associated with the regions w and w_0, and denote by ww_0 the region common to w and w_0. Then we have

$$(\lambda_1 a_1 + \lambda_2 a_2 + \cdots)\beta_0 = \int_{w_0} (\lambda_1 f_1 + \lambda_2 f_2 + \cdots) \, dv$$

$$\geq \int_{w_0 - ww_0} f_0 \, dv + \int_{ww_0} (\lambda_1 f_1 + \lambda_2 f_2 + \cdots) \, dv$$

$$= \int_{w - ww_0} f_0 \, dv + \int_{ww_0} (\lambda_1 f_1 + \lambda_2 f_2 + \cdots) \, dv$$

$$\geq \int_{w - ww_0} (\lambda_1 f_1 + \lambda_2 f_2 + \cdots) \, dv$$

$$+ \int_{ww_0} (\lambda_1 f_1 + \lambda_2 f_2 + \cdots) \, dv$$

$$= \int_w (\lambda_1 f_1 + \lambda_2 f_2 + \cdots) \, dv$$

$$= (\lambda_1 a_1 + \lambda_2 a_2 + \cdots)\beta$$

If $(\lambda_1 a_1 + \lambda_2 a_2 + \cdots)$ is positive, then $\beta_0 \geq \beta$. To prove that $(\lambda_1 a_1$

$+ \lambda_2 a_2 + \cdots)$ is positive we observe that

$$\int_{w_0} (\lambda_1 f_1 + \lambda_2 f_2 + \cdots)\, dv \geq \int_{w_0} f_0\, dv$$

i.e.,

$$(\lambda_1 a_1 + \lambda_2 a_2 + \cdots)\beta_0 \geq \alpha$$

Since β_0 and α are positive, it follows that $(\lambda_1 a_1 + \lambda_2 a_2 + \cdots)$ is necessarily positive. The lemma is proved.

This lemma gives us a method of determining a region with respect to which the powers of the various alternative hypotheses are in assigned ratios, and, subject to this condition, every alternative hypothesis has the maximum power.

A5   Two Lemmas Useful in Classificatory Problems

Consider an array of elements

$$a_{11} \quad a_{21} \quad \cdots \quad a_{p1}$$

$$a_{12} \quad a_{22} \quad \cdots \quad a_{p2}$$

$$\cdot \qquad \cdot \qquad \cdots \qquad \cdot$$

$$a_{1n} \quad a_{2n} \quad \cdots \quad a_{pn}$$

consisting of p columns and n rows. Let P denote the product and S the sum of n elements chosen one from each row such that the total number of elements coming from the first column is equal to a specified non-zero value n_1, from the second n_2, and so on from the pth column n_p. Obviously $n \geq p$ and $n = n_1 + \cdots + n_p$.

Lemma 1.   If the elements a_{ij} are not negative and if there exist quantities $\lambda_1, \cdots, \lambda_p$ such that each element a_{ik} of the n_i elements chosen from the ith column satisfies the relationships

$$\lambda_i a_{ik} \geq \lambda_j a_{jk} \qquad j = 1, \cdots, p \qquad (A5.1)$$

and if similar relationships are satisfied for all $i = 1, \cdots, p$ with the same set $\lambda_1, \cdots, \lambda_p$ then for this choice of $n_1, \cdots, n_p$ elements the product P defined above is a maximum.

To prove this consider any other choice of n_i elements

$$a_{im_1}, a_{im_2}, \cdots$$

from the ith column. If we remember that the subsubscript refers to the row number, the elements from the m_1th, m_2th, $\cdots$ rows occurring in the proposed selection may be represented by

$$a_{i_1 m_1}, a_{i_2 m_2}, \cdots$$

from which by definition it follows that the product

$$a_{i_1 m_1}, a_{i_2 m_2}, \cdots$$

is not less than

$$\frac{\lambda_i}{\lambda_{i_1}} a_{im_1} \frac{\lambda_i}{\lambda_{i_2}} a_{im_2} \cdots$$

Since each λ is positive by definition, division by λ does not change the inequality sign. Considering all the groups of elements in the second selection we find

$$\prod_i a_{i_1 m_1} a_{i_2 m_2} \cdots \geq \prod_i \frac{\lambda_i}{\lambda_{i_1}} \frac{\lambda_i}{\lambda_{i_2}} \cdots a_{im_1} a_{im_2} \cdots$$

$$\geq \prod_i a_{im_1} a_{im_2} \cdots$$

since

$$\prod_i \frac{\lambda_i}{\lambda_{i_1}} \frac{\lambda_i}{\lambda_{i_2}} \cdots = 1$$

the terms in the numerator canceling with those in the denominator in the final product.

Corollary 1.1. If the object is to maximize the product P without the restriction on the number of elements coming from each column, then obviously the best procedure is to choose the biggest element from each row.

Corollary 1.2. The product P will be a minimum if the inequality relationship (A5.1) is reversed.

Corollary 1.3. If $p = 2$, the method described in lemma 1 reduces to evaluating the ratios

$$\frac{a_{11}}{a_{21}}, \frac{a_{12}}{a_{22}}, \cdots, \frac{a_{1n}}{a_{2n}}$$

and arranging them in descending order of magnitude and choosing the elements in the numerator from the first n_1 ratios and the elements in the denominator from the second n_2 ratios.

Lemma 2. If there exist quantities $\mu_1 \cdots, \mu_p$ such that each element a_{ik} of the n_i elements chosen from the ith column satisfies the relationships

$$a_{ik} + \mu_i \geq a_{jk} + \mu_j \qquad j = 1, \cdots, p$$

and if similar relationships hold for all $i = 1, \cdots, p$ with the same set $\mu_1, \cdots, \mu_p$, then for this choice of $n_1, \cdots, n_p$ elements the sum S defined above is a maximum.

The result follows from lemma 1 by considering exp (a_{ik}) and maximizing the product. The existence of $\mu_1, \cdots, \mu_p$ leads to the existence of positive quantities $\lambda_1, \cdots, \lambda_p$ used in lemma 1. The sum S is minimized when the reverse relationships hold good.

Appendix B

B1   On a Transformation Useful in Multivariate Computations

In multivariate analysis one is often confronted with the task of inverting a covariance matrix which is laborious when the number of variates exceeds four or five. This and the further use of the elements of the inverse matrix in the computation of statistical constants and test criteria can be considerably simplified by working with a set of transformed variates derivable from the original variates. The method of construction of these transformed variates and the mechanization it introduces on the computational side are given in this appendix with special reference to the statistical methods used in Chapters 8 and 9.

Let $x_1, \cdots, x_p$ be the original variables, and λ_{ij} the covariance between the ith and jth variates. The transformed variables $Y_1, Y_2, \cdots$ are defined by

$$Y_1 = x_1$$

$$Y_2 = x_2 - a_{21}Y_1$$

$$Y_3 = x_3 - a_{32}Y_2 - a_{31}Y_1$$

$$. \qquad \cdots$$

$$Y_p = x_p - a_{pp-1}Y_{p-1} - \cdots - a_{p1}Y_1$$

The constants a_{ij} are chosen such that Y_i are independent. The actual evaluation of these coefficients is carried out in successive stages so that, if the coefficients in $Y_1, \cdots, Y_i$ are known, any coefficient in Y_{i+1} can be calculated in a simple manner.

To find a_{21}, the covariance of Y_1, Y_2 denoted by cov $(Y_1 Y_2)$ has to be equated to zero.

$$\text{cov}\,(Y_1 Y_2) = \text{cov}\,(x_1 x_2) - a_{21}V(Y_1) = 0$$

$$= \lambda_{21} - a_{21}\lambda_{11} = 0$$

$$a_{21} = \frac{\lambda_{21}}{\lambda_{11}}$$

$$V(Y_2) = \lambda_{22} - \lambda_{21}a_{21}$$

where V denotes variance. For Y_3, a_{31} and a_{32} are to be calculated in order. With the constants b_{ij} as defined below introduced merely to facilitate computation, the steps may be given as follows

$$b_{31} = \lambda_{31} \qquad\qquad a_{31} = \frac{b_{31}}{V(Y_1)}$$

$$b_{32} = \lambda_{32} - a_{21}b_{31} \qquad a_{32} = \frac{b_{32}}{V(Y_2)}$$

$$V(Y_3) = \lambda_{33} - b_{31}a_{31} - b_{32}a_{32}$$

To find Y_4, the steps are

$$b_{41} = \lambda_{41} \qquad\qquad a_{41} = \frac{b_{41}}{V(Y_1)}$$

$$b_{42} = \lambda_{42} - a_{21}b_{41} \qquad a_{42} = \frac{b_{42}}{V(Y_2)}$$

$$b_{43} = \lambda_{43} - a_{32}b_{42} - a_{31}b_{41} \qquad a_{43} = \frac{b_{43}}{V(Y_3)}$$

$$V(Y_4) = \lambda_{44} - b_{41}a_{41} - b_{42}a_{42} - b_{43}a_{43}$$

With $Y_1, \cdots, Y_{i-1}$ known, the steps for the evaluation of Y_i are

$$b_{i1} = \lambda_{i1} \qquad\qquad a_{i1} = \frac{b_{i1}}{V(Y_1)}$$

$$b_{i2} = \lambda_{i2} - a_{21}b_{i1} \qquad a_{i2} = \frac{b_{i2}}{V(Y_2)}$$

$$b_{i3} = \lambda_{i3} - a_{32}b_{i2} - a_{31}b_{i1} \qquad a_{i3} = \frac{b_{i3}}{V(Y_3)}$$

$$\quad \bullet \qquad \cdots \qquad\qquad \bullet \qquad \cdots$$

$$b_{ij} = \lambda_{ij} - \sum_{t=i-1}^{1} a_{jt}b_{it} \qquad a_{ij} = \frac{b_{ij}}{V(Y_j)} \qquad j \le i-1$$

$$V(Y_i) = \lambda_{ii} - \sum_{j=1}^{i-1} a_{ij}b_{ij}$$

The method needs checking at each stage since the constants derived at any stage depend on those previously calculated. Errors may accumulate due to rounding off in earlier calculations, but the accuracy can be maintained by retaining a sufficient number of decimal places at each stage.

It is unnecessary to express Y as a function of x only. This would mean another set of successive operations starting with $Y_1 = x_1$ and substituting for Y_1 in Y_2, for Y_1, Y_2 in Y_3, and so on. In any problem $Y_1, \cdots, Y_i$ will be successively calculated, and for this the transformation derived above can be directly used. If Y_i has to be directly calculated from the original measurements, then the computational method given in B2 is much simpler.

B2   An Alternative Computational Scheme

An alternative method which directly yields the functions of x is suggested by the following theoretical considerations. Let the dispersion matrix of $x_1, x_2, \cdots, x_p$ be

$$
\begin{matrix}
\lambda_{11} & \cdots & \lambda_{1p} \\
\cdot & \cdots & \cdot \\
\lambda_{p1} & \cdots & \lambda_{pp}
\end{matrix}
$$

Consider the extended matrix

$$
\begin{matrix}
\lambda_{11} & \cdots & \lambda_{1p} & x_1 \\
\cdot & \cdots & \cdot & \cdot \\
\lambda_{p1} & \cdots & \lambda_{pp} & x_p
\end{matrix}
$$

Taking λ_{11} as the first pivotal element, replace the first row by

$$
1 \quad \frac{\lambda_{12}}{\lambda_{11}} \quad \cdots \quad \frac{\lambda_{1p}}{\lambda_{11}} \quad \frac{x_1}{\lambda_{11}}
$$

Sweeping out the first column and using the first pivotal row, we obtain the reduced matrix

$$
\begin{matrix}
\lambda_{22}' & \cdots & \lambda_{2p}' & x_2' \\
\cdot & \cdots & \cdot & \cdot \\
\lambda_{p2}' & \cdots & \lambda_{pp}' & x_p'
\end{matrix}
$$

where

$$
\lambda_{ij}' = \lambda_{ij} - \frac{\lambda_{i1}}{\lambda_{11}} \lambda_{1j} \qquad x_i' = x_i - \frac{\lambda_{i1}}{\lambda_{11}} x_1
$$

Now

$$V(x_i') = V(x_i) - \frac{2\lambda_{i1}}{\lambda_{11}} \operatorname{cov}(x_i x_1) + \left(\frac{\lambda_{i1}}{\lambda_{11}}\right)^2 V(x_1)$$

$$= \lambda_{ii} - \frac{\lambda_{i1}^2}{\lambda_{11}} = \lambda_{ii}'$$

Similarly,

$$\operatorname{cov}(x_i' x_j') = \lambda_{ij}'$$

This shows that the reduced matrix at any stage is the dispersion matrix of the new variables on the right-hand side, provided that the first matrix is the dispersion matrix of the original variables. This property has been discussed in 3a.6 in connection with the solution of normal equations and their intrinsic properties. Also

$$\operatorname{cov}(x_1 x_i') = \operatorname{cov}(x_1 x_i) - \frac{\lambda_{i1}}{\lambda_{11}} V(x_1)$$

$$= \lambda_{i1} - \lambda_{i1} = 0$$

so that the new variables are all uncorrelated with the variable of the pivotal row. We now consider the second pivotal row

$$1 \quad \frac{\lambda_{23}'}{\lambda_{22}'} \quad \cdots \quad \frac{\lambda_{2p}'}{\lambda_{22}'} \quad \frac{x_2'}{\lambda_{22}'}$$

and find the further reduced matrix

$$\lambda_{33}'' \quad \cdots \quad \lambda_{3p}'' \quad x_3''$$
$$\cdot \quad \cdots \quad \cdot \quad \cdot$$
$$\lambda_{p3}'' \quad \cdots \quad \lambda_{pp}'' \quad x_p''$$

We thus obtain the variables

$$x_1, x_2', x_3'', \cdots$$

with variances

$$\lambda_{11}, \lambda_{22}', \lambda_{33}'', \cdots$$

They are all mutually uncorrelated as shown above, and further x_2' depends on x_1 and x_2, and x_3'' on x_1, x_2, and x_3, only, and so on. Thus the transformation is of the type considered in B1. We thus obtain a relatively simple scheme for obtaining uncorrelated linear functions of the original variables, provided that the number and variables to be included are fixed in advance. In the earlier method the transformed variables are calculated one after the other so that we are free to choose the variable to be added at any stage and in any order we like. There are a few problems where the decision to add a new character depends on tests to be made with the help of the transformed variates up to that stage. In situations like this only the earlier method is open to us. It is enough to compute the transformation (B1.1) in such a case since successive values of Y_1, Y_2, $\cdots$ will be obtained. There is no need to express Y as functions of x only. In problems where a transformation of a chosen set of correlated variables is required, the alternative method of B2 is better.

Having obtained Y_1, Y_2, $\cdots$, Y_5 (say) directly as functions of the original variables, if we want to extend the transformation to a sixth variable x_6 we write

$$Y_6 = x_6 - a_{65}Y_5 - a_{64}Y_4 - a_{63}Y_3 - a_{62}Y_2 - a_{61}Y_1$$

as in the earlier method. The coefficients are determined from the equations

$$\text{cov } (x_6 Y_i) = a_{6i}V(Y_i)$$

Since Y_i is a known function of x, it is easy to calculate cov $(x_6 Y_i)$ and $V(Y_i)$ is already available.

References

BIRNBAUM, Z. W., and D. G. CHAPMAN (1950). On optimum selections from multi-normal populations. *Ann. Math. Stats.*, **21**, 443.

BROGDEN, H. E. (1946). An approach to the problem of differential prediction. *Psychometrika*, **11**, 139.

FAIRFIELD SMITH, H. (1936). A discriminant function for plant selection. *Ann. Eugen. London*, **7**, 240.

GOODWIN, C. N., and G. M. MORANT (1940). The human remains of Iron Age and other periods from Maiden Castle, Dorset. *Biom.*, **31**, 295.

HOOKE, B. G. E. (1926). A third study of the English skull with special reference to the Farringdon Street crania. *Biom.*, **18**, 1.

JEFFREYS, H. (1948). Theory of probability. Oxford University Press. Oxford.

MARTIN, E. S. (1936). A study of an Egyptian series of mandibles with special reference to mathematical methods of sexing. *Biom.*, **28**, 149.

MISES, R. V. (1945). On the classification of observation data into distinct groups. *Ann. Math. Stats.*, **16**, 68.

MORANT, G. M. (1926). A first study of craniology of England and Scotland from neolithic to early historic times, with special reference to Anglo-Saxon skulls in London museums. *Biom.*, **18**, 56.

NEYMAN, J., and E. S. PEARSON (1928). On the use and interpretation of certain test criteria for purposes of statistical inference. *Biom.*, **20A**, 175 and 263.

NEYMAN, J., and E. S. PEARSON (1933a). On the problem of the most efficient tests of statistical hypotheses. *Philos. Trans. Roy. Soc.* **A**, **231**, 281.

NEYMAN, J., and E. S. PEARSON (1933b). On the testing of statistical hypotheses in relation to probability a priori. *Proc. Cam. Phil. Soc.*, **29**, 492.

PANSE, V. G. (1946). An application of the discriminant function for selection in poultry. *Jour. Genetics (London)*, **47**, 242.

PEARSON, K. P. (1894). Contributions to the mathematical theory of evolution. 1. Dissection of frequency curves. *Philos. Trans. Roy. Soc.* A, **185**, 71.

PEARSON, K. P. (1930, 1931). Editor. Tables for statisticians and biometricians, Parts I and II. Cambridge University Press.

PENROSE, L. S. (1947). Some notes on discrimination. *Ann. Eugen. London*, **13**, 228.

RAO, C. R. (1948). The utilization of mutiple measurements in problems of biological classification. *J.R.S.S. Suppl.*, **10**, 159.

RAO, C. R. (1950). Statistical inference applied to classificatory problems. *Sankhyā*, **10**, 229.

RAO, C. R., and P. SLATER (1949). Multivariate analysis applied to differences between neurotic groups. *British Jour. Psychology*, Statistics Section, **2**, 17.

WALD, A. (1949). Statistical decision functions. *Ann. Math. Stats.*, **20**, 165.

CHAPTER 9

The Concept of Distance
and the Problem of Group Constellations

9a   Distance between Two Populations

9a.1   The Need for a Distance Function

One important object of obtaining biometric measurements is to study the possibilities of classifying different groups of individuals in the form of a significant pattern. Here we are concerned not with the individual variations within a group which played a prominent part in the investigations of Chapter 8, but with the group characteristics or the statistical constants related to the distributions of measurements. The configuration of several groups or, to be more precise, of the group characteristics may admit a description in terms of a few group constellations and their interrelationships. The groups within a constellation must necessarily be closer, in some sense, to one another than those belonging to different constellations. Such a description, based only on measurements, quantitative or qualitative in character, may be of use in the study of evolution of the various groups.

A word of caution is necessary. Although it is possible to refute any statement concerning the relationships of some groups, it cannot be asserted that any closeness as indicated by a study of measurements alone is due to some common stock from which the groups have evolved. Historical and ethnological evidence and also geographical contiguity of localities inhabited by various groups have to be considered in interpreting the observed differences.

The first step in the problem of group constellations is the construction of an index by which we can measure the resemblance between two groups. With such an index it is possible to speak of a generalized distance between two groups and to compare the distances between any two pairs of groups. We may, then, be able to say that groups G_1 and G_2 resemble each other more than G_2 and G_3 or G_3 and G_4, and so on.

If groups G_1 and G_2 are close together and G_3 is distant from both, we can talk of G_1 and G_2 as forming a cluster. It may be that all the distances between G_1, G_2, and G_3 are small but the distances of these from the others are large. Then G_1, G_2 and G_3 can be considered to be a closely associated cluster of groups. By sorting out such clusters it may be possible to arrange the various groups in some simplified pattern.

9a.2   Mathematical Concepts (Discriminatory Topology)

In 8b statistical criteria were developed for specifying an individual as a member of one of two groups to which he can possibly belong. These criteria depend on the evaluation of the likelihood ratio and on the assignment of all individuals providing a ratio higher than a predetermined value λ to one group, and the rest to the other. Errors are inevitable in such a procedure, and for any given λ the chances of incorrect classification of individuals of the first and second groups are calculable. For a suitable choice of λ these errors can be made equal, thus supplying the *least possible proportion* α of individuals who are liable to be misclassified. In other words the two groups can be said to overlap to the extent of 100α per cent. The overlap is a maximum when the two groups are identical, in which case the method of classification reduces to a toss of the coin. The overlap decreases with an increase in the divergence between the two groups. If the two groups are distinct in the sense that the ranges of measurements are non-overlapping in the two cases, then the individuals have a distinct identity so that no error is committed. The percentage of overlap is thus zero. The extent of separation or divergence between two groups can thus be judged by α, the least proportion of overlapping individuals who are liable to be misclassified. If a measure of distance is necessary to express the amount of separation, one might choose a decreasing function of α so that the zero value of α may correspond to the maximum distance. One such function is $(1 - \alpha)$.

This satisfies the two fundamental postulates of distance in topological spaces:

(i) The distance between two groups is not less than zero.

(ii) The sum of distances of a group from two other groups is not less than the distance between the two other groups (triangle law of distance).

The first postulate follows since $\alpha \leq 1$, in which case the distance $1 - \alpha \geq 0$. To prove the second, we consider three groups, G_1, G_2, G_3. Let $R_1(1, 2)$, $R_2(1, 2)$ be the best divisions of the space corresponding to G_1 and G_2. Similar definitions hold for $R_1(1, 3)$, $R_3(1, 3)$, $R_2(2, 3)$,

$R_3(2, 3)$. Defining

$$\int_{R_i(i,j)} f_i \, dv = 1 - \alpha_{ij}$$

the proposition required to be proved may be stated as follows.

$$(1 - \alpha_{12}) \gtrdot (1 - \alpha_{13}) + (1 - \alpha_{23})$$

From definition it follows that

$$\int_{R_i(i,j)} f_i \, dv \lessdot \int_{R_i(i,j)} f_j \, dv$$

so that

$$\int_{R_i(i,j)} f_i \, dv + \int_{R_j(i,j)} f_j \, dv \lessdot 1$$

Hence

$$\int_{R_1(1,2)} f_1 \, dv \gtrdot 1 \gtrdot \int_{R_1(1,3)} f_1 \, dv + \int_{R_3(1,3)} f_3 \, dv$$

and

$$\int_{R_2(1,2)} f_2 \, dv \gtrdot 1 \gtrdot \int_{R_2(2,3)} f_2 \, dv + \int_{R_3(2,3)} f_3 \, dv$$

Adding, $2(1 - \alpha_{12}) \gtrdot 2(1 - \alpha_{13}) + 2(1 - \alpha_{23})$, which proves the desired result. The distance function defined above must satisfy some further empirical requirements if it is to be of any value in biological classifications.

(i) The distance must not decrease when additional characters are considered.

(ii) The increase in distance by the addition of some characters to a suitably chosen set must be relatively small so that the group constellations arrived at on the basis of the chosen set are not distorted when additional characters are considered.

The first requirement is reasonable since adding some characters to a basic set must necessarily reduce the errors of classification. In fact, this requirement is satisfied when the distance function is as chosen above. Let $P_1(x_1, \cdots, x_p)$ and $P_2(x_1, \cdots, x_p)$ denote the probability densities of two groups with $R_1(p)$ and $R_2(p)$ as the best divisions of the p-space. When an additional character is considered, the probability densities can be written $P_1(x_1, \cdots, x_{p+1})$ and $P_2(x_1, \cdots, x_{p+1})$ with $R_1(p + 1)$ and $R_2(p + 1)$ as the best division of the $(p + 1)$-space. If Ω denotes the region obtained by considering $R_1(p)$ and the complete range for x_{p+1}, then by definition it follows that

$$\int_{R_1(p+1)} P_2(x_1, \cdots, x_{p+1})\, dv' \leq \int_{\Omega} P_2(x_1, \cdots, x_{p+1})\, dv'$$

$$= \int_{R_1(p)} P_2(x_1, \cdots, x_p)\, dv$$

so that if α and α' represent the proportions of overlapping individuals in the two cases it follows that $\alpha' \leq \alpha$, which proves the result.

The second requirement has been introduced merely as a practical necessity. Owing to considerations of cost in obtaining the information and the numerical reduction of data, there must be some limit to the number of characters used in order to arrive at stable judgments. This should be empirically verified in any situation.

9a.3   Mahalanobis' Generalized Distance

Consider two multivariate normal populations with a common dispersion matrix (λ_{ij}) and having mean values $\mu_{11}, \cdots, \mu_{p1}$ and $\mu_{12}, \cdots, \mu_{p2}$ so that the probability densities $f_1(x)$ and $f_2(x)$ are

$$f_1 = \text{const. exp}\left\{ -\tfrac{1}{2}\Sigma\Sigma\lambda^{ij}(x_i - \mu_{i1})(x_j - \mu_{j1}) \right\}$$

$$f_2 = \text{const. exp}\left\{ -\tfrac{1}{2}\Sigma\Sigma\lambda^{ij}(x_i - \mu_{i2})(x_j - \mu_{j2}) \right\}$$

where (λ^{ij}) is reciprocal to (λ_{ij}). The surfaces of constant likelihood ratios are defined by

$$L(x) = \sum_j \left(\sum_i \lambda^{ij} d_i \right) x_j = \text{const.}$$

where $d_i = \mu_{i1} - \mu_{i2}$, $(i = 1, \cdots, p)$. The common value of the least proportion of wrong classifications is

$$\int_{L(x) \geq a} f_2\, dv = \int_{L(x) \leq a} f_1\, dv$$

This can be determined by considering only the distribution of $L(x)$, which, being a linear function of x, is normal. The mean $L(x)$ in the first group is

$$L(\mu_1) = \sum (\Sigma\lambda^{ij} d_i)\mu_{j1}$$

and in the second group

$$L(\mu_2) = \sum_j (\Sigma\lambda^{ij}d_i)\mu_{j2}$$

$$V\{L(x)\} = D^2 = \Sigma\Sigma\lambda^{ij}d_id_j = L(\mu_1) - L(\mu_2)$$

$$\alpha = \int_{L(x) \leq a} e^{-\frac{1}{2}[L(x) - L(\mu_1)]^2/D^2} \frac{dL(x)}{D\sqrt{2\pi}}$$

By symmetry it follows that

$$a = \frac{L(\mu_1) + L(\mu_2)}{2}$$

On making the transformation $y = [L(x) - L(\mu_1)]/D$, the above integral reduces to

$$\alpha = \frac{1}{\sqrt{2\pi}} \int_{D/2}^{\infty} e^{-\frac{1}{2}y^2} \, dy$$

and hence

$$1 - \alpha = \frac{1}{\sqrt{2\pi}} \int_{-\infty}^{D/2} e^{-\frac{1}{2}y^2} \, dy$$

which shows that $(1 - \alpha)$ is an increasing function of D. The measure $(1 - \alpha)$ may then be conveniently replaced by the functionally dependent quantity D,* which was first introduced by P. C. Mahalanobis. The above analysis supplies a logical derivation of this tool suggested on intuitive considerations. It also shows that Mahalanobis' generalized distance function is applicable only to groups in which the measurements are normally distributed.

9a.4 Karl Pearson's Coefficient of Racial Likeness

In 1921, in a paper by Miss M. L. Tildesley, Karl Pearson proposed a measure of racial likeness (C.R.L.) which has been used since then by anthropologists of the biometric school for purposes of classifying skeletal remains (Morant, 1923). If n_{1i} and n_{2i} denote the number of observations on which the means m_{i1} and m_{i2} of the ith character for the first and second groups are based, s_i is the standard deviation of the ith

---

* D is the ordinary Euclidean distance in a space defined by a set of oblique axes. Therefore it also satisfies the triangular law of distance.

character, and p is the number of characters used, then C.R.L. is defined by

$$\frac{1}{p} \sum_{i=1}^{p} \frac{n_{1i}n_{2i}}{n_{1i} + n_{2i}} \left(\frac{m_{i1} - m_{i2}}{s_i}\right)^2$$

This is meant to be an estimate of a measure of distance between two populations. Since this estimate depends to a large extent on the sample sizes a reduction factor is employed for comparing the C.R.L. values arising out of two pairs. The reduced coefficient of racial likeness (R.C.R.L.) is

$$\frac{\bar{n}_1 + \bar{n}_2}{\bar{n}_1 \bar{n}_2} \frac{1}{p} \left\{ \sum_{i=1}^{p} \frac{n_{1i}n_{2i}}{n_{1i} + n_{2i}} \left(\frac{m_{i1} - m_{i2}}{s_i}\right)^2 - 1 \right\}$$

where

$$\bar{n}_1 = \frac{\Sigma n_{1i}}{p} \qquad \bar{n}_2 = \frac{\Sigma n_{2i}}{p}$$

It may be seen that

$$E(\text{R.C.R.L.}) = \frac{1}{p} \frac{\bar{n}_1 + \bar{n}_2}{\bar{n}_1 \bar{n}_2} \sum_{1}^{p} \frac{n_{1i}n_{2i}}{n_{1i} + n_{2i}} \left(\frac{\mu_{i1} - \mu_{i2}}{\sigma_i}\right)^2$$

where μ_{i1} and μ_{i2} are the population mean values and it is assumed that s_i is not subject to variations. This is not independent of the sample sizes unless $n_{1i} = \bar{n}_1$ and $n_{2i} = \bar{n}_2$ for all i.

With skeletal material there is a good deal of variation in the number of observations available for various characters, which makes the above coefficient ill-suited to such applications. In the expected value, which is supposed to measure the differences in the group characteristics, the various characters are not weighted according to any criteria; the weights are determined by the number of observations available. This, at the same time, makes the coefficient uncomparable unless by some happy coincidence the relative numbers of observations are such that in two R.C.R.L. values to be compared the weights happen to be the same. Also, the R.C.R.L. values calculated from the same two groups in two different situations with different sample observations for the various characters may be widely different. The effect of sample size in the estimate of D^2 is not very serious and can be easily corrected if necessary, as shown later, by subtracting some value which depends solely on the sample sizes and whose value is negligible (tending to zero) in large samples. Comparability is retained because the weights attached to the various characters are not functions of sample sizes.

C.R.L. differs from D^2 in another important aspect. In C.R.L. all the characters are treated as independent. All biological experience points to the fact that some amount of correlation exists between any two characters, and the effect of this is to make C.R.L. increase rapidly with an increase in the number of characters. It is difficult to say from the changes in C.R.L. whether some newly added characters supply additional information for purposes of discrimination. It was seen in the examples of Chapter 8 that, if differences in some characters have already been considered, the absolute differences in some other characters do not throw any light on discrimination between the groups. There is no provision in the construction of C.R.L. to distinguish which characters are more useful for discrimination. For instance, when a character highly correlated with a set of characters is used in addition to those in the set, the C.R.L. may be considerably altered although the change may be inappreciable when the high correlation is taken into account. The change in D^2 may not be appreciable if such superfluous characters are used. If any character alters D^2 considerably, it may be taken to be of additional value in discrimination. In view of the fact that the D^2 statistic satisfies some logical requirements, it may be used in preference to the C.R.L.

9b   An Illustrative Example

9b.1   Calculation of D^2

The mean values of 9 characters for 12 castes and tribes of the United Provinces (Mahalanobis, Majumdar, and Rao, 1949) are given in Table 9b.1α, and the pooled intragroup correlations and standard deviations in Table 9b.1β. The first step in the analysis is the evaluation of all possible D^2 values. The formula

$$D^2 = \Sigma\Sigma\lambda^{ij}d_id_j$$

for the computation of D^2 is not useful since it requires the inversion of a ninth-order determinant and then the evaluation of $9(9 + 1)/2$ terms whose sum is D^2. In an earlier example, the classification of the Highdown skull, it was found convenient to work with a set of uncorrelated characters constructed from the original measurements. The D^2 with such transformed variables reduces to the evaluation of a simple sum of squares. Two simple methods of obtaining this transformation are given in Appendix B of Chapter 8, and one method is actually illustrated in the problem of the Highdown skull. The other method is followed in the present example. If the original characters expressed in standard deviation units are represented by lower-case letters, then

TABLE 9b.1α.   Mean Values by Groups and Characters

Group	Head Length		Head Breadth		Bizygomatic Breadth		Nasal Height		Nasal Breadth		Nasal Depth		Stature		Sitting Height		Frontal Breadth	
	n	Mean	n	Mean	n	Mean	n	Mean	n	Mean	n	Mean	n	Mean	n	Mean	n	Mean
Brahmin (Basti, B₁)	86	191.92	86	139.88	86	133.36	86	51.24	85	36.55	86	25.49	85	164.51	85	86.43	86	104.74
Brahmin (Other, B₂)	92	191.35	92	139.50	92	132.68	91	50.40	90	36.13	91	24.74	92	165.07	92	86.25	92	104.46
Chattri (Ch)	139	192.58	139	131.72	139	131.70	137	52.72	137	35.64	139	24.73	139	163.33	139	82.25	139	103.98
Muslim (M)	167	190.78	168	137.40	168	131.52	168	51.38	168	36.36	168	24.49	168	162.45	131	81.83	72	103.28
Bhatu (C₁)	148	186.10	150	138.58	150	133.55	150	52.06	150	35.65	150	25.09	149	163.38	57	84.49	150	99.34
Habru (C₂)	124	186.94	123	137.40	124	131.16	124	50.30	124	35.82	124	24.19	124	164.91	71	85.53	124	100.18
Bhil (Bh)	187	181.87	186	137.62	186	131.18	187	48.60	187	37.49	186	24.05	186	162.92	: : : :	. . . .	187	103.36
Dom (D)	113	186.40	113	137.52	113	132.64	113	50.34	113	38.11	112	25.33	113	166.53	102	84.19	113	104.16
Ahir (A₁)	68	187.45	67	138.12	68	131.70	68	48.98	68	35.60	68	24.29	67	161.37	68	84.35	68	102.76
Kurmi (A₂)	94	188.86	94	137.86	94	131.82	94	49.22	94	36.21	94	24.03	94	161.35	94	83.41	94	102.62
Other Artisan (A₃)	173	187.69	173	136.84	173	131.30	173	48.72	173	36.27	171	23.73	172	161.34	172	83.09	173	102.44
Kahar (A₄)	57	188.83	57	136.28	57	130.70	57	48.62	57	36.61	57	23.84	57	160.53	57	81.47	56	101.68

TABLE 9b.1β.   Pooled Estimates of Correlations and Standard Deviations

	HL	HB	B_zB	NH	NB	ND	St	SH	FB
HL	....	0.1982	0.2792	0.1758	0.1930	0.1537	0.2698	0.2651	0.2270
HB		......	0.5407	0.1735	0.1413	0.1308	0.1927	0.2069	0.4461
B_zB			......	0.1852	0.2729	0.1575	0.2891	0.2995	0.4930
NH				......	0.0438	0.2910	0.1974	0.2170	0.1139
NB					......	0.1139	0.1412	0.1182	0.1831
ND						......	0.1774	0.2094	0.1243
St							......	0.5849	0.2173
SH								......	0.3012
FB									......
Standard deviation	6.60	4.50	4.58	3.50	2.57	1.75	5.74	3.20	3.92

the transformed variables $y_1, y_2, \cdots, y_9$, which are all uncorrelated and which have standard deviation unity, are as given below.

$$y_1 = Y_1 = hl$$

$$0.980162 y_2 = Y_2 = hb - 0.198200 Y_1$$

$$0.822702 y_3 = Y_3 = b_z b - 0.505209 Y_2 - 0.279200 Y_1$$

$$0.970893 y_4 = Y_4 = nh - 0.097610 Y_3 - 0.144326 Y_2 - 0.175800 Y_1$$

$$0.953943 y_5 = Y_5 = nb + 0.023239 Y_4 - 0.246667 Y_3 - 0.107261 Y_2$$
$$- 0.193000 Y_1$$

$$0.944814 y_6 = Y_6 = nd - 0.069643 Y_5 - 0.258066 Y_4 - 0.094404 Y_3$$
$$+ 0.104439 Y_2 - 0.153700 Y_1$$

$$0.924222 y_7 = Y_7 = st - 0.084080 Y_6 - 0.045612 Y_5 - 0.122926 Y_4$$
$$- 0.211917 Y_3 - 0.144918 Y_2 - 0.269800 Y_1$$

$$0.788187 y_8 = Y_8 = sh - 0.507938 Y_7 - 0.115274 Y_6 - 0.018904 Y_5$$
$$- 0.141858 Y_4 - 0.217927 Y_3 - 0.160669 Y_2$$
$$- 0.265100 Y_1$$

$$0.826753 y_9 = Y_9 = fb - 0.162016 Y_8 - 0.054612 Y_7 - 0.027845 Y_6$$
$$- 0.044106 Y_5 + 0.006423 Y_4 - 0.335334 Y_3$$
$$- 0.417533 Y_2 - 0.227000 Y_1$$

The normalized mean values of the characters are given in Table 9b.1γ, and the mean values of the transformed characters $y_1, \cdots, y_9$ in

TABLE 9b.1γ.   Normalized Mean Values of Characters

Group	hl	hb	b_xb	nh	nb	nd	st	sh	fb
Brahmin (Basti, B₁)	0.534	0.423	0.310	0.293	0.070	0.566	0.238	0.815	0.508
Brahmin (Other, B₂)	0.448	0.338	0.161	0.053	−0.093	0.137	0.336	0.759	0.436
Chattri (Ch)	0.634	0.165	−0.053	0.715	−0.284	0.131	0.033	−0.491	0.314
Muslim (M)	0.361	−0.128	−0.092	0.333	−0.004	−0.006	−0.120	−0.622	0.135
Bhatu (C₁)	−0.348	0.134	0.351	0.527	−0.280	0.337	0.041	0.209	−0.870
Habru (C₂)	−0.220	−0.128	−0.171	0.024	−0.214	−0.177	0.308	0.540	−0.655
Bhil (Bh)	−0.988	−0.079	−0.166	−0.462	0.436	−0.257	−0.039	−0.401	0.156
Dom (D)	−0.302	−0.101	0.152	0.035	0.677	0.474	0.590	0.115	0.360
Ahir (A₁)	−0.143	0.032	−0.053	−0.353	−0.300	−0.120	−0.309	0.165	0.003
Kurmi (A₂)	0.071	−0.026	−0.027	−0.285	−0.062	−0.269	−0.312	−0.129	−0.033
Other Artisan (A₃)	−0.107	−0.253	−0.140	−0.427	−0.039	−0.440	−0.314	−0.229	−0.079
Kahar (A₄)	+0.066	−0.377	−0.271	−0.456	0.093	−0.377	−0.455	−0.735	−0.273

Table 9b.1δ.   First the values of $Y_1, Y_2, \cdots$ are obtained by substituting the values from Table 9b.1γ, and then by division by the corresponding standard deviations $y_1, \cdots, y_9$ are derived.   The D^2 corresponding to

TABLE 9b.1δ.   Mean Values of Transformed Characters

	y_1	y_2	y_3	y_4	y_5	y_6	y_7	y_8	y_9
Brahmin (Basti, B₁)	0.534	0.323	0.001	0.158	−0.066	0.440	−0.003	0.705	0.189
Brahmin (Other, B₂)	0.448	0.254	−0.109	−0.054	−0.194	0.081	0.223	0.656	0.206
Chattri (Ch)	0.634	0.040	−0.303	0.641	−0.350	−0.090	−0.157	−0.773	0.441
Muslim (M)	0.361	−0.204	−0.111	0.316	−0.023	−0.116	−0.213	−0.756	0.339
Bhatu (C₁)	−0.348	0.207	0.420	0.541	−0.322	0.235	−0.040	0.150	−1.207
Habru (C₂)	−0.220	−0.086	−0.083	0.084	−0.152	−0.148	0.435	0.545	−0.760
Bhil (Bh)	−0.988	0.119	0.062	−0.319	0.623	−0.089	0.236	−0.301	0.381
Dom (D)	−0.302	−0.040	0.313	0.071	0.711	0.461	0.592	−0.260	0.388
Ahir (A₁)	−0.143	0.061	−0.053	−0.342	−0.289	0.005	−0.235	0.462	−0.015
Kurmi (A₂)	0.071	−0.041	−0.032	−0.298	−0.075	−0.205	−0.286	0.081	−0.016
Other Artisan (A₃)	−0.107	−0.237	0.009	−0.387	−0.004	−0.321	−0.196	0.020	0.064
Kahar (A₄)	0.066	−0.399	−0.112	−0.414	0.142	−0.258	−0.360	−0.530	−0.012

any two groups is the sum of squares of the differences in the values of $y_1, \cdots, y_9$. The values of D^2 are given in Table 9b.1ϵ where corresponding to each group the other groups are arranged in increasing order of D^2.

TABLE 9b.1ε. Values of D^2 (Based on 9 Characters) Arranged in Increasing Order of Magnitude

Brahmin (Basti, B_1)		Brahmin (Other, B_2)		Bhatu (C_1)		Habru (C_2)		Dom (D)		Bhil (Bh)	
B_2	0.27	B_1	0.27	C_2	1.32	A_1	1.26	Bh	1.15	D	1.15
A_1	1.17	A_1	0.78	A_1	2.68	C_1	1.32	C_2	2.11	A_3	1.75
A_2	1.48	A_2	1.03	A_2	2.98	A_2	1.53	A_3	2.31	A_2	2.23
A_3	2.13	A_3	1.47	A_3	3.35	B_2	1.63	A_2	2.41	A_4	2.24
C_2	2.23	C_2	1.63	B_1	3.48	A_3	1.67	M	2.47	C_2	2.43
M	2.86	M	2.62	B_2	3.61	D	2.11	A_4	2.66	A_1	2.53
D	2.86	A_4	2.72	A_4	4.20	B_1	2.23	B_2	2.81	M	3.16
Ch	3.05	D	2.81	M	4.46	Bh	2.43	B_1	2.86	B_2	3.82
A_4	3.30	Ch	2.87	D	4.52	A_4	2.87	A_1	2.91	B_1	4.45
C_1	3.48	C_1	3.61	Bh	5.08	M	3.74	Ch	3.84	Ch	5.02
Bh	4.45	Bh	3.82	Ch	5.25	Ch	4.68	C_1	4.52	C_1	5.08

Chattri (Ch)		Muslim (M)		Ahir (A_1)		Kurmi (A_2)		Other Artisan (A_3)		Kahar (A_4)	
M	0.40	Ch	0.40	A_2	0.30	A_3	0.12	A_2	0.12	A_3	0.43
A_2	2.12	A_4	0.90	A_3	0.49	A_1	0.30	A_4	0.43	A_2	0.58
A_4	2.24	A_2	1.34	B_2	0.78	A_4	0.58	A_1	0.49	M	0.90
A_3	2.72	A_3	1.45	B_1	1.17	B_2	1.03	M	1.45	A_1	1.52
B_2	2.87	A_1	2.45	C_2	1.26	M	1.34	B_2	1.47	Bh	2.24
B_1	3.05	D	2.47	A_4	1.52	B_1	1.48	C_2	1.67	Ch	2.24
A_1	3.38	B_2	2.62	M	2.45	C_2	1.53	Bh	1.75	D	2.66
D	3.84	B_1	2.86	Bh	2.53	Ch	2.12	B_1	2.13	B_2	2.72
C_2	4.68	Bh	3.16	C_1	2.68	Bh	2.23	D	2.31	C_2	2.87
Bh	5.02	C_2	3.74	D	2.91	D	2.41	Ch	2.72	B_1	3.30
C_1	5.25	C_1	4.46	Ch	3.38	C_1	2.98	C_1	3.35	C_1	4.20

9b.2 The Determination of Group Constellations

A scrutiny of Table 9b.1ε reveals that there is a pattern exhibited by the 12 groups. The Brahmins B_1 and B_2 cluster together in almost each column and may be treated as a single unit, and also the four Artisans A_1, A_2, A_3, and A_4, which appear to be linearly arranged in the order A_1, A_2, A_3, and A_4 with A_4 being most distant from A_1. Bhatu (C_1) and Habru (C_2) go together, with C_2 being nearer to the Brahmin and

Artisan clusters and C_1 far removed from them. Bhil (Bh) and Dom (D) are closer, and so also are Muslim (M) and Chattri (Bh).

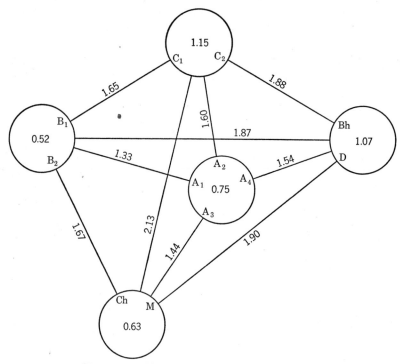

FIGURE 1.   Clusters and their interrelationships.

The average D^2 within and between clusters found above is given in Table 9b.2α. The configuration of the clusters and their mutual relationships is approximately indicated in Figure 1 where the square root of average D^2 (of Table 9b.2α) represents the distance.

TABLE 9b.2α.   Intra- and Inter-Cluster Average D^2

Cluster	Groups	A	B	C	Ch	D
A	A_1, A_2, A_3, A_4	0.57	1.76	2.57	2.07	2.38
B	B_1, B_2	1.76	0.27	2.74	2.85	3.48
C	C_1, C_2	2.57	2.74	1.32	4.53	3.58
Ch	Ch, M	2.07	2.85	4.53	0.40	3.62
D	D, Bh	2.38	3.48	3.58	3.62	1.15

No formal rules can be laid down for finding the clusters because a cluster is not a well-defined term. The only criterion appears to be that any two groups belonging to the same cluster should at least on the average show a smaller D^2 than those belonging to two different clusters. A simple device suggested by K. D. Tocher is to start with two closely associated groups and find a third group which has the smallest average D^2 from the first two. Similarly, the fourth is chosen to have the smallest average D^2 from the first three, and so on. If at any stage the average D^2 of a group from those already listed appears to be high, then this group does not fit in with the former groups and is therefore taken to be outside the former cluster. The groups of the first cluster are then omitted, and the rest are treated similarly.

It is also useful to calculate the change in average D^2 within a cluster due to the inclusion of an additional group. If the change is appreciable, then the newly added group has to be considered as outside the cluster. The calculations arising from the D^2 table (9b.1ϵ) are given in Table 9b.2β.

TABLE 9b.2β.   Computational Scheme for Finding Clusters

Group Added to a Cluster	D^2	No. of Terms (n)	Increase in D^2 —————— Increase in n	Average D^2 $(\Sigma D^2/n)$	Cluster
A$_2$, A$_3$	0.12	1	....	0.12	
A$_1$	0.91	3	0.39	0.30	A$_1$, A$_2$, A$_3$, A$_4$
A$_4$	3.44	6	0.84	0.57	
M	13.02	10	2.39	1.30	
B$_1$, B$_2$	0.27	1	....	0.27	B$_1$, B$_2$
C$_2$	4.13	3	1.93	1.38	
M, Ch	0.40	1	....	0.40	M, Ch
D	6.71	3	3.15	2.24	
Bh, D	1.15	1	....	1.15	Bh, D
C$_2$	5.69	3	2.27	1.90	
C$_1$, C$_2$	1.32	1	....	1.32	C$_1$, C$_2$

There is a sharp increase in the average increase in D^2 when M is added to A$_1$, A$_2$, A$_3$, A$_4$. This indicates that A$_1$, A$_2$, A$_3$, A$_4$ form a cluster; therefore these are omitted and the rest are considered. Thus the other clusters are determined.

For comparison of D^2 values it must be ascertained that they estimate the corresponding population distances. This is one reason why
C.R.L. was found to be not useful. The bias in D^2 when the dispersion is estimated on a large number of degrees of freedom is given by

$$\Sigma\Sigma\lambda^{ij}\lambda_{ij}\frac{n_{ij1}+n_{ij2}}{n_{ij1}\times n_{ij2}}$$

where n_{ij1} is the number of samples supplying observations on both the
ith and the jth character in the first group, and similarly n_{ij2} for the
second group. The value $n_{ii1} = n_{i1}$, the number of observations on the
ith character. This quantity, which depends only on the sample sizes
and variances and covariances, can be calculated and subtracted from
D^2. If $n_{ii} = n_1$ for all i and $n_{j2} = n_2$ for all j, then the bias is simply

$$p\frac{n_1+n_2}{n_1n_2}$$

where p is the number of characters. If n_{i1} and n_{j2} are individually
large, the correction is trivial and need not be carried out. Also, if the
sample numbers are such that the quantities

$$\frac{n_1+n_2}{n_1n_2}$$

are of the same order for all pairs of groups under consideration, then
no correction is needed because the D^2 values become comparable. In
the illustration chosen above, the value of $p(n_1 + n_2)/n_1n_2$ is very
nearly the same and also small for all pairs of groups, and hence no
correction was carried out.

9c   The Use of Canonical Variates in Deriving Group Constellations

9c.1   Graphical Methods of Representing the Groups

The method of finding the group constellations, as described in 9b,
becomes much simpler if the groups are characterized by two or three
measurements. In the case of two characters x_1 and x_2, we can represent the mean values, expressed in standard deviation units, of the k
populations under consideration on a two-dimensional chart with axes
inclined at an angle $\cos^{-1} r$, where r is the correlation between x_1 and x_2.
In such a chart, the distance between two points is equivalent, apart
from a constant multiplier, to Mahalanobis' D between the two populations represented by the two points. This is valuable as it facilitates

the study of group constellations and also serves as a pictorial representation of the configuration of various groups.

For three characters we can construct a three-dimensional model representing the characters along three mutually inclined axes. In order that the distance between two points might be equal to the D, apart from a constant multiplier, between the two populations represented by them, the angle between the axes corresponding to x_1 and x_2 should be chosen as $\cos^{-1} r_{12,3}$ and the scale of x_1, x_2, x_3 be properly adjusted.

If the object of representation is only to measure D by the actual distance in space, we can transform the characters to independent variables, in which case they can be represented along three mutually orthogonal axes. This method of representation fails when we are dealing with more than three characters. In such cases it might be useful to examine whether the configuration of the mean values with respect to $p > 3$ characters can be preserved, as far as possible, by representing the groups with respect to two or three suitably chosen functions of the p characters. A convenient measure for examining the adequacy of such a simpler representation is given by the ratio of the sum of squares of all possible $k(k - 1)/2$ distances arising out of the k populations in the simpler representation to the sum of squares of the p-dimensional representation. The former sum of squares is not greater than the latter, and the two representations are identical when the ratio is unity. When this ratio is close to unity, the simpler model might be considered as a fair representation of the groups in the total character space.

9c.2 The Problem of Maximal Average D^2

The general problem to be solved is what are the best $t(<p)$ linear combinations of the p variates which make the sum of all possible D^2 values arising out of a number of populations as calculated with these t variates a maximum?

Let

$$m_{11} \quad \cdots \quad m_{p1}$$

$$m_{12} \quad \cdots \quad m_{p2}$$

$$m_{1k} \quad \cdots \quad m_{pk}$$

represent the mean values of p characters for the first, second, $\cdots$ kth populations, and Λ the common dispersion matrix. Suppose that $t = 1$ and the required linear function is $l_1 x_1 + l_2 x_2 + \cdots + l_p x_p$ with its variance $l \Lambda l'$ where l is the vector $(l_1, l_2, \cdots, l_p)$. The D^2 with respect to $l_1 x_1 + \cdots + l_p x_p$ between the ith and jth populations is

$$[l_1(m_{1i} - m_{1j}) + \cdots + l_p(m_{pi} - m_{pj})]^2$$

The sum of all possible D^2 values is proportional to

$$\Sigma\Sigma l_i l_j b_{ij}$$

where

$$b_{ij} = \Sigma(m_{ir} - \bar{m}_i)(m_{jr} - \bar{m}_j)$$

and $\bar{m}_i = (\Sigma m_{ir})/k$. This is nothing but between populations variance with respect to the chosen linear compound.

To find the best linear function, $\Sigma\Sigma l_i l_j b_{ij}$ is maximized, subject to the condition $\Sigma\Sigma l_i l_j \lambda_{ij} = 1$. Introducing the Lagrangian multiplier λ, the vector $\mathbf{l}$ is obtained as the solution of

$$\mathbf{l}(B - \lambda\Lambda) = 0$$

where $B = (b_{ij})$, $\Lambda = (\lambda_{ij})$, and λ is the greatest root of the equation (see 1c.4).

$$|B - \lambda\Lambda| = 0$$

Suppose that we want the best two functions $\mathbf{lx}'$ and $\mathbf{mx}'$ where $\mathbf{l}$ and $\mathbf{m}$ can be chosen to satisfy the conditions $\mathbf{l\Lambda l}' = 1 = \mathbf{m\Lambda m}'$ and $\mathbf{l\Lambda m}' = 0$. Introducing Lagrangian multipliers c_1, c_2, c_3, the expression to be differentiated is

$$\mathbf{l}B\mathbf{l}' + \mathbf{m}B\mathbf{m}' - c_1\mathbf{l\Lambda l}' - 2c_3\mathbf{l\Lambda m}' - c_2\mathbf{m\Lambda m}'$$

The equations are

$$\mathbf{l}B - c_1\mathbf{l\Lambda} - c_3\mathbf{m\Lambda} = 0$$

$$\mathbf{m}B - c_2\mathbf{m\Lambda} - c_3\mathbf{l\Lambda} = 0$$

The value of c_3 can be shown to be zero by multiplying the first equation by $\mathbf{m}'$ and the second by $\mathbf{l}'$ and adding. This shows that c_1 and c_2 are roots of the equation

$$|B - \lambda\Lambda| = 0$$

Since the maximized value of $\mathbf{l}B\mathbf{l}' + \mathbf{m}B\mathbf{m}'$ is $c_1 + c_2$, it follows that c_1 and c_2 correspond to the first two largest roots. Also the vectors corresponding to any two roots satisfy the condition $\mathbf{l\Lambda m}' = 0$ (see 1c.3), so that $\mathbf{lx}'$ and $\mathbf{mx}'$ are uncorrelated. The best two linear functions are thus the first two canonical vectors associated with the matrices B and Λ as discussed in 1c.3.

Similarly, the first t canonical variates give the best t linear functions. The sum of all possible D^2 values with respect to all the p characters is equal to the sum of all the roots $\lambda_1 + \cdots + \lambda_p$, and the corresponding sum for the t largest canonical variates is $\lambda_1 + \lambda_2 + \cdots + \lambda_t$, so that the adequacy of the fit is judged by the smallness of the sum of the residual roots $\lambda_{t+1} + \cdots + \lambda_p$ or its ratio to the total.

9c.3   An Illustrative Example

In the example of 9b, the original variables have been already transformed into an uncorrelated set, so that, if the transformed values (for which $\Lambda = I$, the unit matrix) are used, the problem reduces to the determination of the latent roots and vectors of the between product sum matrix. From the table of mean values of the transformed characters the between group sum of squares and products are calculated (Table 9c.3α). It may be observed that the mean values of Table

TABLE 9c.3α.   Between Product Sum Matrix Using Mean Values of the Transformed Characters

Matrix A

	y_1	y_2	y_3	y_4	y_5	y_6	y_7	y_8	y_9
y_1	2.296	0.067	−0.567	0.709	−0.991	0.074	−0.561	0.014	0.682
y_2	0.067	0.499	0.113	0.311	−0.158	0.403	0.239	0.708	−0.104
y_3	−0.567	0.113	0.417	0.070	0.270	0.314	0.254	0.197	−0.489
y_4	0.709	0.311	0.070	1.472	−0.503	0.437	0.192	−0.424	−0.412
y_5	−0.991	−0.158	0.270	−0.503	1.295	0.187	0.571	−0.604	0.806
y_6	0.074	0.403	0.314	0.437	0.187	0.731	0.447	0.498	−0.020
y_7	−0.561	0.239	0.254	0.192	0.571	0.447	1.022	0.488	−0.059
y_8	0.014	0.708	0.197	−0.424	−0.604	0.498	0.488	3.075	−1.140
y_9	0.682	−0.104	−0.489	−0.412	0.806	−0.020	−0.059	−1.140	2.722

9b.1δ are so adjusted that their sum for any character over all the groups is zero, in which case no correction is necessary for the raw sum of squares and products.

One method of determining the canonical vectors is by iteration. We start with a trial vector, multiply each row of the matrix with this vector, and thus obtain a derived vector which is a better approximation than the trial one. The convergence will be quicker if we start not with the original matrix but with a suitable power of it (Hotelling, 1936). The canonical vectors associated with a symmetric matrix, A, and A^{2^p}, a suitable power of A, are the same; the canonical roots of A^{2^p} are those of A raised to the power 2^p. If $\mathbf{l}$ is the vector associated with the root λ of A, then

$$\mathbf{l}(A - \lambda I) = 0$$

Multiplying by $(A + \lambda I)$, the equation reduces to

$$\mathbf{l}(A^2 - \lambda^2 I) = 0$$

Multiplying by $(A^2 + \lambda^2 I)$,

$$1(A^4 - \lambda^4 I) = 0$$

and so on. Hence the result stated above is true.

From matrix A of Table 9c.3α first A^2, the square of A, is obtained and then A^4 by squaring A^2. Finally, by squaring A^4, A^8 is obtained, as in Table 9c.3β. Choosing the trial vector $(1, \cdots, 1)$, the first approxi-

TABLE 9c.3β.   Matrix A^8

19264	− 3164	− 7381	5938	− 4662	− 3405	− 8659	−17324	16812
− 3164	5954	4195	1770	− 8053	4452	4133	24372	−21019
− 7381	4195	4480	− 703	− 3115	3437	4788	18446	−16589
5938	1770	− 703	3506	− 6092	918	− 1344	5443	− 4487
− 4662	− 8053	− 3115	−6092	15902	− 5395	− 2130	−30993	26424
− 3405	4452	3437	918	− 5395	3421	3515	18386	−15884
− 8659	4133	4788	−1344	− 2130	3515	5313	18398	−16351
−17324	24372	18446	5443	−30993	18386	18398	101184	−87841
16812	−21019	−16589	−4487	26424	−15884	−16351	−87841	77651

mation is

$$-2581, 12640, 7558, 4949, -18114, 9445, 7663, 50071, -41284$$

which are simply the column totals. If we divide by the highest quantity in the set, the vector reduces to

$$-0.0515, 0.2524, 0.1509, 0.0988, -0.3618, 0.1886, 0.1530, 1, -0.8245$$

Multiplying each row of A^8 by this vector, we derive a second approximation, and so on; the operations are repeated until stable values are obtained. After five operations the following vector is obtained.

$$-0.1849, 0.2400, 0.1865, 0.0507, -0.3008, 0.1816, 0.1855, 1, -0.8755$$

The highest value used in the last stage of division is 206,926, and this gives the eighth power of the first canonical root.

$$\lambda_1^8 = 206{,}926 \quad \text{or} \quad \lambda_1 = 4.620$$

This vector is standardized by dividing each element by the square root of the sum of squares of all the elements. The standardized vector is

$$-0.129, 0.167, 0.130, 0.035, -0.210, 0.127, 0.129, 0.698, -0.611$$

From the (i, j)th element of the matrix A^8 is subtracted the product $\lambda_1^8 \times i$th element $\times j$th element of the first vector to obtain the reduced matrix given in Table 9c.3γ. The above process of choosing a trial vector and finding better approximations is repeated on this reduced matrix.

TABLE 9c.3γ. The Reduced Matrix Eliminating the First Root and the Vector

15821	1306	3907	6883	−10266	− 22	−5202	1304	503
1306	151	− 315	543	− 778	61	− 354	190	151
− 3907	− 315	976	−1656	2538	24	1302	− 346	−138
6883	543	−1656	3247	− 4554	− 10	−2292	331	− 11
−10266	− 778	2538	−4554	6783	109	3494	− 678	115
− 22	61	24	− 10	109	98	121	88	135
− 5202	− 354	1302	−2292	3494	121	1844	− 298	17
1304	190	− 346	331	− 678	88	− 298	413	381
503	151	− 138	− 11	115	135	17	381	416

The second vector is found to be

$$0.722, 0.062, -0.193, 0.342, -0.508, -0.004, -0.259, 0.058, 0.013$$

and the second root is
$$(27{,}347)^{1/8} = 3.629$$

The first two canonical vectors supply the best two linear functions.

	y_1	y_2	y_3	y_4	y_5	y_6	y_7	y_8	y_9
z_1	−0.129	0.167	0.130	0.035	−0.210	0.127	0.129	0.698	−0.611
z_2	0.722	0.062	−0.193	0.342	−0.508	−0.004	−0.259	0.058	0.013

From the mean values of $y_1, y_2, \cdots$ given in Table 9b.1δ the mean values of z_1, z_2 are calculated as shown in Table 9c.3δ.

TABLE 9c.3δ. Mean Values of the Canonical Variates

	B_1	B_2	Ch	M	C_1	C_2	Bh	D	A_1	A_2	A_3	A_4
z_1	0.437	0.380	−0.859	−0.856	1.088	0.920	−0.410	−0.357	0.372	−0.012	−0.129	−0.576
z_2	0.535	0.423	0.918	0.405	0.031	−0.133	−1.217	−0.783	0.028	0.070	−0.170	−0.106

The sum of squares for $z_1 = 4.619$ and for $z_2 = 3.630$. They correspond to the first two canonical roots, thus providing a check on the calculations. These two roots alone account for a total variation $4.619 + 3.630 = 8.249$ out of a total of 9, corresponding to 9 transformed characters. The percentage of variation absorbed is 91.7, so that a two-dimensional representation gives a fairly accurate picture of the configuration of the groups in the nine-dimensional space. The two-dimensional representation with the canonical variates as coordinate axes is given in Figure 2. A third root may absorb some more variation, in which case a three-dimensional representation will supply an almost true picture of the configuration of the groups.

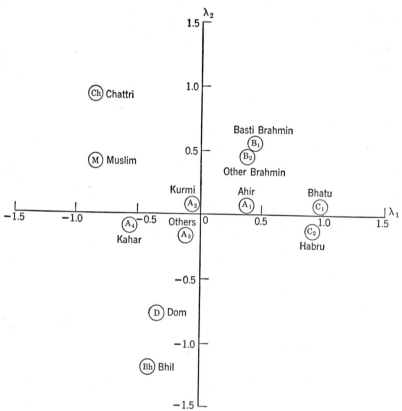

FIGURE 2.   U.P. Anthropometric survey group constellations in the $(\lambda_1-\lambda_2)$ chart.

9d   A Test for Reduction in the Number of Dimensions

9d.1   The Analysis of Neurotic Cases

In the previous section no sampling problem was considered, the object being to obtain the best method of representation of p-dimensional data in a smaller number of dimensions. No question was asked whether the variation between the groups is entirely confined to a smaller space or whether it can be explained by variations with respect to a smaller number of hypothetical characters. Such a question would require the estimation of these hypothetical characters, if they exist, and a test of significance for the residual variation. The algebra is the same as in the previous section, but sample sizes come into the calculations when tests of significance are considered. The method is illustrated by an example discussed elsewhere by the author and Patrick Slater who supplied the material and who also provided a suitable psychological interpretation of the statistical analysis.

The mean values of scores on 5 types of neurotics and normal cases and the within dispersion matrix have already been given in Table 8b.9α. For the following analysis we need the between and within product sum matrices.

TABLE 9d.1α. Analysis of Dispersion

	S.P. Matrix between Groups 5 D.F.			S.P. Matrix within Groups 250 D.F.		
	A	B	C	A	B	C
A	367.7248	161.7773	76.2389	575.2127	62.8946	118.5423
B	161.7773	76.4732	33.0330	62.8946	151.8666	8.9436
C	76.2389	33.0330	17.7109	118.5423	8.9436	148.7735

A glance at the mean Table 8b.9α shows that the most conspicuous single difference is between the normal cases and the neurotics, but there are also marked differences between the groups of neurotics. The five cases of post-traumatic personality change approximate the normal cases. Closely similar to one another but distinctly different from the normal and the remaining neurotic groups are the hysterias and anxiety states. Still further removed from the normal are the obsessional and psychopathic cases; but between these two groups some differences appear to exist. Whereas the obsessionals exhibit more pointers per person than the psychopaths, this difference is wholly due to an excess of symptoms of inadequacy and shyness; there is less evidence of instability among them than among the psychopaths. This suggests that, in addition to variations in the degree to which the neurotic groups differ from normal, a further source of variation may be found and may prove useful for differential diagnosis. We may ask the following problem.

Is there sufficient evidence to demonstrate variation between the groups in more than one dimension, or can the observed differences between them be treated as differences simply in degree?

The determinantal equation for λ, giving the canonical variances, is

$$| \text{Between matrix} - \lambda \text{ Within matrix} | = 0$$

$$\begin{vmatrix} 367.7248 - \lambda 575.2127 & 161.7773 - \lambda 62.8946 & 76.2389 - \lambda 118.5423 \\ 161.7773 - \lambda 62.8946 & 76.4732 - \lambda 151.8666 & 33.0330 - \lambda 8.9436 \\ 76.2389 - \lambda 118.5423 & 33.0330 - \lambda 8.9436 & 17.7109 - \lambda 148.7735 \end{vmatrix} = 0$$

Various methods have been suggested for obtaining the solutions of this equation and the canonical vectors associated with the roots. To apply the method described in the previous section it is necessary to multiply the determinantal equation by the reciprocal of the dispersion matrix given after Table 8b.9α. This is equivalent to multiplying the between sum of products matrix by the reciprocal of the dispersion matrix and subtracting 250λ times the unit matrix (250 being the degrees of freedom of the within matrix). The resulting equation is

$$\begin{vmatrix} 135.2909 - \mu & 58.6725 & 27.3495 \\ 209.8339 & 101.4343 - \mu & 42.7341 \\ 7.7001 & 2.6617 & 5.4009 - \mu \end{vmatrix} = 0$$

where $\mu = 250\lambda$. This is of the form already considered. In the above example it is convenient to expand the determinant because the resulting equation is a simple cubic.

$$\mu^3 - 242.1261\mu^2 + 2365.848134\mu - 5455.7616654 = 0$$

The three roots of this equation are

$$\mu_1 = 232.0312 \qquad \mu_2 = 6.4481 \qquad \mu_3 = 3.6468$$

The total variation is 242.1261, out of which the variations absorbed by the 3 roots are 95.8%, 2.7%, and 1.5%; so the second and third are relatively unimportant.

Since the dispersion matrix is estimated on a large number of degrees of freedom, the total variation 242.1261 is approximately distributed as χ^2 with $p(k-1)$ (the number of characters $\times$ 1 minus the number of groups), equal to 15 degrees of freedom. This is an alternative test to the Λ criterion (see 7d.1) for judging the overall group differences.

If the whole variation is concentrated in the first canonical (hypothetical) variate, then the residual variation

$$242.1261 - 232.0312 = 10.0949$$

should be attributed to chance. The first canonical variance is distributed as χ^2 with $(p + k - 2) = 7$ degrees of freedom, so that the residual is a χ^2 with $(15 - 7) = 8$ degrees of freedom. The value of $\chi^2 = 10.0949$ has more than 20% probability on 8 degrees of freedom, thus providing no evidence of variation in the other dimensions.

If this χ^2 is significant, we proceed to test whether the first two canonical variates are sufficient to explain the total variance. In this case the significance of the sum of the other variances has to be tested.

The distribution of the degrees of freedom among the various roots is

$$p(k - 1) = (p + k - 2) + (p + k - 4) + \cdots$$

each term being 2 less than the previous one. The degrees of freedom for the residual in any case are the total minus the degrees of freedom for the roots accounting for the total variation on the specified hypothesis. This is equivalent to the sum of degrees of freedom of the smallest canonical variances added to form the residual.

The χ^2 approximation can be slightly improved (Bartlett, 1948) by using $[N - \frac{1}{2}(p + k)] \log_e (1 + \lambda)$ instead of $\mu = 250\lambda$ itself, where N is the total sample size for all groups put together. In the present example:

Root	Term	χ^2	D.F.
First	$[255 - \frac{1}{2}(p + k)] \log_e (1 + \lambda_1)$	165.14	7
Second	$[255 - \frac{1}{2}(p + k)] \log_e (1 + \lambda_2)$	6.35	5
Third	$[255 - \frac{1}{2}(p + k)] \log_e (1 + \lambda_3)$	3.62	3

The χ^2 for the residual after the first root is eliminated is $6.35 + 3.62 = 9.97$, with $5 + 3 = 8$ degrees of freedom. In the previous approximation the residual χ^2 is 10.0949, which is very nearly the same. Although no exact test is known, the two tests described above are equivalent in large samples.

In the present example only the first root is significant, but in problems of this nature it is of practical importance to consider at least some of the smaller roots in determining the configuration of the various groups. It might happen that the variation in the dimension corresponding to a smaller root is concentrated among a few of the groups, in which case very large samples would be necessary to establish significance. Any noticeable difference between two groups in the mean values of the canonical variate corresponding to such a root cannot be strictly interpreted as real when the overall test does not establish the significance of this root. But this additional analysis may throw some light on the prospects of future investigations. In the present case the canonical variates corresponding to the first two roots have been calculated. The configuration of the various groups is indicated in Figure 3.

The coefficients k_1, k_2, k_3 of the best linear fit or the first canonical variate are obtained from the equations

$$(135.2909 - 232.0312)k_1 + 58.6725k_2 + 27.3495k_3 = 0$$

$$209.8339k_1 + (101.4343 - 232.0312)k_2 + 42.7341k_3 = 0$$

$$7.7001k_1 + 2.6617k_2 + (5.4009 - 232.0312)k_3 = 0$$

The matrix of these equations is obtained by substituting for μ the maximum root 232.0312 in the matrix of the determinantal equation for μ. Putting $k_3 = 1$ arbitrarily, we find that the proportional values of k_1 and k_2 are $k_1 = 18.84886$, $k_2 = 30.61225$.

The variance of $k_1A + k_2B + k_3C$ is $a_{11}k_1{}^2 + a_{22}k_2{}^2 + a_{33}k_3{}^2 + 2a_{12}k_1k_2 + 2a_{13}k_1k_3 + 2a_{23}k_2k_3$, where a_{ij} are the elements of the dispersion matrix within the groups. Using the values of k_1, k_2, k_3 obtained as above, we find the variance as 1697.6281 or the standard deviation as $\sqrt{1697.6281} = 41.2023$. Dividing k_1, k_2, k_3 by this value we find the standardized best linear function $0.4575A + 0.7430B + 0.0243C$.

Similarly, the standardized linear function for the second dimension is $0.4071A - 1.0473B + 0.3292C$. The mean values of these variates for all the groups are given in Table 9d.1β.

TABLE 9d.1β.   Mean Values of the First Two Cannoical Variates

Group	λ_1	λ_2
Normal	0.3879	0.1637
Personality change	0.7891	0.3604
Anxiety state	2.2249	0.2105
Hysteria	2.3227	0.1120
Psychopathy	3.1339	−0.1115
Obsession	3.3601	0.6204

These values can be used for a pictorial representation of the groups as shown in Figure 3. In the first dimension the normal group occupies a position at one end of the scale; the neurotic groups are spread out towards the other extreme, the small group of cases of post-traumatic personality change being the only one which is not clearly distinct

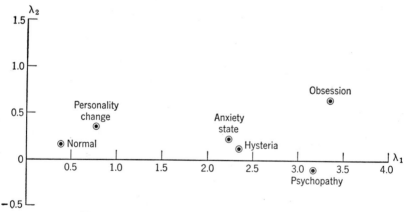

FIGURE 3.   The configuration of neurotic groups.

from normal. At the other extreme are the psychopathic personalities and the obsessionals; in terms of this dimension they lie very close together. The anxiety states and the hysterias are also found to approximate one another closely, but they lie a considerable distance from the the other groups.

The preponderance of the part of the total variation between the groups which occurs in this dimension is the most striking finding in the analysis. That it is the first of the dimensions found, that each of the original scores makes a positive contribution to the variation in it, and, above all, that in it the normal group appears at one pole and the various neurotic groups diverge all towards the other—these facts suggest that it can be identified with the general factor among neurotic characteristics described by Eliot Slater, Eysenck, and other writers. Whether this general dimension of neuroticism indicates the existence of any unitary psychological trait or whether it is simply a reflection of the fact that most neurotic characteristics are non-specific and are found with varying degrees of frequency among all neurotic states is a controversial question upon which it is unnecessary to enter here. Mayer Gross, Moore, and Patrick Slater prefer the latter alternative.

Although the variation in the second dimension is very much smaller, the arrangement of the groups it discloses invites some psychological consideration. The equation defining variation in this dimension contrasts the scores for inadequacy with the scores for instability by giving them opposite signs. At one extreme is the obsessional group, which in terms of average scores is the most highly inadequate but not the most unstable; at the other extreme is the psychopathic group—the most unstable but not the most inadequate. The psychological picture presented by this arrangement of the groups is a familiar one: obsessional cases are notoriously fixed in their habits; psychopaths are notoriously irresponsible and unreliable. What is surprising is not that some contrast of this kind was found but that the observations exhibit so little variation in this respect. But, as the score is based on a summation of three pointers only, it is more likely that variation in this dimension is insignificant than that it has been insufficiently accurately measured.

Example 1. If B and W denote the between and within sum of product matrices and T the total, then the roots of

$$| W - \psi T | = 0$$

and

$$| B - \lambda W | = 0$$

are connected by the relation

$$\psi = \frac{1}{1 + \lambda}$$

and the canonical vectors

$$1(W - \psi T) = 0 \qquad \text{and} \qquad 1(B - \lambda W) = 0$$

are the same.

Example 2. The equation for ψ can be deduced as follows. Evaluate the determinant

$$u(\psi) = \left| \, W - \psi T \, \right|$$

for $\psi = 0, 1, 2, 3, \cdots$ and construct the equation for ψ by the method of finite differences.

[Hint: If $u_0, \Delta u_0, \Delta^2 u_0, \cdots$ denote the forward differences, then

$$u(\psi) = u_0 + \psi \Delta u_0 + \frac{\psi(\psi - 1)}{2!} \Delta^2 u_0 + \frac{\psi(\psi - 1)(\psi - 2)}{3!} \Delta^3 u_0 + \cdots].$$

Example 3. If ψ_0 is an approximate solution of

$$u(\psi) = u_0 + \psi \Delta u_0 + \frac{\psi(\psi - 1)}{2!} \Delta^2 u_0 + \cdots$$

then the correction δ to ψ_0 is given by

$$-u(\psi_0) = \delta \left[\Delta u_0 + (\psi_0 + \overline{\psi_0 - 1}) \frac{\Delta^2 u_0}{2} \right. $$
$$\left. + \frac{d}{d\psi_0} \psi(\psi - 1)(\psi - 2) \frac{\Delta^3 u_0}{3!} + \cdots \right]$$

Example 4. All the solutions for ψ lie between 0 and 1. [Hint: $\psi = 1/(1 + \lambda)$.]

Examples 1 to 4 supply an alternative method of evaluating the canonical variances without reducing the determinantal equation $\left| B - \lambda W \right| = 0$ to the form $\left| C - \mu I \right| = 0$. It is convenient to find first the values of ψ, which all lie between 0 and 1. It is easy to guess an approximate root and then obtain the correction terms by iteration.

If in any problem all the roots are needed, they may be obtained by Graff's root-squaring method, which is illustrated below. If the equation is

$$a_0 x^p + a_1 x^{p-1} + \cdots + a_p = 0$$

then the equation whose roots are squares of the above roots is computed in the following manner

x^p	x^{p-1}	x^{p-2}	.	.	.
a_0^2	$2a_0a_2$	$2a_0a_4$			
	$-a_1^2$	$-2a_1a_3$	$-2a_1a_5$	$\cdots$	
		a_2^2	$2a_2a_4$	$2a_2a_6$	$\cdots$
		$\cdots$	$\cdots$	$\cdots$	
Total b_0	b_1	b_2	b_3	b_4	$\cdots$

This gives the first approximation to the square of the roots

$$\psi_1^2 \sim \frac{b_1}{b_0} \qquad \psi_2^2 \sim \frac{b_2}{b_1} \qquad \psi_3^2 \sim \frac{b_3}{b_2} \qquad \cdots$$

Starting from this equation, the first operation is repeated. If c_0, c_1, $\cdots$ are the coefficients, then

$$\psi_1^4 \sim \frac{c_1}{c_0} \qquad \psi_2^4 \sim \frac{c_2}{c_1} \qquad \cdots$$

By using logarithms, the values ψ_1, ψ_2, $\cdots$ at any stage are obtained. The process can be terminated as soon as stable values of ψ_1, ψ_2, $\cdots$ are obtained. Each time, the powers of roots obtained are 2, 4, 8, 16, 32, $\cdots$, and so on, and the convergence will depend on the separation of roots in the equation. This method is suitable only when all the roots are different. In problems of the nature discussed in this chapter, cases of exactly equal roots rarely occur.

Example 5. If **b** is an arbitrary vector, show that

$$\lim_{n \to \infty} \frac{\mathbf{b}A^n}{\lambda_1^n} = \mathbf{x}_1$$

where λ_1 is the dominant root and $\mathbf{x}_1$ is the first characteristic vector arising out of the determinantal equation

$$\left| A - \lambda I \right| = 0$$

This justifies the iterative method adopted on p. 368.

Example 6. Taking an arbitrary vector **k**, form the matrix P, whose rows are the vector,

$$\mathbf{k}, \mathbf{k}A, \cdots, \mathbf{k}A^p$$

where A is a symmetric matrix of order p. Solve the equations

$$\mathbf{b}P = 0$$

and show that the expansion of $\left| A - \lambda I \right| = 0$ is

$$b_p \lambda^p + b_{p-1} \lambda^{p-1} + \cdots + b_0 = 0$$

where $\mathbf{b} = (b_0, \cdots, b_p)$.

[Hint: First show that A satisfies the equation

$$b_p A^p + \cdots + b_0 I = 0]$$

References

BARTLETT, M. S. (1947). Multivariate analysis. *J.R.S.S. Suppl.*, **9**, 76.

HOTELLING, H. (1936). Simplified calculation of principal components. *Psychometrika*, **1**, 27.

MAHALANOBIS, P. C. (1936). On the generalized distance in Statistics. *Proc. Nat. Inst. Sc. (India)*, **12**, 49.

MAHALANOBIS, P. C., D. N. MAJUMDAR, and C. R. RAO (1949). Anthropometric survey of the United Provinces, 1941: A statistical study. *Sankhyā*, **9**, 90.

MORANT, G. M. (1923). A first study of the Tibetan skull. *Biom.*, **13**, 176.

RAO, C. R., and PATRICK SLATER (1949). Multivariate analysis applied to differences between neurotic groups. *British J. Psy.*, Statistics Section, 2, 17.

TILDESLEY, M. L. (1921). A first study of the Burmese skull. *Biom.*, **13**, 176.

Appendix.

Miscellaneous Problems

The following problems are intended to serve as exercises and discussion problems.

1. Distinguish between a mathematical limit and a stochastic limit. Show that if $x_n \to x$ stochastically then the limiting distribution of x_n is the same as the distribution of x.

2. If x is a stochastic variable assuming only non-negative values and $E(x) = t$, then

$$P(x < \lambda^2 t) > 1 - \frac{1}{\lambda^2}$$

3. Find the general form of the probability law which has the median as the maximum likelihood estimator of a parameter.

4. On the basis of a sample of size n how do you test whether the observations have arisen from a rectangular population with an unknown range?

This is equivalent to testing whether the middle $(n - 2)$ observations have a rectangular distribution in the range determined by the smallest and the biggest observation.

5. From the joint distribution of $\bar{x}$ and s^2 as defined in 2b.1 find the distribution of $\bar{x}/s$ when $\mu \neq 0$ and show how this can be used to test for an assigned value of the coefficient of variation in the population.

Derive a locally most powerful unbiased test for the null hypothesis that the coefficient of variation has an assigned value.

6. Show without actually working out the distribution that, for samples from a multivariate normal distribution, the distribution of the computed multiple correlation coefficient contains only the corresponding population parameter and a similar result is true for the partial correlation coefficient.

7. Prove that

$$\mathbf{a}G\mathbf{a}' \not> (\mathbf{a}T\mathbf{a}')^{\frac{1}{2}}(\mathbf{a}GT^{-1}G\mathbf{a}')^{\frac{1}{2}}$$

where $\mathbf{a}$ is an arbitrary vector and T and G are positive definite matrices. Make use of the fact that the ratio of the left-hand expression to that of the right is the correlation between the vectors $\mathbf{x} = \mathbf{a}D$ and $\mathbf{y} = \mathbf{a}GD^{-1}$ where $DD' = T$.

Hence, following the notions of 8c.2, show that the genetic advance

379

as determined by the discriminant function is greater than that for the straight selection function.

8. Calculate the information limits to the variances of unbiased estimates of μ_1 and μ_2 in the problem of 4c.1 and show that they are actually attained for the maximum likelihood estimates.

9. A coin is tossed a number of times till x heads appear. Find the average and the variance of the number of tosses. Determine a recurrence relation for the evaluation of higher moments.

10. Using the data considered in 7d.5, obtain the function of the measurements which characterizes most effectively the secular changes in progress. Assume that regressions with time are linear.

Hint: The probability density for any time t can be written

$$\text{const. exp} - \tfrac{1}{2}\Sigma\Sigma\lambda^{ij}(x_i - a_i - b_i t)(x_j - a_j - b_j t)$$

The likelihood ratio for two different time points gives the best discriminating function. In this case it is linear in the measurements. Estimate the constants.

11. Give any method by which the number of fishes in a pond can be estimated.

In an investigation to estimate the number of births in a locality during a particular month the following data are obtained: 350 families reported no birth and 100 reported a single birth of which 25 took place in the government hospital. Knowing the exact number of births in the hospital, how do you estimate the total number of births in the locality? Find the standard error of this estimate.

12. Comment on the following anecdote: On examining the chart giving the standard heights and associated weights of persons a husband remarked that his wife weighs more than she should. The wife retorted saying that she is not so tall as she should be.

13. A total number of 130 heads was observed when 100 rupee coins and 100 half-rupee coins were thrown together. Knowing that the rupee coin is unbiased, what can you say about the half-rupee coin?

14. Show that under conditions of random mating the blood group frequencies in the four classes O, A, B, AB, can be expressed in terms of gene frequencies only.

15. The following data relate to the distribution of age at death in a particular year classified according to civil conditions.

Civil Condition	Age at Death					
	0–15	15–30	30–45	45–60	60–75	Over 75
Bachelor	300	120	50	60	45	10
Married	10	70	100	120	50	12
Widowed	...	...	12	45	30	20

What conclusions can you draw about the effect of civil condition on the age at death? What more is needed for a proper comparison of these distributions?

16. How do you collect material to study whether the correlation coefficient between the measurements of head length and head breadth on the skull is greater than the correlation coefficient between the corresponding measurements on the living? What is the appropriate statistic to test the above null hypothesis if all four measurements are available for each of n individuals?

17. Find on the basis of a sample of size n the best estimate of the correlation coefficient in a bivariate normal population when both the variables have the same mean and variance. This coefficient is known as the intra-class correlation.

Suppose that p measurements are available on each of two brothers from a number of families. Determine the best linear compound of the measurements which has the highest intra-class correlation coefficient between the brothers.

Obtain the large and small sample distributions of the maximum correlation and indicate their use in tests of significance.

18. The following estimates of the correlation coefficients between intelligence test scores were found in an investigation to study the relative influences of environmental and heredity factors.

	Two Brothers Reared Apart	Two Brothers Living Together	Twins Reared Apart	Twins Living Together
Correlation coefficient	0.235	0.342	0.451	0.513
Sample size	50	40	45	55

Comment on these figures, using tests of significance wherever necessary.

19. It is said that man's stature is variable during the day and that the range is half an inch, the maximum stature being observable when the man gets up in the morning and the minimum when he retires to bed. How will you proceed to study this variability? Also comment on the precision with which the stature has to be measured for such studies.

20. To determine the sex ratio three procedures were adopted: (1) A number of boys were asked to state the number of brothers (including himself) and sisters they have. (2) A number of girls were asked to state the number of sisters (including herself) and brothers they have. (3) Finally a number of parents were asked to give the number of sons and daughters they have. The totals of brothers, sisters, and families for the three procedures are given below.

	Procedure		
	1	2	3
Brothers	203	140	120
Sisters	130	220	115
Total families	80	95	60

Test whether the family size is the same in the three investigations. Find the estimates of the sex ratio for the three procedures, and test whether they are significantly different.

Index

(Names occurring in references are indicated by r, and those in footnotes by n.)

Aitken, A. C., 29r, 127r, 253, 271r
Analysis of covariance, concomitant variation, 119
Analysis of dispersion, 258
Analysis of variance, concomitant variation, 119
  equality of regression equations, 112
  least square method, 83
  one-way classification, 89
  significance of regression coefficients, 105
  test for an assigned regression function, 115
  two-way classification, 91
  unequal numbers in cells, 94
Anscombe, F. J., 209, 210, 220r
Anthropological illustrations, asymmetry and kurtosis of nasal height distributions, 219
  asymmetry of right and left femora, 87
  classification of the Highdown skull, 291
  cranial capacity, 103
  differences in boys of different schools, 262
  differences of the first and second born, 245
  differences in sexing of skulls, 197
  differences in variabilities of males and females, 225
  estimation from incomplete data, 161
  femur and humerus differences in groups, 252
  group constellations of castes in United Provinces, 357
  group constellations using canonical variates, 370
  group differences in head breadth, 90
  group differences in nasal height, 94
  inheritance in man, 124

Anthropological illustrations, regression of nasal index on weather factors, 115
  secular variations in skull characters, 266
  sexing of osteometric material, 304
  stature of prehistoric man, comments, 115
  use of indices, 155
Asymmetric matrix, canonical reduction, 27
Asymptotic distribution, of quantiles, 156
  of the median, 157
  of maximum likelihood estimates, 157

Backcross data, 188
Barnard, M. M., 266, 267, 271, 271r
Bartlett, M. S., 201, 220r, 226, 228, 235r, 236, 259, 261, 271r, 373, 378r
Bateson, 180, 194
Bayes' theorem, 308
Bernstein, F., 170, 174r
Beta variable, distribution, 41
  distribution of product, 42
  moments of, 42
Bhattacharya, A., 143, 174r
Bias in an estimate, 151
Binomial proportion, estimation, 134
  $\sin^{-1}$ transformation, 210
Binomial variate, distribution, 32
  distribution function, 33
  moments of, 34
Biological illustrations, differential thickness of bark in different directions, 241
  feeding experiment on pigs, 121
  milk feeding experiment, 217
  see also Anthropological illustrations, Genetic illustrations, Psychological illustrations

Birnbaum, Z. W., 336, 349r
Bivariate normal distribution, estimation
    of parameters, 161
  moments of, 153
Bliss, C. I., 255, 256, 271r
Blood groups, *O*, *A*, *B*, comparison of
    gene frequencies, 187
  consistency test, 184
  estimation of gene frequencies, 169
Boas, 124
Bose, R. C., 74r, 80n
Brogden, H. E., 338, 349r
Brookner, R. J., 236, 272r

Canonical reduction, of asymmetric
    matrix, 27
  of symmetric matrix, 24
Canonical variates, illustrations, 367,
    370
  use in group constellations, 364
Cauchy population, distribution, 42
  distribution of the mean in samples, 43
  efficient estimate of the parameter, 166
  inconsistent estimate of the parameter,
    152
Central limit theorem, 174
Chapman, D. G., 336
Characteristic vectors, 21
Chi-square, χ^2, approximations to distri-
    bution of, 222
  distribution of least squares, 58
  distribution of sum of, 41
  general large sample theory of χ^2 test,
    179
  goodness of fit test, 183
  limits to χ^2 in test for specified vari-
    ance, 223
  multivariate tests of, 257, 294, 372
  non-central distribution of, 50, 57
  ratio of, 45
  test of homogeneity, 185
  tests in contingency tables, 192
Classificatory problems, allocation of
    individuals to groups in a fixed
    ratio, 322
  differential predictors, 337
  discriminant function, 287
  doubtful region, 296
  in genetic selection, 329
  in job selection, 336

Classificatory problems, with more than
    two groups, 307
  resolution of a mixed series, 300
  single predictor, 336
  with two groups, 286
  uncertainty of the a priori information,
    290
Cochran's theorem, 49, 55
Cochran, W. G., 74r, 255, 256, 271r
Coefficient of correlation, *see* Correlation
    coefficient
Coefficient of racial likeness, C.R.L.,
    355
  reduced form, R.C.R.L., 356
Combination of data from various
    sources, 172
Combination of tests, P_λ, 44, 217
Concomitant variation, adjustment for,
    119
Conditional tests, 201, 205
Confidence interval, 276
Consistency in estimation, 151
Consistency relation of moments, in
    population, 27
  in samples, 17
Contingency tables, with small samples,
    200
  tests of independence, 192
Convergence theorems, 172, 173
Correction for grouping, 301
Correlation coefficient, estimate from
    parallel samples, 234
  multiple, distribution of, 63, 65
  partial, distribution of, 69
  simple, distribution of, 68
  $\tanh^{-1}$ transformation, 231
  tests of significance, 230, 232
Coupling data, 167
Covariance analysis, concomitant vari-
    ation, 119
Cramér, H., 158, 172, 174r
Cranial capacity, estimation of mean,
    110
  prediction formula for, 103
  preservation of skulls with small, 111

D^2(Mahalanobis), applications, 246, 354,
    357
  distribution, 70
  generalization to many groups, 257

Dandekar's correction for continuity, 203
  see also Yates' correction, 203
Deficiency matrix, 3
Degrees of freedom, of χ^2, 177, 179
  of least squares, 84
Dependence of vectors, 2
Determinantal equation, 22
Determinants, 10
  reduction of, 31
Discriminant function, construction of, 247
  difficulties in its use, 289
  in genetic selection, 329
  in job selection problems, 336, 337
  as ratio of likelihoods, 287
  successive evaluation of these functions, 254
  test for an assigned, 248
  test for equality of functions, 250
  test for its coefficients, 251
Discriminant score, linear, 316
Discrimination of neurotic conditions, 316
Discriminatory problems, *see* Classificatory problems
Discriminatory topology, 352
Dispersion matrix, 52
Dissection of a compound frequency curve, 300
Distance between two populations, 352
  Mahalanobis' D^2, 70, 246, 354, 357
Distribution, of χ^2 goodness of fit, 177, 179
  of correlation coefficient, 68
  of Fisher's z, 48
  of Hotelling's T, 70
  of L- and M-statistics for homogeneity of variances, 226, 227
  of Λ-statistic (Wilks), 261
  of least squares, 58
  of linear functions of normal variates, 53
  of Mahalanobis' D^2, 70
  of maximum likelihood estimates, asymptotic, 157
  of mean and variance in normal samples, 46
  of multiple correlation coefficient, 63, 65
  of non-central χ^2, 50

Distribution, of non-null t^2, 48
  of P_λ of Pearson, 44
  of partial correlation coefficient, 69
  of product of beta variables, 42
  of quadratic forms, 49, 55
  of quantiles, asymptotic, 156
  of regression coefficients, 63
  of square of a normal variable, 40
  of Students' t, 47
  of U-statistic, comparison of two D^2 values, 74
  of V-statistic, generalization of D^2, 257
  of variances and covariances (Wishart), 66
  of W-statistic, the difference of two D^2 values, 255
Distribution of sum of variates, Cauchy, 43
  gamma, 41
  normal, 39
  Poisson, 36, 37
Distribution function, binomial, 33
  Poisson, 38
Doubtful region in classification, 296
Dugue, 158, 174r

Efficiency of an estimate, 155
Elderton, E. M., 220r
Elementary matrix, 13
Equations, linear, homogeneous, 5
  nonhomogeneous, 6
  numerical solutions, 31
Estimation, linear, with correlated variables, 81
  intrinsic properties of normal equations, 79
  normal equations, 76
  observational equations, 75
  of regression coefficients, 103
  with restrictions on parameters, 81
  standard errors of estimates, 78
  with two sets of parameters, 118
  with weighted observations, 85
  method of maximum likelihood, 150
  combination of data, 172
  consistency and bias, 151
  efficiency, 155
  estimation from incomplete data, 161
  method of scoring, 165

Estimation, method of maximum likelihood, optimum properties of estimates, 157
the primitive postulate, 151
relation to sufficient statistics, 151
minimum variance, information limit to variance, 130
a lower bound to variance, 143
the problem of several parameters, 144
relation to sufficient statistics, 135, 139
Eysenck, 375

F, f distributions, 45, 48, 49
Factors of neurosis, 370
Fairfield Smith, H., 330, 349r
Fiducial interval, 276
Fisher, R. A., 74r, 87, 87n, 124, 127r, 128r, 131, 150, 168, 174r, 175r, 200, 211, 220r, 231, 236, 237, 247, 271r, 272r, 276, 287, 288, 289, 301
Fisher's z distribution, 48
Frets, G. P., 245, 272r

Gamma variate, distribution of sum of variates, 41
estimation of parameters of distribution of, 134, 141
moments of, 41
Gauss, K. S., 76
Generalized distance, see D^2
Generalized variance, 147
Genetic advance, 332
Genetic illustrations, comparison of gene frequencies, 186
comparison of recombination fractions, 188, 211
consistency of blood group frequencies, 184
detection of linkage, 181, 195
discrimination between Iris versicolor and Iris setosa, 248
estimation of blood group frequencies, 169
estimation of linkage, coupling and repulsion, 167
inheritance in man, 124
selection of poultry by discriminant function, 330

Genetic selection, discriminant function in, 329
Goodwin, C. N., 292, 349r
Gosset, W. S. (Student), 87n, 128r
Gray, H., 124, 127r
Gross, Mayer, 375
Grouping correction, 301

Hartley, H. O., 228, 235r
Homogeneity tests, contingency table, 185
of correlations, 233
of variances, 226
Hooke, B. G. E., 103, 111, 128r, 292, 349r
Hotelling, H., 74r, 201, 220r, 236, 272r, 286, 367, 378r
Hotelling's T, 70
Hsu, P. L., 74r, 237, 272r
Huzurbazar, V. S., 158, 175r
Hypothesis, composite, 176
linear, 82, 83
Neyman-Pearson theory, 278
null, 274
simple, 176

Illustrations, see Anthropological, Biological, Genetic, and Psychological
Incomplete data, estimation from, 161
Index, consistent estimate of, 155
moments of, 154
Information, 131
Information limit, 131
Intercross data, 180
Intrinsic properties of normal equations, 79
Invariance, under orthogonal transformation, 19
of some statistics, 72

Jeffreys, H., 275, 349r

k-statistic, 301
Kemsley, W. F. F., 225, 235r
Kintchine's theorem, 174
Kolodzieczyk, St., 128r
Koopman, B. O., 149, 175r
Kurtosis, test for deviation from normal, 219

L test, 226, 227
Large sample, standard errors of, index, 154
  median, 157
  moments, 215
  quantiles, 156
  transformed statistics, 207
Large sample tests, χ^2 goodness of fit, 179
  of deviation from symmetry and normal kurtosis, 219
  difference between means, 217
  homogeneity of parallel samples, 185
  homogeneity of Poisson samples, 205
  independence in contingency tables, 192
  with transformed statistics, 207
Latent roots of a matrix, 21
Least squares, in estimation, 80, 81, 82
  evaluation of, 85
  two fundamental distributions in, 58
Levi, F. W., 29r
Levy, P., 175r
Levy's theorem, 174
Liapounoff, A., 175r
Liapounoff's theorem, 174
Likelihood, 150
Likelihood ratio test, 226, 259, 285
Limiting distribution, of binomial variate, 38
  of maximum likelihood estimates, 157
  of quantiles, 156
Limiting theorems, central limit, Lindberg-Levy's, 174
  convergence of sum, product and ratio, 173
  Kintchine's, 174
  Levy's, 174
  Liapounoff's, 174
  Slutsky's, 173
Linear equations, homogeneous, 5
  nonhomogeneous, 5
  numerical methods of solution, 31
Linear estimation, see Estimation, linear
Linear hypothesis, nature of, 82
  test of, 83
Linear transformation, 18
Lindberg, J. W., 175r
Lindberg-Levy theorem, 160, 174

M test, homogeneity of variances, 227

Macdonell, W. R., 104n, 128r
Mahalanobis, P. C., 246, 258, 272r, 355, 357, 378r
Mahalanobis' D^2, see D^2
Majumdar, D. N., 318, 357, 378r
Markoff, A. A., 76, 128r
Martin, E. S., 349r
Mather, K., 167, 175r
Matrix, characteristic vectors of, 21
  the determinant of, 10
  elementary, 13
  latent roots of, 21
  of linear transformations, 18
  numerical computations with, 31
  partitioned, 9
  of a quadratic form, 18
  rank of, 2
  reciprocal, 13
  reduction of an asymmetric form, 27
  sweeping out a, 2
  unit matrix, 8
Maximum likelihood, see Estimation, method of maximum likelihood
Merril, A. S., 175r
Minimax, some comments on, 313
Minimum variance, see Estimation, minimum variance
Mises, R. V., 312, 349r
Mixed series, resolution of, 300
Moments, of beta distribution, 42
  of binomial distribution, 34
  of bivariate normal, 153
  of gamma distribution, 41
  of multinomial distribution, 35
  of normal distribution, 39
  of Poisson distribution, 36
  of moment statistics, 215
Moore, 375
Morant, G. M., 292, 349r, 355, 378r
Multinomial distribution, moments of, 35
Multiple correlation, distribution of, 63, 65
  test for, 104
Multivariate analysis, of dispersion, 259
  generalization of D^2, 257
  internal analysis of variates, 264
  of neurotic patients, 370
  problem of secular variations in skull characters, 266

Multivariate analysis, problems of a single sample, 239
problems of two samples, 246
review of work on, 236
successive evaluation of discriminant functions, 254
test for additional information due to some characters, 252
test for an assigned contrast of p correlated variables, 243
test for an assigned discriminant function, 248
test for an assigned ratio of discriminant function coefficients, 251
test for asymmetry, 245
test of differences in mean values, 262
test for differences in two samples, 248
test for equality of discriminant functions in parallel samples, 251
test for equality of means of p correlated variables, 240
use of the W-statistic, difference of two D^2 values, 255
Wilks's criterion, 258
Multivariate normal population, distribution of linear functions from, 53
distribution of quadratic forms in, 55
variances and covariances in, 52
Multivariate distributions, Hotelling's T, 70
Mahalanobis' D^2, 70
multiple correlation, 63, 65
partial correlation co-efficient, 69
U-statistic, comparison of two D^2 values, 74
variances and covariances, 66
Wilks's Λ criterion, 260
Münter, A. H., 128r, 163, 175r

Nair, U. S., 52, 74r, 260, 272r
Nandi, H. K., 74r
Neurosis, the discrimination problem of, 316
factors of, 370
Neyman, J., 130, 175r, 224, 235r, 236, 272r, 277, 278, 280, 282, 285, 349r, 350r
Neyman-Pearson lemma, 309, 339
generalization of, 339
a slight variation of, 341

Neyman-Pearson theory of hypothesis testing, 278
Noncentral χ^2 distribution, 50
Non-null t distribution, 48
Normal equations, 76
intrinsic properties, 79
Normal population, distribution of mean and variance, 46
distribution of the square, 40
distribution of sum of variates, 39
estimation of parameters, 133, 139, 140, 148, 150
moments of, 39
see also Multivariate normal population
Nuisance parameter, 201
Null hypothesis, 274
Null vector, 1

Observational equations, 75
see also Estimation, linear
Orthogonal transformation, 19
Orthogonal vector space, 3

P_λ distribution, 44
application of, 217
Pairs of quadratic forms, 25
Panse, V. G., 330, 350r
Partial correlation coefficient, 69, 365
Partitioned matrix, 9
Pearson, E. S., 224, 228, 235r, 236, 272r, 277, 278, 280, 282, 285, 349r, 350r
Pearson, K., 33, 38, 74r, 112, 115, 128r, 227n, 300, 321, 350r, 355
Pearson's (Karl) P_λ, 44
coefficient of racial likeness, 355
Penrose, L. S., 307, 350r
Pivotal condensation, 29
Poisson variate, conditional distributions, 36, 37
distribution function, 38
distribution of the sum, 36, 37
estimation of the mean, 135
large sample tests, 205
moments of, 36
Power function, 277
a lemma on, 342
Prediction formula, 103
for cranial capacity, 103
Psychological illustrations, discrimination of neurotic conditions, 316

Psychological illustrations, factors of neurosis, 370
  sociability of village and city recruits, 202
  speech and physical defects, 199

Quadratic forms, classification of, 19
  distribution of, 55
  reduction of two forms, 25
Quantiles, asymptotic distribution, 156

Range, estimation of, 142
Rank of a matrix, 2
Rao, C. R., 74r, 128r, 150, 175r, 220r, 272r, 316, 350r, 357, 378r
Reciprocal matrix, 13
  numerical evaluation, 31
Recombination fraction, 167
Regression coefficients, distribution of, 63
  estimation of, 103
  test for, 104
Residual sum of squares, see Least squares

Scoring method, 165
  combination of data, 172
  in estimating linkage, 167
  gene frequencies, 169
Similar regions, 286
Sin^{-1} transformation, 210
Slater, Eliot, 375
Slater, Patrick, 316, 350r, 371, 375, 378r
Slutsky, E., 175r
Slutsky's theorem, 173
Statistics used in tests of significance, see χ^2, D^2, F, f, L, M, P_λ, T, t, U, V, W, Λ (Wilks'), z
Student (W. S. Gosset), 87, 87n, 128r
Student's distribution, 47
Student's generalization of t, 239
Student's t test, 87
Sufficient statistics, 135
  distributions admitting, 137, 149
  an optimum property of, 139
  minimal set of, 144
Sweep-out method, 2

t, Student's, distribution, 47
  non-null distribution, 48

t, Student's, test, 87
T, Hotelling's, applications, 239
  distribution, 70
Tanh^{-1} transformation, 231
Tests, distance power, 284
  likelihood ratio, 226, 259, 285
  locally most powerful unbiased, 280
  uniformly most powerful, 278
  see also Analysis of variance, Chi square, Homogeneity tests, Large sample tests, Multivariate analysis
Tildesley, M. L., 355, 378r
Tocher, K. D., 363
Transformation of statistics, expression for variance under, 207
  log of standard deviation, 214
  sin^{-1} root of binomial proportion, 210
  square root of Poisson variate, 209
  tanh^{-1} of correlation coefficient, 214
Tschebysheff's lemma, 152
Turnbull, H. W., 29r

U-statistic, application, 243, 250, 251, 253
  distribution, 74
Unbiased estimation, general, 129
  an important aspect of, 130
  linear, 75
Unbiased minimum variance, see Estimation, minimum variance
Uniformly most powerful test, 278

V-statistic, generalization of D^2, 257
Variance, distribution of, in normal samples, 46
  information limit to, in estimation, 130, 143, 144
  log transformation, 214
  test for a given inequality of variances, 224
  test for homogeneity of variances, 226
  test for a specified value of, 221
  unbiased minimum variance, estimate of, 148
  see also Analysis of variance
Vectors, linear independence of, 2
  orthogonality of, 2
Vector space, basis of, 2

Vector space, orthogonal, 3
  rank of, 2
Von Mises, R., 312, 349r

W-statistic, difference of two D^2 values, 255
Wald, A., 160, 175r, 178, 220r, 236, 272r, 329, 350r
Wilks, S. S., 236, 259, 260, 272r

Wilks' Λ criterion, 258
Wishart, J., 74r, 121, 128r, 236, 272r
Wishart's distribution, 66

Yates, F., 87n, 168, 175r, 203, 220r
Yates' correction for continuity, 203
  see also Dandekar's correction, 203

z distribution, 48